Grassland into the 21st Century:
Challenges and Opportunities

Occasional Symposium No. 29, British Grassland Society, 1995

Proceedings of the 50th Anniversary Meeting of the British Grassland Society
held at The Cairn Hotel, Harrogate, 4-6 December, 1995

Lacock
Chippenham
W.

~214

Edited by
G. E. POLLOTT
Wye College - University of London
Ashford
Kent
TN25 5AH
UK

OCCASIONAL SYMPOSIUM NO. 29

British Grassland Society

Disclaimer
Occasional reference is made in this publication to trade names and proprietary products. No endorsements or criticism of named products is intended nor is any criticism implied of similar products which are not mentioned.

British Library Cataloguing-in-Publication Data available

1995
ISBN 0 905944 34 8
ISSN 0572 7022

Copyright British Grassland Society

Cover design by R. J. L. Pollott

Printed by Rexam Digital Imaging Ltd., 14 Portman Road, Reading, RG30 1LZ

CONTENTS

Offered poster papers

Offered poster papers

PRODUCTION AND UTILIZATION
Offered theatre papers

Offered poster papers

SUSTAINABLE SYSTEMS
Offered theatre papers

Offered poster papers

SECTION 4 - TECHNOLOGY INTERACTION
Invited papers

Offered poster papers

THE AIM AND OBJECTIVES
OF THE BRITISH GRASSLAND SOCIETY

The aim is to provide a forum for all those with an active interest in the science and the practice of temperate grassland production and utilisation by bringing together research workers, advisers, farmers and technical members of the agricultural industry.

The objectives of the Society are:

1)   To encourage research and practice in all aspects of grassland and forage husbandry which will lead to improvements in the efficiency of its use.

2)   To communicate as widely as possible the results of research and practice in grassland and forage crops.

Membership
Membership is open to all those with a keen interest in grassland and the furtherance of the Society's objectives.

Membership is drawn from research, advisory services, agricultural education, farmers and allied interests.

There are 70 local grassland societies affiliated to BGS.

Publications
An international journal, *Grass and Forage Science*, is published quarterly and supplied to members free of charge. Three times a year, the Society publishes *Grass Farmer*, a practically orientated publication which gives reports of farm practices, together with research and development findings in digest form. This is also available to members free of charge.

Other occasional publications include textbooks, symposia proceedings and reports of meetings and surveys.

Further information on any aspect of BGS can be obtained from:

> The Secretary
> British Grassland Society
> No. 1 Earley Gate
> University of Reading
> Reading RG6 2AT

FOREWORD

In his Foreword to the first number of the Journal of the British Grassland Society in 1945, Sir George Stapledon said that 'The function of the British Grassland Society may truly be said to be the evolutionary outcome of the ever growing attention given to grassland problems by agricultural scientists'. This evolution is still in progress, with the attention to grassland problems (and opportunities) not being confined to agricultural scientists, but, of course, involving also farmers, agri-business, advisors and teachers. All of these interests play major roles in the British Grassland Society.

Grassland is important not only for the provision of feed for ruminants to produce milk, meat and fibre but also for amenity and recreation use, for wildlife, water collection and soil conservation. Grassland is a key part of the British landscape. It is fitting that the Society should celebrate its 50th Anniversary by a Conference which looks forward rather than backward with the theme 'Grassland into the 21st Century: Challenges and Opportunities'. Contributions to the Conference are made by individuals from sectors representing all the interests of the Society and deal with grassland in the widest context. Sessions dealing with 'The economic and social framework' and 'The environmental framework' provide the basis for considering 'Future technology' and 'Technology interaction'. These papers are published in full together with summaries of some 60 contributions reporting new R and D results. The international standing of the Society is indicated by the large number of papers that are from overseas authors.

Whilst wishing to focus our discussion on the future, it is also a time to celebrate and mark the achievements of the past. It gives me great pleasure that the Proceedings include two specially commissioned papers. The paper by Dick Powell, Jim Corrall and Rosemary Corrall outlines the history of the Society, whilst the second by John Frame, Dick Baker and Nancy Henderson describes advances in grassland technology over the 50 years existence of the British Grassland Society.

The Society has already achieved much during its first 50 years and is well placed to at least emulate these achievements over the next 50 years. I pay tribute here to the contribution made by members of the Society and particularly its Office-bearers and members of Executive Council over the years. I specifically thank those who joined with me to form the committee responsible for organising the Conference - Jim Corrall, Jan Crichton, John Farmer, Mike Helps, Joe Johnson, Scott Laidlaw, Steve Peel, Geoff Pollott, Giles Tedstone and Cled Thomas.

R. J. WILKINS
President, British Grassland Society, 1995-96

SPECIAL PAPERS

A History of the British Grassland Society, 1945 - 1995

R. A. POWELL[1], A. J. CORRALL[2] AND ROSEMARY G. CORRALL[2]

[1]Goldacre, 102 St. Thomas Street, Wells, Somerset, BA5 2UZ

[2]210 Greys Road, Henley on Thames, RG9 1QX

EXTRACT FROM BGS CONSTITUTION

Objects: the advancement of methods of production and utilization of grass and forage crops for the promotion of agriculture and the public benefit. The advancement of education and of research in grass and forage crop production and utilization, and the publication of the results of any research.

INTRODUCTION

BGS is the agency that brings together all those with an interest in the science and practice of the production and utilization of grass and forage crops. Through its activities, i.e. conferences, competitions, visits and regular and occasional publications, it provides a forum for the full and open exchange of knowledge and experience, particularly facilitating the two way exchange between scientist and practitioner.

At this time it is appropriate to look back upon the history of these last 50 years, at the Society's origins, its objectives, development and achievements. But, because a fairly detailed history of its first 40 years (1945-85) was published only 10 years ago (Powell and Corrall, 1985), the account herein deals relatively briefly with those earlier years, while devoting proportionately more space to the events and development of the last 10 (1986 - 95). These latter years have been a period of accelerated progress, in ideas, expansion of activities and provision of new services to members. They provide the springboard for the future, as the agricultural industry faces the new challenges of market deregulation and increasing economic, social and environmental pressures.

The primary aim of agriculture is to supply food in the quantity required and at a price the public can afford. It is no coincidence that the golden jubilee of the BGS so nearly coincides with the fiftieth anniversary of the final defeat of the Axis Powers. Only people whose adult life encompassed the war years can properly appreciate how close the UK came to defeat by starvation. At one time so many ships were being sunk that, reportedly, little more than one week's supply of major staple foods remained in stock; this despite a level of rationing which few who did not experience it can readily believe. Even for several years after victory had been won, only quite tiny weekly allocations of meat, dairy products, eggs and even bread were made to each individual, and rationing did not finally come to an end until well into the 1950s. The immense range of foods of all kinds now freely available in supermarkets from all parts of the world was no more than a distant dream. The founding of the BGS in 1945 could not have been more timely. In the immediate post-war period the emphasis in British farming, so vital in time of war, was still on maximum production, with cost almost a minor consideration, and the price to the consumer moderated by direct Government subsidy to the producer. Wartime priority had been on arable crops for direct human consumption, but as the tide turned decisively in the Allies' favour increasing attention was being given to livestock products, which had been in especially short supply. Such as there were had come mainly from home-grown food resources; concentrate feeds, traditionally then the production element in ruminant feeding (and especially the vital protein constituent) were largely of imported materials and therefore themselves no less tightly rationed than human foods. They were also much more expensive than grassland and home-grown forages, even when subsidised.

British grassland had been contributing little more - sometimes less - than maintenance, although R and D workers and a handful of pioneering farmers were already proving its capacity to produce milk and meat at much lower cost, and devising the management systems required for it to do so. Thus when in the 1950s the emphasis shifted from maximum production towards technical and economic efficiency, and later towards efficient use of natural resources and minimising inputs, the Society's programmes reflected and often even anticipated these changes. More recently it has been accepted that these objectives are not necessarily mutually exclusive and that there is a place for both intensive and extensive systems. Also in the last few years, increasing public concerns about the impact of agriculture on the environment and anxieties about animal welfare have been reflected in the Society's programme. For instance, in 1989 the subject of the Winter Meeting was 'Environmentally Responsible Grassland Management', and in 1993 a joint meeting with the British Ecological Society and the Joint Nature Conservation Council explored the problems and opportunities of 'Grassland Management and Nature Conservation'. The subject matter of individual papers at Research Conferences and other events has consistently reflected, and often led, changing attitudes, circumstances and objectives.

Despite all the political, economic, environmental and associated regulatory problems which have assailed it, British agriculture has been a great success story since the Second World War, especially in ruminant livestock production. The British Grassland Society has made a major contribution to this success, and it is the aim of this History to record and demonstrate how this has been achieved. Part 1 is a mainly chronological account, identifying the main milestones on the road from 1945 to 1995. It is followed in Part 2 by an examination, in greater detail, of the individual institutions and activities of the Society, and the contribution they have severally made.

PART 1 BIRTH AND DEVELOPMENT: A BGS CHRONOLOGY

Initiation of a British grassland society was first discussed by a group of British grassland scientists attending the 4th International Grassland Congress held in Britain in 1937. Among them was Professor R. George Stapledon, at that time Director of the Welsh Plant Breeding Station at Aberystwyth, and later to be knighted for services to agriculture. But the outbreak of the Second World War in 1939 and the international crises which preceded it delayed its further consideration until November, 1944. On 21st of that month, when the Allies' European campaign was still at its height, the impatient Sir George, by then Director of the Grassland Improvement Station at Drayton, brought together at Stratford-upon-Avon 20 hand-picked grassland scientists and technicians of like enthusiasm from all parts of the British Isles. They duly appointed from among their number a representative organising committee with Sir George as Chairman and his deputy at Drayton, Dr William Davies, as Vice-Chairman. They were to draw up a draft constitution, recruit members from the research, advisory and academic ranks, and prepare a 3-day grassland meeting based on Stratford, in June 1945, at which the first AGM of the new Society was to be held. This, in Stratford's Town Hall on the evening of the first day, 20th June, was attended by 53 of the 196 people by that time recruited as members-in-waiting. The new Society was formally voted into being, the Organising Committee confirmed *en bloc* as its first Executive. Sir George was elected President, William. Davies as Vice-President, and their designated Secretary, Treasurer and Journal Editor were also agreed. The tour of the GIS, which had preceded the AGM, and the two following days of farm visits in Gloucestershire and Leicestershire together constituted, in effect, the Society's first Summer Meeting.

The initial objectives may be summarised as:-

1. To provide opportunities for those concerned in grassland (and forage crop) research, development and husbandry to meet and exchange information, ideas and experiences relating to all aspects of grassland and forage crop management, production and utilization.
2. To encourage the investigation of problems pertaining to these matters.
3. To collect and publish information relating to grassland and forage husbandry, and to publish any periodicals, books and leaflets considered desirable.
4. To stimulate the incorporation into practice of advances resulting from research, experimental work and practical experience.
5. To cooperate with any other organisation in furthering the Society's objects.

How these objectives have been pursued, and what progress has been made in achieving them, are the main business of the remainder of this paper.

Production of the *Journal of the British Grassland Society* (since 1979 entitled *Grass and Forage Science*) was a high priority of the first Executive Committee and Dr. H.I. Moore of Leeds University (later Principal of Seale-Hayne College) the designated Editor. He embarked upon the task with vigour, and the first issue (Vol.1 No.1) was published in March 1946 with No. 2 the following December. Since then an annual volume of 4 quarterly issues has appeared, without a break, in March, June, September and December. The first (March) issue of Volume (50) begins with a brief summary of the Society's origins, aims and development.

In pursuance of a policy to include the whole United Kingdom in the Society's activities, the second Summer Meeting was held in Scotland (Aberdeen, 1946), the third in Wales (Aberystwyth, 1947) and the fourth in Ulster (Belfast, 1948). Subsequently these key meetings have been located at venues distributed throughout the British Isles, thus obtaining a wide coverage of soil, climatic and topographical conditions, environmental constraints and local problems.

The first Winter Meeting of the Society was held in London in 1947 on the subject 'Grass Conservation and the Crisis', drawing an attendance of over 100 members. The next, in January, 1949, was a 2-day event held in Newcastle, the first day devoted to farm visits and the second to conference papers. It again attracted about 100 members and was the only Winter Meeting held outside London for a number of years.

So the fledgling Society began the building of today's impressive edifice on the foundation of three main activities - the Summer Meeting, the Winter Meeting, and the Journal.

In 1949 the Society awarded five travel scholarships to assist young members to attend the 5th International Grassland Congress in the Netherlands (the first after the war). In the same year a joint meeting was held with the Agricultural Education Association, the first of a number of joint meetings with other organisations whose kindred interests overlap with those of the BGS.

In the early 1950s the Society appointed a sub-committee to study the measurement and recording of pasture yields. The resultant 'Barker Report' began the Society's involvement in grassland recording, covered more fully in Part 2.

The 1950s were a period of rapid growth and development, and by 1960 membership had risen to around 900. In July, 1954 the first local grassland society was formed, in Surrey. Although indirectly inspired by the BGS, it was a home-grown organisation, but one which was to set in train a nationwide network of local societies which has effectively complemented the work of the BGS and contributed very significantly to its success in raising standards of grassland management and use throughout the British Isles.

The first visit made outside UK had been to Eire in 1948, based on Dublin, by 40 members following the Summer Meeting in Ulster, and in June, 1952, 36 members visited the Netherlands. The success of these two events sparked off a series of overseas tours in later years.

In 1955 the Society celebrated its tenth anniversary, and a short account of these ten formative years, by Mr. J. T. Kernohan, as Secretary/Treasurer, was given in the Journal (Kernohan, 1955). In 1956 the Society elected its first farmer President, Mr A. S. Cray of Hampshire (see Part II, Membership, Farmers). In the following year, when Dr. Ken Baker (GRI) succeeded Jim Kernohan as Secretary/Treasurer, the BGS Office, originally established in Aberystwyth, moved via Belfast, Cambridge and Fakenham to a more permanent home at GRI, Hurley, where it remained until 1991. Thus the Society was brought into even closer and more rewarding relationship with the GRI Director and his staff, which was of immense benefit to it.

The Grassland Recording Investigation had begun in 1959, when the Executive also accepted an invitation jointly from the participating counties, Surrey, Sussex and Hampshire, for the 1962 Summer Meeting to be held in their area, so that some of the farms co-operating in the Investigation could be featured and preliminary results discussed.

The Society was invited by the Ministry of Agriculture to participate in the organisation of the 8th IGC, to be held in Reading in 1960, and, in the event, became mainly responsible for it (see Part 2). The Executive Committee accepted an offer from the Yorkshire Grassland Society, formed in 1957, to host the 1960 Summer Meeting, timed to follow immediately after the International Grassland Congress for the convenience of overseas visitors who might wish to attend. This also set a precedent for local society involvement, and the hosting of Summer Meetings by local societies soon became the norm.

Nineteen-sixty, an important year in the Society's history, was to be marred by the death of its illustrious founder. Sir George Stapledon died on 16th September. Widely acclaimed as the father of modern grassland husbandry and the inspirational leader of a countrywide determination to make best use of its greatest natural asset, he was sorely missed, especially by BGS members. In perpetual memory of him and his achievements the Society played a leading part in setting up the Stapledon Memorial Trust. The careers of many young grassland scientists have benefited substantially from the financial help which the Trust has provided.

By 1962 there were seven local societies affiliated to BGS, and at Surrey's suggestion a Local Societies' Committee was formed, responsible to the Executive, and a Local Societies' News Sheet published, ultimately developed, via *Herbivaria* and *Grass Today*, into *Grass Farmer*.

As part of agriculture's contribution to 1963's National Productivity Year a British Grassland Convention was held with full BGS participation in 'Off the Grass' demonstrations at the Great Yorkshire and Royal Dairy Shows. 1963 also saw the formation of the European Grassland Federation, largely on BGS initiative, at a special symposium held at Hurley in September, The proceedings of that symposium were later published under the title 'The Agronomic Evaluation of Grassland' as No. 1 in the BGS Occasional Symposium Series. This series now contains some 29 titles which, apart from two or three Winter

Meetings, are the proceedings of symposia designed to cover the current state of scientific knowledge and practical experience on specific topics.

Notable events in 1964 included the first of only two Summer Meetings to be held outside the UK (in Eire), while in 1965, marking the Society's twentieth anniversary, a special meeting was called by the President, Dr. Baker, of prominent senior members of the Society to review current and possible future activities. While no major changes resulted, it established the principle of a periodical review which has kept the Society always in tune with the march of events.

In the Society's 21st anniversary year an article by Mr. R. S. Tayler of Reading University (who had succeeded Dr. Baker as Secretary/Treasurer in 1964), entitled 'The British Grassland Society Comes of Age' was published in the 1966 RASE Review. It briefly reviewed the Society's history, emphasising both its domestic and international roles, with some speculation as to its future direction. Membership at this time was around 1100 and the number of local societies already totalled 38. As well as a special dinner to celebrate the occasion, the twenty-first anniversary was further commemorated by the award of three travel scholarships, and also a grant to assist a young member to attend the 11th IGC in Australia in, 1970. Then in 1968 and 1969 a further 10 travel grants, generously donated by the Grasshoppers, the prestigious farming club based in Hampshire, were also awarded to assist young members in investigative studies on which written reports were submitted and some published.

Early in 1970 a special meeting of the Executive Committee reviewed the Constitution and Rules to take account of changing conditions and to reorganise the Society's management. The Executive Committee was re-named the Executive Council, to which a new Programme Committee and all other subordinate committees reported. The title of the Journal Committee was changed to Publications Committee, which was given overall supervisory responsibility for the increasing number of publications which the Society was producing. In that year, also, the Society was accepted by the Charity Commissioners as a registered charity.

By the mid-1970s the Society was hit by a severe financial crisis which caused the suspension of its practical magazine *Grass Today* and threatened the Journal. The immediate solution came from a successful appeal for financial support, launched by a generous private donation, and this was followed by the adoption of a number of measures to safeguard the future. These included the budgeting of each activity to be financially self supporting, a contract with Blackwell Scientific Publications to publish the Journal with editorial control retained by the Society, the relaunch of *Grass Today* as *Grass Farmer*, with a professional editor and sponsored by a consortium of commercial companies, and a number of organisational changes. These latter included the re-establishment of the separate post of Treasurer (initially to be filled by Mr. Norman Coward, Midland Bank Agricultural Specialist), the appointment of a Finance Sub-committee to oversee financial policy and make recommendations to the Executive Council and the initiation of regional representation on the Council. These measures together achieved a remarkable and sustained financial recovery, which was further developed through the 1980s to lay the foundations of the sound position enjoyed by the Society today.

During the late 1970s, and since, much thought and energy has been devoted to laying the foundations of a 'new' BGS - a phoenix risen from the ashes of near disaster - on which has been built, through the 1980s and 1990s, the vibrant and bubbling activity which characterises the Society of today. Council recognised that both the range and variety of services to members needed to be increased and more effective publicity introduced to enhance the Society's image and attract and sustain the support of new members. The Society introduced the competition element into its programme when it set up the BGS National Silage Competition in 1979. This had two main objectives - the identification and demonstration of technical excellence, and the development of closer co-operation with local societies for mutual benefit. The Grass-to-Meat Awards were also established that year , again with the aim of demonstrating excellence.

The Society's most prestigious award, known simply as the BGS Award, was introduced in 1978 and first awarded in 1979. It is made annually (if a suitable candidate is identified) to a member adjudged to have made an outstanding contribution to the understanding or appreciation of grassland husbandry and technology. More detail is given in Part 2.

In 1988 another type of conference was introduced into the Society's programme. Offered research papers, as short presentations or as posters, had long been a feature of Winter Meetings and, for three trial years in the 1970s, of Summer Meetings, but in both they suffered from competition for time and attention from the full programmes of invited papers and visits respectively. Therefore, to provide a forum for presentation of work at an early stage of development and for young workers at an early stage in their careers, Dr. Wilkins in his first presidential year (1986/7) initiated the series of BGS Research Conferences, with the first held in 1988 at the Welsh Agricultural College, Aberystwyth.

A special BGS discussion meeting for members was held at Nice, France in association with the 16th International Grassland Congress, in 1989. This was well attended and a welcome opportunity for members from many countries to come together for discussion of research topics of mutual interest.

The Society's main programme is planned well in advance to ensure the best speakers and all the other advantages of careful preparation. However, the Executive Council has been aware of the need to be able to respond quickly to new areas of interest or concern as they arise. To meet this need a series of Discussion Meetings has been added, to provide an opportunity to discuss the present state of knowledge on a chosen subject and current work in progress thereon, and to encourage thorough debate among the delegates. The first of these, in April 1994, on 'High Dry Matter Silage', and the second, in April 1995, on 'Extending the Grazing Season' were widely popular and attracted excellent attendances. Though both were far from 'new' subjects, circumstances had projected them urgently back into current concern, calling for early reassessment and consideration.

For the future, two further meeting initiatives are under active consideration. Recognition of the existence of a number of special interest groups within the Society's membership suggested that they might be encouraged and their needs catered for within the Society's programme rather than that they be driven to form a separate organisation. The Executive Council is currently exploring how this may be done. The second desirable initiative is to organise, from time to time, 'members only' meetings. Both initiatives should also give an added incentive for recruitment.

Apart from a continued intensification of the meetings programme during and since the 1980s, other services to members have also much increased. Biannual newsletters, containing a wide spectrum of news items, by no means confined to Society items, but including Council thinking and proposals on current problems, and a calendar of forthcoming events of grassland interest in the British Isles, Europe and throughout the world, are much appreciated.

The 1980s and 1990s to date have seen a continued enhancement of the Society's image. Well-timed press releases and an excellent relationship with leading agricultural journalists and broadcasters have ensured good coverage of BGS events. This publicity has encouraged good attendances for a constantly expanding programme of events, with a useful effect on the recruitment of new members. The consistently high quality of the content and organisation of meetings and other activities has resulted in many speakers being fully reported in the agricultural press, and farmer members are increasingly featured as individuals when brought to notice by Summer Meeting visits or as winners of BGS Competitions. Recently several members have been featured regularly in the Farmers Weekly 'Farm Focus' series, with frequent mention of BGS activities. Even the occasional adverse press comment has been turned to good account; an authoritative response letter, as for instance that of the President to a highly critical report on the 1993 Winter Meeting which appeared in the 'Dairy Farmer', can provide useful publicity.

In 1988 the Executive Council brought into being a special BGS R&D Group. This was in response to the cuts which had been made in government support for R&D in agriculture, coming to a head with the announcement of its intention to withdraw from the support of all 'near-market' R&D except in a few prescribed circumstances. The Group has proposed a comprehensive national strategy for the funding and coordination of R&D in grassland and related animal production, and drawn up a priority list of essential R&D to be continued or initiated. It has established dialogue at the highest level with government and the commissioning agencies, research establishments and farmers' unions - in short all who may have an influence in these matters - and by doing so, has won for the Society a valued and much respected voice.

PART 2   THE SOCIETY'S INSTITUTIONS AND ACTIVITIES

In this second section of the Society's History the authors enlarge upon the more important aspects of its composition, institutions and activities not covered in detail in Part 1. It is their development which has contributed so much to the formidable reputation, both at home and abroad, which the Society has achieved over the last 50 years and to setting the scene from which an even more successful future can unfold.

Membership

The rapid growth in membership over the first 30 years is well illustrated in Table 1 which shows a peak in 1990 and some reduction to the present day. By April, 1946 (only 10 months after inauguration) membership had risen to 234. The original restriction of membership to 300 was progressively increased, in 1947 to 600 and to 800 in 1952. Not long after all restrictions were removed.

Table 1.   BGS Membership, 1945 - 1995 (No. of members).

June 1945	196
April 1946	234
March 1950	553
July 1960	900
Dec. 1969	1042
March 1980	1070
March 1990	1343
March 1995	919

Despite inflation, fortunately at a relatively modest rate over the first period, and considerable cost increases through development of existing activities and the institution of new ones, the subscription level has been well-contained. Even as recently as 1972, 27 years after the Society's foundation, it was still only £4 per annum. Then, soaring inflation and rapidly rising costs, especially of printing and publishing, forced a subscription rise in 1973 of 50% to £6 - too little, too late, as it proved - and only three years later, another to £10. Loss of members, sadly so often associated with a subscription increase, and a virtual halt in recruitment, caused a dramatic fall in fully-paid membership to about 550 by the end of 1976. But the vigorous action then taken, and subsequent organisational changes and introduction of new activities, largely restored the situation, so that by the end of the decade membership had risen again modestly above that at its beginning.

Further developments through the 1980s brought about a steep rise in membership to a peak of nearly 1350 by 1990. Then came the recession with sharp reductions in the number of scientific staff in both public and private employment, and the doubling of the subscription to £30, forced upon the Society in 1992 by rising costs after being unchanged for ten years. These factors combined to bring about another steep fall in membership, to the present total of around 900. The Executive Council has been taking steps to improve both recruitment and the retention of existing members, and there are signs currently of a turn round in membership numbers.

At the very beginning membership had been restricted to 'technical people employed by public authority' but even within the first year, and despite the qualifying restriction, a small number of both farmers and technical employees of the ancillary industries ('trade') had already been accepted as members. It had always been envisaged that both farmers and 'trade' technicians would have a part to play in the new Society, and, as the initial restriction was progressively relaxed, trade technicians eagerly took up the places allocated to them, though farmers were at that time much less ready to join such a scientifically-orientated society. In 1947 the desirable balance between the three main categories of membership had been defined by the Executive as 67% technical, 25% farmers and 8% 'trade'. It is perhaps remarkable that, as at April, 1995, the actual figures for declared areas of interest were 63% technical (i.e. scientists, advisers and teachers), 29% farmers and 8% 'trade'! The presence in the Society's membership of a balance of all sections of the industry gives a unique - and envied - quality to all BGS activities, because of the benefit each group gains from close contact with the others. It must be said that each of these categories into which the membership can be divided has made a major contribution to the Society's success. Overseas members have always been important to the Society. As early as 1947 they were already representative of 10 countries in 4 continents. They now total 219 in some 42 countries. Although distance makes full participation difficult for many, it is usual to find a number of overseas members at the Society's conferences.

'Technical people employed by public authority' As defined by Sir George Stapledon, this category of membership includes scientists from research institutes, academics from universities and colleges, and technicians from the Government advisory services and thus those for whom the Society was originally designed. As befits an essentially scientific society, scientists, advisers and teachers have always provided the majority of both its members and its Presidents.

The scientists have included the only three to have received the ultimate accolade of a second term of Presidential office. The first of course was its illustrious founder, Sir George himself, who oversaw the Society's development over its first two years; the second his immediate successor, Dr. W. Davies, who was reelected for a second term in 1959/60; and now Professor Roger Wilkins,

President first in 1986/7 and re-elected in 1995 to lead the Society into its second half-century. Each in his own way has made an immense contribution to the Society's high reputation, both at home and abroad. The incomparable Sir George remains an icon of scientific grassland management throughout the world. William Davies, first Director of the Grassland Research Institute at Hurley, is remembered for his warm humanity as well as for his wise leadership of a dedicated research team, a tireless champion of the BGS, especially in enhancing its reputation abroad. In 1946 he played a prominent part in reviving and reestablishing the International Grassland Congress, and organising the Fifth Congress in the Netherlands in 1949, after a break of 12 years. In 1963 he was again in the forefront in helping to initiate the European Grassland Federation and was himself made an Honorary Life President of that organisation. His support and enthusiasm for the local grassland societies movement was reflected in the encouragement he gave to GRI staff to accept speaking engagements at their meetings throughout the country. Roger Wilkins has very much followed in Dr. Davies' footsteps, with a formidable reputation, both nationally and internationally. He has also been behind a number of the initiatives which the Society has successfully developed. Future BGS historians will undoubtedly have in him a most suitable subject for eulogy.

One of the most useful contributions made by members in the advisory services - both public and private - has been the part they have played in the formation and organisation of local grassland societies. They have frequently played a vital role in these, often as Secretary, committee member or even taking their turn as Chairman. Public and private advisory services together have formed a most valuable link between the local societies and BGS, not least in the organisation of the various BGS competitions.

Farmers As Sir George and his 'fellow conspirators' had visualised from the start, farmers have played an increasingly important part in the Society's affairs. They have indeed a vital role, in the translation of science into practice and, in reverse, as originators of practical methods, techniques and problems to stimulate further scientific investigation and research. Farmers attracted to the Society have always been people with a keen appreciation of the value of science to farming progress. In these 50 years such farmers have multiplied many fold as more and more of the younger men and women entering the industry have enjoyed the advantage of formal scientific training at universities and agricultural colleges.

From its earliest days, when farmers accounted for less than 10% of membership, there have been among them men of great vision and ability who have to date provided 9 Presidents from among their ranks. Mr. Sam Cray, from Medstead in Hampshire, was the first farmer President. He was a deeply thoughtful innovator and student of the scientific approach to grassland farming and livestock management. Being also a director of the company Cow and Gate, he had an intimate knowledge of both sides of the dairy industry. Like his contemporary and later President (1966/7) Mr. Rex Paterson, he was a pioneer of grassland recording, and a fluent and lucid speaker who played a major part in BGS debates.

The other farmers who, over the years, succeeded to the Presidential role, are also household names in the farming industry, each bringing his own gifts to the office and one, Mr. David Cray, following his father into that office. Many other well-known farmer members (not all can be President) have made major contributions to the Society's success, particularly, but not exclusively, through serving as BGS Regional Representatives and involvement with Summer Meetings.

'Trade' members - contribution of the ancillary industries When in 1947 research workers and other technically qualified staff of the ancillary industries were officially encouraged to join the Society, the 8% of membership allocated was quickly taken up, and these 'trade' members soon began to make a substantial contribution to its benefit, both individually, often as members of the Executive and other BGS committees, and through financial support given by their employers in various forms of sponsorship. Employees of major national companies supplying fertilizers, seed and machinery have naturally been the more prominent numerically, and their companies have given the greatest support financially, although smaller, more local firms have always given marvellously generous support to Summer Meetings especially, which depend heavily on sponsorship to keep attendance fees at an affordable level.

The first 'trade' President was elected in 1977. Mr. R. A. (Dick) Powell - appropriately enough in the 21st year of his membership - had been deeply involved in the local societies movement from its beginnings and, as with other Presidents, had served on the Executive and other BGS Committees. Other 'trade' members who have served as President include Dr. John Brockman (a 'trade' member prior to his lectureship at Seale-Hayne), Mr. Ken Nelson and Mr. John Farmer, each making a significant contribution to the Society's development.

Affiliated local grassland societies
It took 3 years for Surrey's example in forming a County Grassland Society (1954) to be followed elsewhere, but once the breakthrough was made the idea spread throughout the country at an accelerating pace. The impetus was given in 1957 when, in response to a request from the BGS Executive, the Surrey Society nominated a member's farm to be included in the programme of the Summer Meeting, based that year at Reading University. Surrey seized the opportunity to display one of the best-managed grassland farms in the county and to publicise through commentary and a photographic exhibit the aims, activities and benefits of a local grassland society, and how it could complement the work of the BGS by bringing advances in grassland management more intimately to the attention of the local farming community. In March 1958 an article describing the

formation and development of the Surrey Society was published in Volume 13 of the BGS Journal (Powell, 1958).

The effect was immediate. Before the end of 1957 the Yorkshire Society and Sussex Association of Grassland Study Groups had been formed and affiliated to BGS, and there were many calls upon leading members of the Surrey Society to speak to meetings in other counties where a local society was contemplated. By 1960 there were 7, by 1970, 48 and by 1992 the peak of 73 local societies. More recently, due to pressures on both time and money and changes in local circumstances, three have ceased operation, and one or two others are teetering on the brink, mainly those in predominantly arable areas, but the great majority continue to flourish.

Local grassland societies have been a fertile source of farmer recruits to BGS, especially as more and more have had the experience of hosting a Summer Meeting in their territory. The BGS in turn assists them in a variety of ways, both practically and financially for the very modest cost of affiliation. It provides their officers and members with 'public liability' insurance, provides the expenses for one speaker per year for the first 3 years, involves them in its competitions, gives them publicity at events and is always ready with guidance and advice. *Grass Farmer* is supplied to them in bulk at a price per issue less than that of many daily newspapers. Competitions, in particular the National Silage Competition, form a valuable bond between the parent Society and the affiliates.

Local grassland societies have tended to be organised somewhat differently in various parts of the United Kingdom. In England it is usually on a county basis, in Wales on a more localised, district basis but with a Welsh Federation of Grassland Societies co-ordinating many activities for Wales as a whole, and in Scotland it tends towards a regional basis round the agricultural colleges. Northern Ireland is ably served by the Ulster Grassland Society and the Fermanagh Grassland Club. In total the membership of affiliated local grassland societies is around 10,000. They represent a very significant part of the forward-looking grassland farmers of the country.

Meetings and Conferences

Until the mid 1980s the programme of the British Grassland Society revolved around three main types of meeting: Summer Meetings, Winter Meetings and Occasional Symposia.

Summer Meetings The Summer Meeting, usually held in July and stretching over 4 to 5 days (including arrival and departure), have been held every year since 1945, except for 1952 and 1968 (cancelled due to Foot and Mouth disease). Planned 3 or 4 years in advance, they are organised by a Local Committee appointed by the host organisation, originally a university, college or research institute, but since the 1960s more usually a local grassland society or a group of them. There are usually one or more locally-based BGS members on the

Committee with experience of Summer Meetings, and advice and guidance given by the BGS Secretary and Regional Representative. The full objectives and detailed procedure for Summer Meetings are set out in the comprehensive 'Guidelines for Summer Meetings' issued by the Executive to assist Local Committees and maintain the high standards which members have come to expect. The Local Committee selects a theme and title suited to the area and their planned programme of visits, allocates areas of responsibility to its members, and prepares a detailed budget. Both plan and budget have to be approved by the Society's Executive Council. The aim is to produce an affordable cost to delegates attending but to avoid any loss, which has to be borne by the parent Society (BGS). Any profit which does accrue is shared equally by the host Society and the BGS. To achieve this delicate balance requires both meticulous planning and a first-class treasurer, whose most important ally is the member of the Committee charged with the task of obtaining sponsorship from both national and local commercial companies. Fortunately generous commercial support has always been forthcoming, though in times of financial stringency the task of fund raiser gets ever more difficult.

The objective of the meeting is an in-depth study of the strengths and problems of grassland farming in the area visited and any R & D being conducted in the vicinity. The programme will include visits to relevant research stations and development farms, where these are available, and to selected examples of farms, systems and methods typical of the area visited and related to the chosen theme, although a completely atypical example may be included where it is of sufficient interest. Recent practice is for the delegates to assemble informally, usually on a Sunday afternoon, and after dinner attend a formal session of welcome, conducted by the Host Vice-President, at which they will be given the history and main physical and climatic features of the area to be visited, together with a brief description of routes to be followed, main farming types to be seen, and the actual visits to be made over the ensuing three days. There is also an Alternative Programme of visits of a more general nature, intended initially for wives accompanying their husband delegates and wishing to see what the area has to offer. In practice many delegates are husband-and-wife farming partnerships and the ladies - and some of the men - opt on a daily basis between the two programmes.

On the evening after the first day's visits the BGS AGM is held, with a Report on the past year from the Executive Council presented by the outgoing President, the Treasurer's Report, and the Address by the incoming President. On the second evening an entertainment is frequently arranged, usually with a strong local flavour, and on the last evening the Society's Annual Dinner is held, a toast to the Society being proposed by a distinguished guest. In 1992 at Cheltenham the Society was honoured by the presence and superb speech of Her Royal Highness, the Princess Royal. There are often one or more optional visits arranged for the morning of the fourth day, usually to see research work, farms or gardens associated with the base at which delegates have been accommodated.

Winter Meetings Held annually since 1947, Winter Meetings were for many years one-day meetings in London on the Friday of Smithfield Week and became an established feature of this important event in the calendar of the whole agricultural industry. However, as recession began to bite towards the end of the 1980s, the annual pilgrimage to the Metropolis began to dwindle, and with it attendance at the Winter Meeting. So following a rather inconclusive survey of members' opinions, the Executive Council decided to try a break with tradition and move the event out of London to a hotel venue and change the format to a residential event, offering much greater opportunity for both formal and informal discussion, often with a broad-based programme. Timing was brought forward from early December to late November, thus also providing a 'slot' in or around February for symposia on specific topics. While not perhaps suiting everyone, the new Winter Meetings which have, until this year, been held at the Abbey Hotel, Great Malvern, are now well-established and have proved popular with the majority. The topics for the Winter Meetings for 1970 onwards are given in Appendix 2.

Proceedings of the Winter Meetings have at different times been produced before the event and also as edited publications in the BGS Occasional Symposium series, with some inevitable delay in the latter case. It has recently been decided to standardise on 'camera ready' submission of text for publication and distribution to delegates at the meetings.

Occasional Symposia These conferences are arranged to explore the latest technical knowledge and its practical application relating to a particular defined topic, e.g. 'Grazing' (1985), 'Big Bale Silage' (1989). They are usually residential, though some are one-day events. Invited speakers include research workers - some from overseas - advisors, and grassland farmers whose experiences illustrate the practical possibilities and problems. Offered papers may be included as theatre or poster presentations, and, as at Winter Meetings, featured in the Proceedings, which thus provide comprehensive statements on the current state of technical knowledge and its practical application and are subsequently much in demand.

Joint Meetings It has always been BGS policy to co-operate as fully as possible with other organisations with kindred and related interests. Thus a number of joint conferences have been held with such as the British Society of Animal Science (formerly BSAP), the British Veterinary Association, the National Sheep Association, British Ecological Society, the former Milk Marketing Board and the Institute of Biology, of which the Society is an affiliate. The Society has also been pleased to host a number of EGF Meetings. The proceedings of most of these have also been published in the Occasional Symposium Series. A list of the various Occasional Conferences is given in Appendix 2.

BGS Research Conferences The first conference of this type was held at the Welsh Agricultural College, Aberystwyth in 1988. It was hoped that presentation to and response from what is largely a peer group (but from differing disciplines) would benefit both work at an early stage and workers early in their careers. Programmes consist of offered papers presenting original research on any aspect of grassland and forage production and utilisation. The plan was to rotate the chosen venues round the UK, with emphasis on work in progress in that particular vicinity. The first was a considerable success, attracting 135 delegates. Three more have since been held, at the Scottish Agricultural College, Auchincruive (1990), Greenmount College, Northern Ireland (1992) and the University of Reading (1994). In each of the last two Research Conferences a single *invited* paper has been included, sponsored by the Stapledon Memorial Trust; they were given, respectively, by Prof. Roger Wilkins (IGER and Reading University) and Prof. Len 't Mannetje (Agricultural University of the Netherlands). The four of these conferences so far held have successfully met their objectives and have between them attracted 150 theatre papers, 160 poster presentations and 445 delegates, including a number from overseas. Planned to be held at 2-year intervals, the next such event would be due in 1996. But because of a congested programme of meetings in the Jubilee year 1995/6, the next Research Conference will be held in September, 1997 based at Seale-Hayne College at the joint invitation of the University of Plymouth and IGER.

The recently developed series of BGS Discussion Meetings has been dealt with in some detail in Part 1. Mention has also been made of possible 'members only' meetings on some occasions and the decision by the Executive Council to explore how recognition and support can be offered to 'special interest groups' within the membership. It is likely that all these will play a significant part in future programmes of activities.

Publications

Grass and Forage Science High on the list of the Society's objectives has always been "the publication of any periodicals, books and leaflets considered desirable." Of these, by far the most important is the Journal, *Grass and Forage Science*, currently demanding a print run of 1,700 copies. Since its second year, in 1947, each annual Volume has consisted of four issues, published in March, June, September and December. Supplied to each member and Local Society, copies also go to subscribers throughout the world. Its main purpose is to publish the results of research and development. The Editor will now consider for publication papers which deal with agricultural production from grass and other forage crops, with recreational and amenity uses of grassland and with the environmental implications of grassland systems, irrespective of climatic zone. Before the Society had a separate magazine (*Grass Farmer*) as a vehicle for more practically-orientated articles, the Journal also included some of these, from time to time, as farmer membership increased.

Now completing its 50th year of publication, the Journal has had 6 Editors. Each in his turn has stamped his own authority upon it and further enhanced the ever higher reputation established by his predecessors. Dr. H. I. Moore, then of Leeds University and subsequently Principal of Seale-Hayne College, was Sir George Stapledon's nominee as first Editor and was responsible for establishing its format and the foundations of the formidable reputation it was to achieve. When he became President, he was temporarily succeeded by Mr. P. Mackintosh before Mr. A. G. G. Hill, Director of the Commonwealth Bureau of Pastures and Field Crops, took over as Editor in 1954. It was during his 20 years in that post that the Journal fully established its reputation as the world's leading scientific grassland publication - a reputation fully maintained by his successors, Dr. J. G. W. Jones of Reading University (1975 - 1985), Dr. R. J. Lewington (1986 - 1987) and, since 1988, Dr. A. Younger, of the University of Newcastle-upon-Tyne.

The Editor is assisted by a deputy editor and a panel of associate editors with expertise in particular fields. There are also advisory editors based throughout the world who promote the Journal's use by the scientists in their areas.

From its early days the Journal's Editor had the powerful support of a Journal Committee, later to become the BGS Publications Committee. It was chaired by Mr. F. R. Horne, Director of the National Institute of Agricultural Botany, until his death in 1975. His place was taken by Prof. W. Holmes of Wye College and subsequently, in 1984, by Dr. John Brockman, a senior lecturer at Seale-Hayne College. On his retirement in 1992, he was succeeded by the present Chairman and former Editor, Dr. J. G. W. Jones, of Reading University.

Grass and Forage Science continues to maintain and even enhance its enviable worldwide reputation, and financially is now not only sound but contributing positively to the Society's income.

Grass Farmer   The launch and development of this practically-orientated publication from its humble beginnings as a *Local Societies' News Sheet* is described quite fully in the 'Forty Year History' (Powell and Corrall, 1985). After its relaunch as *Grass Farmer* in 1977 it was supported by a small group of commercial companies who made three-year commitments to take an agreed number of pages of advertising space. It has been published regularly, at first twice yearly and later three times a year, with a professional editor assisted by an editorial panel representative of the main categories of membership. Its two Editors, Mr. John Parry first and, since 1980, Mr. Herbert Daybell, have achieved for this publication an excellent reputation and a circulation of 8,500 copies, mainly to BGS members and to the members of affiliated local societies. It has increasingly become the link between science and practice which its progenitors visualised and is highly valued by grassland farmers throughout the UK.

The system of support by a group of advertisers, with periodic changes in the composition of the group, continued until the late 1980s. In recent years changes in the market place have seen the demise or change of many of the larger companies ancillary to grassland farming. This, together with a generally depressed market, has made it increasingly difficult to attract the level of advertising revenue needed. In 1993 and 1994 the Society's accounts showed losses against this publication. The Executive Council is currently engaged in a comprehensive review of the content, format and all other aspects of this magazine. So far the response from affiliated local grassland societies has strongly supported the Council's own belief in its intrinsic value as a communication admirably fulfilling the objectives of the Society.

Text books The first book commissioned by BGS was a comprehensive volume entitled *Grass; its Production and Utilisation*, written by a consortium of authors expert in their particular field, and edited by Prof. W. Holmes, then Dean of the Agricultural Faculty of London University and also Chairman of the BGS Publications Committee. First published in 1980, it quickly became a popular textbook. A second edition, with extensive revision and several new authors, was published in 1981. Currently a third edition is under consideration. Two further commissioned textbooks followed *Grass. The Sward Measurement Handbook*, again prepared by a panel of authors and published in 1981, with Dr. John Hodgson as senior editor, now in its second edition (1993) edited by Alison Davies, and *Herbage Intake Handbook* edited by Dr. David Leaver published in 1982, with a second edition in preparation under the editorship of Mr. Peter Penning.

The Occasional Symposium Series This series of publications was introduced in 1963 to group under one heading the edited proceedings of meetings and conferences, and includes those of a variety of different types. For instance, the first in the Series was the Proceedings of the Hurley Symposium in 1963 at which the European Grassland Federation was inaugurated, and subsequently those of other EGF Meetings held in the UK were included (Nos. 1, 4, 11 and 14). It also includes the proceedings of some BGS Winter Meetings and joint meetings with other organisations. The normal practice is to reproduce full texts of all invited papers and extended summaries of the offered papers given. Because of the structure of the programmes at these conferences this series provides statements of the up-to-date technical knowledge and practical experience of the subjects studied by each conference.

Proceedings of Research Conferences The proceedings of each of the four BGS Research Conferences so far have been published, containing extended summaries of each of the papers given, as theatre or poster presentations, and also, in the later two, the full texts of the Stapledon Memorial Lectures.

The above BGS publications, together with Winter Meeting proceedings, have built up a formidable library of technical and practical literature which has contributed substantially to the Society's worldwide reputation. Apart from the special arrangements with Blackwell Science in the case of the Journal and the textbook *Grass*, BGS publications are marketed direct from the BGS Office. In addition to the Society's own publications the Office also acts as sole distributor for the practical textbook *Milk from Grass*, which was published jointly by GRI and ICI Fertilizers in 1982, with a second edition published in 1991, this time with a team of authors from IGER, SAC and ICI.

Competitions and Awards

The most well-known, and longest-running, BGS competition has been the National Silage Competition. It has always been much more than merely an assessment of silage quality. For example silage analysis accounts for only 30 of the 100 possible marks. All aspects of the production and *utilisation* of the silage are taken into account. Over the 16 years the marking system has evolved to take account of changing knowledge and circumstances so that, for example, marks are now given for effective effluent control and waste management, safe practice and animal welfare.

The National Silage Competition was sponsored by ICI Fertilizers from the start in 1979 until 1991, and since 1992 by Kemira Fertilisers. Both ADAS and SAC provide sponsorship in kind by the help given by their staff in various stages of the competition. The competition, held annually, begins with competitions within local societies, the winners going on to participate in a regional round, in each of the nine BGS regions of UK, and the winners of that proceeding on to the National Final. A team of three judges travels round the nine finalists' farms, making a very thorough assessment of all aspects of the competition. The three rounds are encompassed within a period of about two months, each judged as far as possible on a common schedule of points. The ultimate National winner becomes the holder, for one year, of a challenge trophy donated by the sponsor and in addition the winner and runner up receive 5 and 3 tonnes of fertilizer respectively.

Awards are presented at a ceremony in London to which all nine finalists are invited, together with the press and representatives of the national bodies with some involvement in the use of silage. The presentation is made by an eminent agriculturalist, and lessons about excellence in silage-making and utilisation are brought out by the national judges. The event is now well established and it has been possible to attract some very eminent presenters, most recently His Grace the Duke of Westminster, and an audience of about 90. Subsequently, wherever possible, farm visits are organised to each of the nine finalists' farms.

The Grass to Meat awards were established in 1979/80 in close association with the Meat and Livestock Commission and based on the results of MLC recording. The 'Golden Hoof' trophies were awarded in four of the eight mainland BGS Regions each year (8 Regions during 'Money from Grass Year' 1983). Again, farm walks were organised on the winners' farms. This competition continued very effectively for 12 years, when continually rising standards made identification of new winners too difficult.

In 1986, a grassland management competition sponsored by UKF was started on a trial basis in the South-Eastern Region. Each local society entered a team of three farmers, a beef, a sheep and a milk producer, with the detailed inspection and marking emphasis put on one enterprise each year. It was held in this region for 4 years, and in the South-West Region for three, with a fourth year involving only one animal species.

Some local societies have run their own grassland management competitions for a number of years. Similar competitions have been held in Northern Ireland and Wales for several years, principally concerned with the management of summer grazing. In 1995 a common set of rules and scoring has been adopted by both these regions and other regions are expected to take up this competition, at least on a trial basis, with the help of some financial support from BGS.

Following the experience of the South-West Scotland Grassland Society, BGS held an 'Innovations' competition for local grassland societies in 1987 and 1990; the final being judged at the National Grassland Demonstration at Stoneleigh, where the finalists' entries were exhibited on the BGS stand.

Grassland Recording

Following publication of the Barker Report in 1954, the Government set up an inquiry (the Caine Committee) to report on grassland utilisation in the UK. The BGS submitted both oral and written evidence to this committee, which in its report (published November 1958) referred to "the BGS grassland recording recommendations" and in their conclusions recommended that grassland recording "should be extensively promoted". This was a major factor in the Society's decision to initiate the 1959/63 investigation into grassland recording methods. Dr. H. K. Baker of GRI Hurley was in charge of this project, assisted by a sub-committee representing the MMB, the Ministry and National Agricultural Advisory Service (at regional level) and the local grassland societies in Surrey and Sussex, which provided 20 of the 23 dairy farms co-operating in the study, with the remaining 3 in Hampshire. The necessary funding was provided in part by BGS, but mainly through the MMB's secondment of a specially recruited consulting officer (Mr. R. D. Baker, who later became a head of department at Hurley) to be the investigation's field officer. Generous logistical support (office accommodation, laboratory and statistical facilities) were provided by GRI. The Report and Recommendations were published in a series of articles which appeared in the Journal in the 1960s.

Further details of this and the subsequent investigation, again with local society participation, for development of a similar beef and sheep recording scheme were given in the 'Forty Year History'. Recording forms and instructions for their use were widely distributed and used, especially by MMB and MLC, and used by the latter as the basis for judging the BGS/MLC Grass-to-Meat Awards. The two grassland recording schemes developed from this BGS initiative played a useful part for some 15-20 years in assisting many dairy, beef and sheep farmers to improve their grassland management and provide an illustration of the value of BGS/local society cooperation, of mutual benefit to both. It suggests a resource of which much more use might be made in the future, especially to fill the development gap between research and practice which has been left by the demise of EHFs and commercially funded development farms.

The BGS Award

Each year nominations are invited from the membership for an individual considered to have made an outstanding contribution to the understanding or appreciation of grassland husbandry and technology. Nominations are assessed by a distinguished panel appointed by Executive Council and an award made if

Table 2.   Winners of the BGS Award

1979 Prof.W Holmes	1980 Dr F J Gordon
1981 Mr E Bushby OBE	1982 Prof. W F Raymond
1983 Dr M E Castle	1984 M G J F Copeman
1985 Mr G Williams	1986 Dr J D Leaver
1987 Dr J Frame	1988 Mr I B Howie
1989 Dr R J Wilkins	1990 Mr A J Corrall
1991 Prof. J Hodgson	1992 Mr P O'Keeffe
1993 Mr J M M Munro	1994 Mr W I C Davies

there is considered to be a suitable candidate. Up to and including 1994, 16 awards have been made. Each winner holds, for a year, the handsome silver trophy, specially commissioned by the BGS, and retains an engraved salver. Those to whom this Award has been made have in every case made a major contribution to the Society's success and the benefit of grassland farming.

Scholarships and Bursary Awards

Reference has already been made in Part 1 to the award of various scholarships and grants, mainly to young members, to facilitate studies of grassland topics in overseas countries. More recently, in 1988, a sum of invested capital was set aside, from which the annual interest (around £1,000) could be allocated to BGS members to help meet travel or education expenses incurred in work or study deemed to be furthering the Society's objectives. To date some 20 awards have been made.

In celebration of the Society's fiftieth anniversary a special research studentship has been established. It was awarded for the first time in 1994 to Miss Sharon Danby to work for three years on the utilization of dairy farm wastes on grazed grassland. She is based at IGER North Wyke and is also registered for a PhD degree at Reading University. It is hoped that support may be attracted to make this the first of a series of BGS Research Studentships.

Participation by BGS in other national and major regional events

Since its beginning the National Grassland Demonstration, later to become the Kemira Grassland Event, has provided free stand space for the Society and, at these and other events, BGS has promoted recruitment and sale of its publications. These events have also been used to promote the affiliated local societies, with a list of secretaries and a map showing their locations, and the National Silage Competition and other BGS activities.

International involvement

The Society is proud of its international role. As well as having a significant number of BGS members resident outside the UK, the Society has always maintained a close relationship with similar organisations overseas. At the invitation of the Ministry of Agriculture the organisation of the 8th IGC, held at Reading in 1960, was largely the work of the Society, including the pre-Congress Research and Farming Tours, with tour managers appointed from members employed in the Ministry and commercial advisory services. This hugely popular and successful event was presided over by HRH The Duke of Edinburgh, who gave the Opening Address. It was attended by 592 delegates from 56 countries.

It was at the European Conference on Forage Production, held in Switzerland in June 1962 that the idea of a European Grassland Federation was strongly promoted by BGS delegates. This resulted in a request to the British delegation to arrange a symposium at Hurley the following year, at which their proposal might be pursued, and the BGS was asked to prepare a draft Constitution for the proposed Federation, for discussion at that meeting. In the event, at the final business session of the Symposium ('The Agronomic Evaluation of Grassland') representatives in attendance from 10 European Grassland Societies (plus the UK and 5 other countries) agreed the formation of the Federation, appointed an Executive Committee charged with organisation of the next Meeting to be held in the Netherlands in 1965, and voted Dr. W. Davies an Honorary Life President.

Especially in the earlier years, BGS organised tours for its members to other European countries, beginning in 1949 with a short tour in Eire. Subsequently there were visits to the Netherlands (1952), Sweden (1953), Denmark (1958), Eire again in 1959, France (1961) in both May and September, and to the Netherlands again in 1962; while in that year also the Society organised a visit to England by about 35 members of the French Society (*Association Francaise pour la Production Fourragere*). This included a visit to the farm of a member of Surrey Grassland Society participating in the BGS Grassland Recording Investigation.

More recently (September 1985) a BGS party visited Brittany, principally to study the use of legumes. An itinerary prepared by Dr. Pflimlin, of ITEB, and his colleagues, who gave full technical support to the farm visits, was greatly appreciated and enjoyed by the BGS party, who also took special note of the important part played here by maize silage in storage feeding in all seasons.

The Society has played an important part in the development of grassland research and practice wherever in the world the farming of ruminant livestock is of importance, especially by providing speakers at international conferences and through distribution of its Journal.

The Secretariat

For the Society's successful establishment and subsequent development an immense debt of gratitude is owed to the dedicated Secretariat which provides the administrative and financial heart. A succession of able Secretaries and Treasurers - for 25 years the two posts combined in one person until, in 1976, the pressure simply became too great - has served the Society magnificently. Those who served the Society so well up to 1985 were severally given due recognition in the Forty Year History (Powell and Corrall, 1985). Mr. Jim Corrall and Mr. Charles Crichton, both appointed, respectively, as Secretary and Treasurer, in 1982 have continued in these posts with distinction. Jim Corrall retired at the 1995 AGM, and the Society's new Secretary, Mr. Michael Helps, previously a senior member of ADAS, now carries the torch forward.

The Secretaries and Treasurers in turn, have had sterling assistance from an equally dedicated office staff. The BGS Office has been run by a succession of valuable contributors to the life and work of the Society in their role, among others, as book-keeper and secretary to the Society Secretary. These have included Mrs. Sheila Baker, Mrs. Shan Parker, Mrs. Rosemary Corrall and Mrs. Mary Johnson. All these have developed the post until it was recognised as having an individual administrative element as well as supporting the work of the Society Secretary. When Mrs. Jan Crichton was appointed in 1985 it was as Administrative Secretary to the Society, a post to which she has brought great energy, skill and dedication.

The volume and variety of work undertaken by the Secretariat has increased enormously, especially in recent years, as the number and scope of the Society's activities have expanded. To deal with this rapidly growing burden it has been essential to install up-to-date computer systems and all the additional office hardware associated with it. For many years the Society was fortunate in being provided with an office at Hurley from which to operate, at no charge or, latterly, a very modest rent. The Society Secretary also was, for a long period, a member of staff at Hurley, or in one case at Reading University, i.e. not paid by the Society. With increasing pressure on the bodies which used to provide services for the Society as 'in kind' support it has become necessary for BGS to become more self sufficient. In 1985 the Secretary became an employee of the Society, albeit on a part time contract. Then, with the closure of GRI, Hurley, the Society needed to rent its own office independently in 1991. Both of these factors have been financially significant. The present office is rented from the University of Reading and has proved a very satisfactory base not least because of the cooperation received from members of the Department of Agriculture. It says a great deal for the sagacity of the Executive Council and the astuteness of the Treasurers, in managing the Society's finances, that at the end of this first 50 years the Society finds itself in robust financial health with a substantial cushion of reserve, wisely invested.

Research and Development

The Special BGS R&D Group was set up in 1988 in an atmosphere of severe reductions in government funding of R&D. Under the chairmanship of Mr. David Cray, a farmer and Past President, its membership was chosen to represent science, advisory bodies and practical farming but, in the interests of independence, the scientists were chosen from those no longer employed in research. It was asked to study the situation and make recommendations to the Executive Council on what action the BGS should take to ensure continuation of essential research already in progress and to identify those areas and topics of research likely to be needed in the foreseeable future. The long-term objective was identified of achieving a satisfactory national strategy for the funding and co-ordination of R & D in grassland, forage crops and related livestock production. A detailed study of possible options led the Group (and subsequently Council) to decide that the only practical and fair way of funding such R & D would be through product levies. In its submission to Government, through the Office of Science and Technology, the Society emphasised the serious effects on the industry already suffered through withdrawal of R & D facilities (e.g. the closure of the IGER Station at Hurley) and that any further reductions would greatly handicap British agriculture in its competitive position *vis-a-vis* its European partners.

At an early stage the Society issued a press release expressing its concerns and began a wide-ranging series of consultations at the highest level with other interested parties such as MAFF, MMB, MLC, the NFU and others. It strongly supported the NFU proposal for a Milk Development Council (ultimately conceded by Government), although the Society would have preferred a joint Milk and Meat Development Council, as so much grassland R & D is of common interest to both product industries.

The R&D Group also drew up a comprehensive list of R & D priorities, subsequently approved by Council, covering 11 areas of study and 28 main subjects requiring investigation. In December 1994 a special newsletter was issued by the President, Dr. Cled Thomas, updating members on progress by BGS in this most important field of activity. He enclosed a copy of the listing of priority areas for R & D, and emphasised the Society's conviction that best progress in deciding research priorities could be made by mutual consultation and co-operation between all interested parties, a view strongly supported by the British Society of Animal Science.

THE FUTURE

This history has attempted to trace the development of the British Grassland Society since its inception and to catalogue the activities and achievements of its first fifty years. A number of individuals are mentioned by name, but many more, too numerous to mention, have also made their vital contributions. It is a proud record and today BGS stands poised to meet the challenges of the future. There are already indications of how these will differ from those of the past - the subject indeed of the 50th Anniversary Conference

In an increasingly competitive European and world environment, research and development will continue to be a no less vital resource than it has been since 1945. The Society has won wide acceptance of its claim to be a major voice in prescribing both the needs for future R&D and how it might be funded. Grassland will continue to be the major resource for Britain's important and valuable livestock industry, the bedrock of an agricultural industry which will be receiving much less Government support than hitherto, and increasingly responsible for the prosperity of its own future against overseas competition.

For the subsequent field development work, too, so essential a link in the translation of the fruits of research into practicable and profitable farming methods, the Society has, in its own broadly-based membership and its affiliated local societies, a rich resource ready for its use. There must be scope here for extension of the kind of collaboration which has already proven its potential in such projects as the BGS Grassland Recording Investigation and more recent surveys of farm practice. To make full use of this resource will not be easy, but the organisational skeleton on which the flesh of achievement might be hung already exists in the Society's regional structure and in the experience gained from the BGS National Silage Competition and others.

There is an urgent need, too, to reconcile what may often appear to be the conflicting interests of livestock production with environmental concern in its various forms. The mainly urban-based public appears still to be convinced that the members of the farming community, which has served this country so well in the past and will continue so to do, are as concerned as their critics for the preservation of the environment in which they reside and earn their living. The BGS and local societies are perhaps uniquely placed to combine and reconcile all these concerns in a management plan which will protect the legitimate interests of both farmer and general public alike. By reason of its membership and its past achievements and experience, the British Grassland Society is well equipped to meet the future with enthusiastic confidence.

REFERENCES

KERNOHAN J. T, (1955) Account of the First Ten Years. *Journal of the British Grassland Society*, **10**, 279-280.

POWELL R. A. (1958) The Surrey Grassland Society. *Journal of the British Grassland Society*, **13**, 76-77.

POWELL R. A. and CORRALL ROSEMARY, G. (1985) The British Grassland Society: the first 40 years. *Grass and Forage Science*, **40**, 383-402.

Appendix 1.   PRESIDENTS AND OFFICERS OF BGS

	President	Secretary	Treasurer	Assistant Secretary
1945-46	Sir George Stapledon	R O White	P A Linehan	
1946-47	Sir George Stapledon			
1947-48	Dr William Davies			
1949-50	Prof.T J Jenkin			
1950-51	Prof. S J Watson		J T Kernohan*	
1951-52	Prof. Martin Jones		J T Kernohan*	
1952-53	Dr H I Moore			
1953-54	Prof. P A Linehan			
1954-55	Prof. E T Jones			
1955-56	Dr H G Sanders			
1956-57	Mr A S Cray			
1957-58	Mr F R Horne		H K Baker*	
1958-59	Prof. M M Cooper			
1959-60	Dr William Davies			
1960-61	Mr J T Kernohan			
1061-62	Mr F H Garner			
1962-63	Mr H G Gill			
1963-64	Mr J Rowsell			
1964-65	Prof. P T Thomas		R S Tayler*	
1965-66	Dr H K Baker			
1966-67	Mr Rex Paterson			
1967-68	Mr I V Hunt			
1968-69	Prof. W Holmes			
1969-70	Prof. E K Woodford			
1970-71	Mr E Bushby			
1971-72	Mr W R Smith		J Morrison*	
1972-73	Dr D J Griffiths			
1973-74	Mr R S Tayler			
1974-75	Mr W F Raymond			
1975-76	Mr R W Waltham			
1976-77	Mr G J F Copeman	J Morrison	N Coward	N E Young
1977-78	Mr R A Powell	N E Young		W I C Davies
1978-79	Prof. J C Murdoch			
1979-80	Mr J L Davies			
1980-81	Mr A S Christensen			R D Sheldrick
1981-82	Dr M E Castle	R D Sheldrick	C Crichton	A J Corrall
1982-83	Dr J S Brockman	A J Corrall		R D Sheldrick
1983-84	Prof. C E Wright			J W G Parker
1984-85	Mr G E C Tedstone			
1985-86	Mr J K Nelson			
1986-87	Dr R J Wilkins			
1987-88	Mr W I C Davies			

Appendix 1 cont'd.   PRESIDENTS AND OFFICERS OF BGS

	President	Secretary	Treasurer	Assistant Secretary
1988-89	Mr D N Cray			Miss HV Knight
1989-90	Dr J Frame			
1990-91	Prof. F J Gordon			
1991-92	Mr J A Farmer			O D Davies
1992-93	Mr J Johnson			
1993-94	Mr R J W Slack			
1994-95	Dr C Thomas			
1995-96	Prof. R J Wilkins	M B Helps		

* = Secretary/Treasurer

Appendix 2.

Summer Meetings

1945	Stratford on Avon
1946	Aberdeen
1947	Aberystwyth
1948	Belfast
1949	Sutton Boninton
1950	Edinburgh
1951	Newton Abbot
1952	Cancelled, Foot & Mouth
1953	Wye, Kent
1954	Ayr, S W Scotland
1955	Cambridge
1956	Hereford
1957	Reading, Berkshire
1958	Northumberland
1959	Larne, N. Ireland
1960	Harrogate, Yorkshire
1961	Aberdeen, N of Scotland
1962	Surrey, Sussex & Hants
1963	Carmarthen, Wales
1964	Dublin & Cork
1965	Carlisle, Cumbria
1966	Sutton Bonington, Notts
1967	Newton Abbot, Devon
1968	Cancelled, Foot & Mouth
1969	Glasgow, S W Scotland
1970	Newport, Shropshire
1971	Wye, Kent
1972	Newcastle upon Tyne
1973	Herefordshire
1974	Yorkshire
1975	Bangor, N Wales
1976	Weymouth, Dorset
1977	Aberdeen, N of Scotland
1978	Norwich, Norfolk
1979	Newcastle-u-Lyme, Staffs
1980	Belfast, N. Ireland
1981	Winchester, Hampshire
1982	Crewe, Cheshire
1983	Newton Abbot, Cornwall & Devon
1984	Caerleon, S E Wales
1985	Sutton Bonington, Derby, Leics. & Notts
1986	Glasgow, SW & Central Scotland

1987	Reading, Berkshire
1988	Preston, Lancashire
1989	Carmarthen, Dyfyd,
1990	Penrith, Cumbria
1991	Cheltenham, Glos..
1992	Cork, Republic of Ireland
1993	Lackham, Wiltshire
1994	Aberdeen, N of Scotland
1995	Newport, Shropshire

Winter Meetings

1970	The Making & Feeding of Silage
1971	Summer Milk Production
1972	Intensification of Lowland Sheep Production
1973	Grassland Intensification
1974	Winter Feeding for Beef Production
1975	Potential of Grassland & Forage Production for Ruminants in Britain
1976	Forage Crops: Complement to Grass?
1977	Challenge of the Future
1978	Grazing Sward Production & Livestock Output
1979	Water Control & Grassland Productivity
1980	Supplementation and Effective Use of Grassland for Dairying
1981	Legumes & Fertilizers in Grassland Systems
1982	Contribution of Grass to Profitable Milk Production (Rex Paterson Mem. Trust*)
1983	Money from Grass (Climax mtg of national campaign)
1984	Adjusting to CAP Pressures
1985	Grassland Manuring
1986	Grassland Planning
1987	Grassland for the '90s
1988	Grassland Options for the Future
1989	Environmentally Responsible Grassland Management

Winter Meetings continued

1990 Management Issues for the Grassland Farmer in the '90s
1991 Grass on the Move
1992 Forward with Grass into Europe
1993 The Place for Grass in Land Use Systems
1994 Quality Milk and Meat foR Grassland Systems
1995 Grassland into the 21st Century

One-Day conferences

Big Bale Silage (1989)
Strategies for Weeds, Disease & Pest Control in Grassland (1992)

Discussion Meetings

High Dry Matter Silage (1994)
Extending the Grazing Season (1995)

Occasional Symposia

1. The Agronomic Evaluation of Grassland (1963) (EGF Mtg)
2. Beef Production & Marketing (1965)
3. Fodder Conservation (1967)
4. Hill Land Productivity (1968) (EGF Conf.)
5. Grass & Forage Breeding (1969)
6. White Clover Research (1969)
7. Forage on the Arable Farm (1972)
8. Pasture Utilization by the Grazing Animal (1975)
9. Green Crop Fractionation (1976)
10. Changes in Sward Composition & Productivity (1978)
11. Forage Conservation in the '80s (1979) (EGF)
12. Effective Use of Forage and Animal Resources in the Hills & Uplands (1980)
13. Plant Physiology & Herbage Production (1981)
14. Efficient Grassland Farming (1982) EGF Mtg)
15. Money from Grass (1983)
16. Forage Legumes (1984)
17. Machinery for Silage (1984)
18. Weeds Pest & Diseases of Grasses & Herbage Legumes (1985) (BCPC*)
19. Grazing (1985)
21. Efficient Sheep Production from Grass (1986) (NSA*)
22. Efficient Beef Production from Grass (1987) (BSAP*)
23. Silage for Milk Production (1988) (MMB*)
24. Milk & Meat from Forage Crops (1990)
28. Grassland Management & Nature Conservation (1993) (BES* & JNCC*)

(* = Joint Sponsor)

Advances in Grassland Technology over the Past Fifty Years

J. FRAME [1], R. D. BAKER [2] AND A.R. HENDERSON [3]

[1] 'Ard Choille', 13 St. Vincent Crescent, Alloway, Ayr KA7 4QW
(formerly SAC, Auchincruive)

[2] 28 Badgers Walk, Shiplake, Henley on Thames, Oxon RG9 3JQ
(formerly IGER, Hurley)

[3] 31 Falcon Avenue, Edinburgh EH10 4AL
(formerly SAC, Edinburgh)

INTRODUCTION

Grassland science is one of the youngest sciences and many notable advances, impressive in number and rate of appearance, have been made over the last half century. Some arose suddenly while others resulted from a slow accretion of knowledge or from refinements of previous technology. Some were rapidly adopted in practice, economic pressures being a powerful incentive. Others were more slowly incorporated or discarded on account of capital and labour requirements, risk or even complexity, though the technology remains 'on the shelf' until some further breakthrough is achieved. Specific external events, such as the energy crisis in 1973 or the imposition of agricultural production quotas, starting with milk in 1984, stimulated the uptake of certain technological advances. When highlighting technological developments it is also fitting to pay tribute to the pioneers Sir George Stapledon and William Davies who, together with their teams, laid the foundations during the pre- and post-Second World War period from which many advances were made, not least the multi-disciplinary approach to grassland research and development. There is also an art in grassland management, as farmers will testify. Sometimes the art preceded the science, as exemplified by the technological innovations by leading grassland farmers such as Rex Paterson, Richard Waltham and Lloyd Forster. Intensification was the watchword for the first forty years but extensification, nature conservation, environmentally-friendly systems and sustainability represent the new ethos which has emerged during the last decade.

AGRONOMY

Plant breeding and evaluation

The increases in grassland productivity and nutritive value that have occurred over the last half century owe a great deal to successful plant breeding. The process of developing and testing a new variety takes some 15 years from initial selection until it reaches the farmer. This time scale explains why many new grass varieties became available, especially from continental Europe, 15-20 years after the Second World War. The introduction of the 1964 Plant Varieties and Seeds Act, enabling breeders to obtain protection for their varieties and royalties

31

for their use, was a major fillip to the flow of varieties with improved production and persistence, particularly winter-hardy perennial ryegrasses from the Netherlands, though increasing numbers of 'home-bred' varieties are now emerging. The development of tetraploid ryegrasses and hybrids between perennial and Italian ryegrass, both diploid and tetraploid, were among marked individual achievements. A steady increase of 0.6% annually in the DM potential of perennial ryegrass varieties added to the National Institute of Agricultural Botany (NIAB) 'Recommended List' has been reported (Aldrich, 1987).

Improvement in white clover production was achieved by the introduction, in 1964, of Grasslands Huia, a New Zealand variety which has since dominated world white clover usage. However, since the 1970s, varieties have been released, notably from the Welsh Plant Breeding Station (WPBS), with improved productivity and cold tolerance and suitable for different methods and intensities of utilization. Red clover varieties, including superior tetraploids, were developed with increased resistance to clover rot (*Sclerotinia trifoliorum*) and stem eelworm (*Ditylenchus dipsaci*), while lucerne varieties, with resistance to stem eelworm and/or Verticillium wilt (*Verticillium albo-atrum*), were bred.

In contrast to early plant breeding, modern programmes are supported by multi-disciplinary teams comprising plant physiologists, agronomists and plant and animal nutritionists, thus extending the range of selection criteria. From advances in genetic engineering and molecular biology, gene transfer systems are now being used to develop new traits such as disease and pest resistance, better nutritive value and more efficient physiological processes in grasses and forage legumes.

Varietal comparisons in the early post-war years were mainly made between single plants, or rows of plants, with the objective of type classification rather than assessment of productivity, but eventually species and variety evaluations were carried out, at a range of UK centres, in small plot cutting trials. Following the OEEC/EPA Project 210 'International Trials with Grass and Clover', which involved evaluating grass and clover varieties at 47 sites in 9 countries (Cowling and Kelly, 1960), varietal testing was expanded on a UK coordinated basis. NIAB published a 'Descriptive List' of grass varieties in 1960 and its first 'Recommended List' in 1968.

After UK accession to the EEC in 1973 statutory performance testing was followed by statutory distinctness, uniformity and stability (DUS) assessment and value for cultivation and use (VCU) trials, with frequent and infrequent cutting of plots to simulate grazing and conservation, respectively. The performance of grass and legume varieties, as judged by their yield, nutritive value and the factors affecting persistence, determined their suitability for the 'National List' and eventually regional 'Recommended Lists'. On-farm grazed trials of perennial ryegrasses and white clovers were also used by NIAB to provide additional information on the suitability of a variety for the 'Recommended List'. The synergistic relationship between evaluators and breeders has undoubtedly had positive effects on the development of improved forage varieties.

Seed production The present-day buyer of certified herbage seed is assured of a product guaranteed in its stated genetic and analytical quality as a result of the evolution of variety maintenance, multiplication and testing. The move towards named varieties has accelerated since 1967 when various seed certification schemes were consolidated into a comprehensive national scheme for pedigree seed certification, which became statutory in the 1970s. This scheme ensured that varieties produced in the UK were maintained true to genetic type and varietal purity by field inspection of seed crops and by maintenance of verification plots for seed stocks. Similar schemes evolved abroad under the auspices of the Organisation for Economic Co-operation and Development (OECD) so that seed companies could trade seed internationally with standard certification descriptions.

Formal testing of seed lots for viability, germination and purity started in 1921 with the establishment of the Official Seed Testing Station (OSTS) but over the years various improvements in methodology and standards were introduced. Statutory seed quality requirements were laid down in the official Seeds Regulations and included minimum standards for certified seed of the different herbage species though there were also Higher Voluntary Standards (HVS) to aim for (MAFF, 1983). Recently there has been a decline in home-produced seed production, compared with the early years, but the remaining specialist seed producers have refined their production procedures and, in conjunction with a high degree of mechanization, have improved seed harvesting, handling, drying, cleaning and storage (WPBS, 1978; NIAB, 1980, 1982).

Seed mixtures and establishment
Ley farming was a traditional method of regenerating soil fertility in alternate husbandry systems but was adapted to permanent grassland during and after the Second World War, when over 2.5 million ha were ploughed up. Researchers and leading farmers began to appreciate grass as a crop and to use newly-bred superior grass varieties in seed mixtures. It was recognized that white and red clovers were vital for good ley productivity and that lime and phosphate were needed to maintain basic soil fertility. While there has always been a case for reseeding run-down and unproductive pastures *inter alia* to exploit the potential of new herbage varieties, the fact that well managed long term or permanent grass could be as productive as new reseeds, at least under low to moderate soil fertility, has been increasingly recognized (Mudd and Meadowcroft, 1964; Hopkins *et al.*, 1990). Nevertheless, as Lazenby (1981) observed, the wartime plough-up campaign resulted in a revitalization of agriculture generally, engendering a spirit of adventure and flexibility of outlook lacking since the late Nineteenth Century.

In the early post-war years complex general purpose or 'shotgun' grass seed mixtures were the norm. These mixtures contained a good proportion of commercial grass species, often landraces or ecotypes. While these were not all 'stemmy and shortlived', as often alleged, most of them were gradually outclassed and replaced by more productive, bred, varieties. Initially these were the 'S' varieties from WPBS, in the 1960s, but later, and increasingly, continental European-bred grass varieties. Simpler special purpose mixtures were devised for use in swards for intensive grazing or silage production under high fertilizer regimes. This was based on the rationale that modern varieties had been bred for specific requirements and therefore for sowing alone, or in a mixture with one or two varieties with compatible characteristics, to realize their potential. In particular, perennial ryegrass was increasingly used in mixtures for medium- and long-term swards, and Italian ryegrass, or hybrid ryegrass, for short term swards because ryegrasses were the most competitive and most responsive to increasing fertilizer N application and had the highest yield and nutritive value. Perennial ryegrass has become by far the most widely sown grass species in UK grassland farming and has dominated grass seed sales for many years. White clover has always been a staple component of most seed mixtures and in the early years its role and potential were well recognized. However, rates of application of fertilizer N increased markedly in the 1960s and 1970s, and management for clover persistence became neglected and its value ignored. This trend has been reversed in recent years with a greater appreciation of the value of clover and of its management needs.

Sward establishment Possibly the most notable advance in sward establishment has been the development of sward renovation as an alternative to conventional reseeding, either where the productivity of a sward had deteriorated or for the improvement of hill and upland pastures. Since the 1950s, interest has waxed and waned in the various techniques, not all successful, devised to introduce seed mixtures to existing swards. Seed introduction by simple surface broadcasting (oversowing) proved successful for open swards (Gardner *et al.*, 1954). Dense swards required pre-conditioning by cutting, heavy grazing or suppressant chemicals to reduce competition to establishing seedlings, while some form of cultivation, such as light rotavation, discing or harrowing, became an option to create soil tilth for the seed. Other supportive measures included rectifying soil fertility deficiencies, weed and pest control and choosing a time for sowing which ensured soil moisture was not limiting (see Newbould 1974; 1975 and Frame *et al.*, 1985, for reviews). Several seed drills of varying design have evolved over the years to overcome the various sward problems encountered, e.g. removal of strips of dense existing sward, creation of slits, strip cultivation by mini-rotavators, with or without fertilizer application attachments, or equipment for band spraying of herbicides to kill or suppress adjacent grass. The management guidelines for successful direct drilling are now more clearly understood (Naylor *et al.*, 1983; Tiley and Frame, 1991).

Grassland surveys and recording

A grassland map *Vegetation : Grasslands of England and Wales* was published by the Ordnance Survey in the mid 1940s, derived from earlier surveys by Sir George Stapledon and William Davies. Pastures were classified according to their botanical composition, which was related to agricultural value. Perennial ryegrass/white clover predominated in the best pastures and meadows while bent grass, bent/fescue or bent/rushes/sedges characterized the poorest. A survey in the 1970s covered all types of enclosed grassland but the format was amended to relate age structure and botanical quality to physical features of the environment and to derive indices of grassland-use capability (Green, 1982). The influences and limitations of soil and climate and the variability of environments in which grass was grown were highlighted and an insight into farmers' attitudes to grassland management was gained. In a comprehensive survey of permanent grassland (Forbes *et al.*, 1980), the factors limiting output, which was measured as utilized metabolizable energy (UME), and their relative importance were investigated on a whole-farm basis as well as field-to-field, and the priorities established for future research and development. The main factors affecting UME output were stocking rate, level of fertilizer N application and land manageability, which was strongly influenced by field drainage status and topography. Rough grazings, though occupying just under half the total area of British grasslands, have been less closely surveyed than other grassland types but many of the ecological, soil and management inter-relationships have been the subject of study (HFRO, 1979).

The need for some form of recording to measure utilized output from grassland has long been recognized. Rex Paterson pioneered a method of using cow grazing days and milk yields in the late 1940s/early 1950s. These records demonstrated the effects of different pasture types and forage crops on stock carrying capacity and milk yields, and the influence of feeding and management. A report by a sub-committee of the BGS set out methods of farm and field recording based on utilized starch equivalent (USE) output (Barker *et al.*, 1955). The energy value of all feeds other than grass and grass products was calculated and deducted from the total energy requirements of ruminant livestock and the residual energy ascribed to grassland. Later, an investigation into grassland recording on dairy farms was sponsored by the BGS to gauge the progress made with recording systems and to derive a simple system for general use which would measure effective grass output on any particular field or farm and the effect of different managements. An individual field system based on a cow day (CD) unit, equivalent to the amount of bulk feed the average lactating cow would eat in 24 hours, was recommended, with conversion factors allocated to other classes of stock and to winter-fed hay and silage (Baker *et al.*, 1964). In the 1970s UME replaced USE as the energy measure and the introduction of computers facilitated recording procedures which were increasingly linked to both financial and physical performance and were a stimulus to economic modelling of livestock enterprises.

Herbage nutritive value

The main cited parameter of herbage quality in the early years was crude protein (CP) concentration, generally determined as total N x 6.25, the N being estimated by the Kjeldahl method followed by distillation or, in later years, by colorimetric estimation of ammonia. Other compositional parameters in use were water soluble carbohydrates (WSC), crude fibre (CF) and oil. The nutritive value of forages and feeding stuffs, including silage, hay and dried grass, was described by percentage protein and starch equivalents, these being derived from chemical composition values. A regression equation linking digestibility to CP content was also in use until the early 1950s, before its drawbacks were recognized. From the early 1960s, forage digestibility, particularly of organic constituents, was used as a guide to energy value because of its association with intake. Expressions used were dry matter digestibility (DMD), organic matter digestibility (OMD) and the content of digestible organic matter in the dry matter (DOMD), popularly known as D-value (Raymond, 1969).

The use of digestibility was facilitated by the two-stage rumen-pepsin *in vitro* method of determination (Tilley and Terry, 1963) which required only small quantities of sample material. The *in vivo* determination of digestibility had been restricted by animal, labour and housing costs, though it is still used for validation of alternative methods including enzyme digestion of herbage and prediction from chemical analyses (Jones and Moseley, 1993). Detergent fibre analysis partitioned herbage DM into the mainly digestible cell contents and mainly indigestible cell wall constituents and was valuable in explaining the changes in DMD as forage plants matured. In reporting herbage quality, OMD is favoured by researchers but D-value is more familiar to farmers. However, when computing livestock requirements the unit of energy measurement to reconcile nutritive value and animal requirements is metabolizable energy (ME), i.e. the digestible energy minus the energy lost as methane gas and in urinary excretion (ARC, 1965). By determining digestibility *in vivo* on a wide range of forages, fresh and conserved, equations have been derived to estimate ME by laboratory estimates of *in vitro* digestibility or the content of modified acid detergent fibre (MADF).

The concept of optimizing yields of digestible nutrients rather than DM from grassland has received greater credence since the 1960s and herbage digestibility work, in general, has contributed enormously to the improvement in quality of herbage cut for silage. Ear emergence (EE) was identified as the critical stage of growth, being the key reference point at which the rate of digestibility decline accelerates, although Italian ryegrass and timothy are exceptions in that decline starts before 50% EE. Heading date differed between species, as did D-value, and varieties at any given date or growth stage (Harkess and Alexander, 1969). Ryegrasses were found to be 'high-digestibility' species, cocksfoot and tall fescue 'low' and timothy and meadow fescue 'intermediate'. Among the legumes, white clover was 'high', red clover and lucerne 'intermediate'. Thus it became possible to construct profiles of DM production, D-value and DOM (Figure 1) for representative varieties of the major forage species (Green *et al.*, 1971; NIAB, 1977). An important outcome of the database collated was the D-value prediction schemes, operated by official advisory bodies, which served as a guide to farmersof the potential qualities and yields of swards cut for silage or hay at specified dates and at particular altitudes/locations.

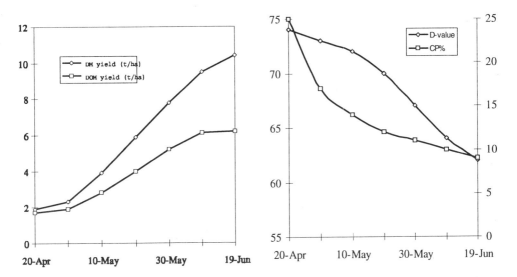

Figure 1. Profile of production and quality of late perennial ryegrass (Aberystwyth S 23) (From Green *et al.*, 1971).

Most recently the development of near infra-red spectroscopy (NIRS) techniques for evaluating herbage quality has been a major advance. Computer assisted NIRS can estimate several parameters such as N (and thus CP), fibre or lignin which are then used to predict digestibility and voluntary intake. The NIRS techniques are particularly suited to large numbers of samples and are applicable to fresh herbage, dried or conserved products (Murray, 1993).

Forage legumes
With widespread use of fertilizer N the role and potential of white clover and its management needs were increasingly disregarded in both research and farming practice. Exceptions were found on lowland beef and sheep farms with low N input and extensive grazing systems, and hill sheep farms where reseeded grass/white clover pastures were incorporated in the 'two-pasture' system (see below).

Against a background of rising fertilizer N costs and a growing realization of the drain on fossil fuel energy which N manufacturing entails and concern about the environmental consequences of high N usage, a reappraisal began late in the 1970s, of white clover and its N-fixing ability. Economic models of animal production from grass/clover *versus* N-fertilized grass swards concluded that the use of mixed swards was potentially profitable when annual fertilizer N usage was below 200 kg/ha, inferring a particular benefit for low-N-input beef and sheep farms. The nutritional superiority of clover in protein, minerals and sustained high digestibility and intake, relative to grass, were reconfirmed (Thomson, 1984) and its key management guidelines elucidated with special reference to choice of suitable clover variety and compatibility with grass, establishment needs, interactions with different fertilizer nutrients, ecophysiological requirements under grazing and cutting regimes and optimum methods of utilization (see review by Frame and Newbould, 1986). Recent research has also shown that grass/white clover swards receiving no fertilizer N can be cut for high quality silage in successive years without detriment to clover productivity and yielding 70-80% of the DM production from a grass sward receiving 300-350 kg N/ha annually. A rest interval within an intensive sheep grazing system and subsequent silage cut has proved beneficial to clover persistence and productivity. This tolerance to flexible grazing and cutting management has been highlighted in dairy systems comparisons with heavily N-fertilized grass (Bax and Thomas, 1992), and in beef and sheep systems in comparisons with moderately N-fertilized grass swards (Stewart and Haycock 1984; Davies *et al.*, 1989). In the late 1970s and early 1980s there was evidence of the high yield potential and quality of red-clover-dominant leys for silage cropping but their relatively short longevity militated against their adoption (Frame, 1990).

Forage crops

Although historically forage crops have played a very important role in the provision of winter feed their use has declined throughout the last 50 years and the area of forage crops grown has fallen by 80%. This has been reflected in the level of research conducted and in breeding new varieties. The dominance of root crops was replaced by kale, rape and cabbage in the 1950s and 1960s and now, with the decline of root and leafy brassica crops, they each constitute about a third of the area grown, the other third being cereals, predominantly maize, for feeding as a conserved crop (Poole, 1990).

Potent reasons for a reduced usage of forage crops were high labour requirements, risks in establishment, pests and diseases, and the difficulties and high costs of harvesting. Research has addressed all of these problems and significant developments occurred. These include monogerm varieties of fodder beet and mangels, which removed the need for hand singling, the breeding of earlier-maturing maize varieties, improved sowing and harvesting machinery, direct-drilling techniques made possible by the discovery of paraquat in 1961 (ICI

Plant Protection, 1976) to kill existing swards and stubble, and improved conservation and storage techniques. Work on the feeding value of maize, mainly for dairy cows (Phipps and Wilkinson, 1985) but also for beef cattle, has contributed to the marked increase in the area grown in recent years.

Soil compaction and drainage

As the intensity of grassland farming increased, swards, particularly those cut for conservation, had to bear more frequent and heavier wheel traffic, with its soil compacting and sward damaging effects. The soil/sward problems engendered, such as decreased water infiltration or disrupted soil structure and resultant losses in herbage production, were first explored in the difficult soils and wet climes of north-west Europe during the rapid expansion in silage making. Reports later emerged from the UK confirming the losses in DM production, broadly in the range 10 to 20% relative to zero or minimal traffic, and noting the associated reductions in N and mineral concentrations, or offtakes, in the harvested herbage (see Douglas, 1994 for review). Major preventative measures were identified as minimizing wheel traffic, undertaking operations over short rather than long periods, keeping equipment size and weight to the minimum for economic effectiveness and decreasing wheel-induced stress on swards by the use of broad, low ground-pressure tyres.

Plastic piping has become a cheaper alternative to traditional fired clay tile pipes and mechanized installation of drains has been introduced. Mole drains have proved effective and economic when used in conjunction with a widely spaced collection system of drains backfilled with permeable gravel, while on lighter soils gravel filling of the mole channels (gravel tunnel drains) has been beneficial. Subsoiling and spiking techniques have been developed to ameliorate compacted swards, by aiding root development and improving soil water/aeration conditions. It has been shown that grass yield, stock carrying capacity and animal performance benefited from good field drainage although the improvements in productivity were less than expected (Garwood, 1988).

Fertilizers

The increased use of NPK compound fertilizers, particularly 'high N' types, and straight N was mainly responsible for the increased productivity of grassland achieved in conjunction with advances in plant breeding, improved knowledge of rates and timing of fertilizer application and an understanding of other management factors. Nutrient concentration in fertilizers has increased; for example, N fertilizers now have 34.5% N (ammonium nitrate) or 46% N (urea) compared with 15.5% N ('Nitro-chalk') or 21% N (sulphate of ammonia) in the early years. A typical NPK compound now has a 40-50% nutrient sum compared with 21% in the 1940s. As well as there being lower bulk to be spread, machinery has been developed with improved precision of application and the once familiar one hundredweight and 50 kg bags have been replaced by one tonne containers for bulk handling. The development of compound fertilizer granules uniform in size, density and composition was a notable technical advance, though in recent times the blending of granules of individual nutrients has increased in popularity, because of lower costs and since it allows manipulation of nutrient ratios.

Nitrogen Recognition that N was the most important nutrient governing grass production led to increasing rates of application from the 1950s onwards and the consequent intensification of stocking. Average usage rose from *circa* 5 kg/ha annually in the 1940s to 120-130 kg/ha (range, 0-450 kg/ha) at present. Other sources of N - soil, excreta at grazing, manures from winter housing, rhizobially-fixed-N from legumes - became completely subsidiary to fertilizer N until a more recent revival.

A plethora of trials covering all the facets influencing sward response to N has been conducted over the past fifty years (see Whitehead, 1970; Wilman and Wright, 1983 for reviews). The effect of increasing fertilizer N application on grass and grass/clover swards is shown diagrammatically in Figure 2. Sward yield response remains linear at higher rates of N application under frequent, compared with infrequent, cutting (Reid, 1978) implying that increased N can lead to higher quality herbage subject to economic maxima. The seasonal distribution of grass has always engendered interest because of its variability in relation to the more constant needs of livestock. Manipulation of N application allows the alteration of the seasonal yield pattern within a specific annual N rate without significantly affecting total yield (Reid, 1982). Under non-limiting fertilizer N, and in some cases irrigation, seasonal grass growth patterns were measured at 33 European sites, with different soil and climatic conditions, in order to provide yield potential data for a model to enable the prediction of seasonal patterns wherever historic meteorological data are available and for the validation of models developed from basic principles of plant physiology (Corrall, 1984). The project made use of a special cutting regime involving a rotational but overlapping sequence of harvesting at short intervals, developed to supersede cutting at set intervals (Anslow and Green, 1967). Several practical attempts, e.g. the 'T-sum 200', have been devised to forecast the optimum timing for the first N application in spring but their use is much influenced by local soil conditions and current weather.

A series of fertilizer N trials on sites differing in soil and climatic conditions highlighted the importance of the level of N applied, and of rainfall, in determining annual herbage yield, and that, due to diminishing yield responses at high N rates, 80-90% of the maximum yield could be achieved from 50-60% of the amount of N needed for maximum yield (Morrison *et al.*, 1980). Fertilizer programmes and models of grassland production and utilization, and expected animal output together with financial implications, have been developed using the concept of site class i.e. soil texture/depth, summer rainfall and water supplying capacity of the soil, and predicted herbage yield at specific N rates (Kilkenny *et al.*, 1978), later refined to take account of previous cropping history on soil N status and the effect of recycled excretal N during grazing (Baker *et al.*, 1991).

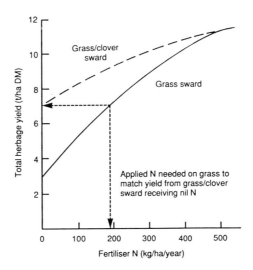

Figure 2.   The effect of increasing fertiliser N application on grass and grass/clover swards.

The use of N on grassland has recently been critically reappraised in response to economic pressures and also as a reaction to concerns about the environment, especially nitrate levels in drinking water supplies and the impact of losses of ammonia and nitrous oxide to the atmosphere. Research has focused on the components of the N cycle and their interactions with special reference to reducing the losses or 'leakage' from animal production systems based on grassland (Ryden, 1984; Jarvis, 1993). Examples of practical measures developed are: more precision in rate, timing and spreading of N and allowing for N returned in excreta; environmentally safer levels of N loading on land; more use of long term swards; reduced autumn reseeding; and greater use of grass/white clover swards.

Lime and other nutrients Advances have been made in precision and timing of application of lime, its effects on trace element availability and in planned application programmes for the long term. There have also been significant improvements in soil sampling and analytical methodology for soil pH and nutrient status, classification and interpretation of the results (MAFF, 1973; Anon, 1985).

Phosphorus fixation/release processes in the soil have been clarified; P is progressively fixed by soil mineral compounds after application so subsequently the sward relies on the release of P from the compounds in the soil solution or humus. Clay soils have high rates of fixation on account of their high humus content and large surface area of soil particles so that heavy textured soils have high P reserves yet availability to plants may be limited. Conversely, P availability can be high from limited supplies of P in light textured soils. Basic slag was widely used as a P source on grassland after the war but was replaced by water insoluble ground mineral phosphate (GMP), the best form being the finely ground, soft mineral apatites from north Africa. The application of water soluble phosphate, preferably in a compound with N, on soils low or very low in P status can lead to increases in spring herbage of up to 52% together with improved herbage P concentration (Swift *et al.*, 1988).

In contrast to P, K is highly mobile in soil solution and accordingly, heavy textured soils, in which K is held on clay minerals, normally have greater reserves and availability than light textured soils; the latter are therefore more prone to K deficiency and leaching. It has also been ascertained that while peaty soils may be high in K status, availability to plants is low. In fertilizer recommendations account is now taken of the high amounts of K needed to replace the large offtakes associated with highly N-fertilized silage crops and conversely, the small amounts needed annually in grazed swards because of recycling of K from excreta.

Grass requires S in similar amounts to P but this requirement was not appreciated in the past since 'free' S was present in the fertilizers used such as sulphate of ammonia and superphosphate. These were replaced by forms such as ammonium nitrate or triple superphosphate with more concentrated N and P, respectively, but with little or no S. In addition the amounts of free wet and dry S deposition onto land have declined due to various government anti-industrial pollution measures. The net result was the appearance and identification of S deficiency in the late 1970s/early 1980s. Maps have been constructed showing average deposition rates for various parts of the country and the soils and areas most likely to be S-deficient have been identified. Non-industrial areas, low rainfall regions and light textured soils have the lowest S reserves.

Soil surveys and herbage analysis have helped to identify and predict mineral deficiencies. Cobalt (Co) and copper (Cu) are the trace elements most commonly required. However, because of the more obvious adverse effects of such deficiencies on stock health, the main advances have been in blood analysis and direct or indirect animal treatment e.g. slow release pellets in the rumen, treatment of drinking water.

Organic manures

Historically, high value and reliance were placed upon animal manures, particularly farmyard manure (FYM), as a plant nutrient source. With increased stocking rates and changes in winter housing from the early 1960s to cubicles, self feeding of silage and slatted floors, the quantities of animal manures, especially as slurries, have increased enormously. Land suitable for spreading slurry was not always close to where it was produced so slurry came to be regarded by many farmers as a waste product, with a disposal problem, rather than a useful resource. However, increased emphasis on lowering farm input costs and minimizing pollution, such as run-off to watercourses, leaching of nutrients, ammonia volatilization and odour release, has resulted in a more positive and rational use of slurries and FYM (Van der Meer *et al.*, 1987).

It is now possible to calculate fertilizer equivalents and their monetary values, and to plan the use of organic manures to complement purchased fertilizers in specific soil fertility programmes. *Official Codes of Good Agricultural Practice for the Protection of Soil, Air and Water* are available as guides for the use of organic manures; for example, the volume of slurry storage facilities required on farms, the maximum volume per ha which should be applied, the timing and frequency of applications, the maximum N loading in a year and the area of land needed to take this loading from various livestock enterprises. The net result is a better appreciation of the need to formulate whole farm balance sheets for nutrient flows combining soil/crop needs with the planned use of both inorganic and organic manures.

Innovations in slurry treatment and handling have been introduced in response to environmental and farm constraints. Slurry can be piped to the fields for slurry 'irrigation' or to waiting spreaders i.e. the 'umbilical cord' method. Injection of slurry rather than swash plate spreading reduces odour emission and ammonia volatilization, while acidification is another means of reducing ammonia loss. Acidification and injection causes loss of slurry N by denitrification in the soil, but the addition of a nitrification inhibitor slows down nitrification thus restricting the nitrate available for subsequent breakdown (Pain, 1991). There are aerobic and anaerobic methods of treatment to decrease the solids, odours and, importantly, the biochemical oxygen demand (BOD), which is a measure of the risk of causing serious pollution in watercourses. Methods for the separation of the liquid and solid fractions of slurry, to aid handling and application, have also been developed. Similar work has begun on the use of sewage sludge on grassland.

Weeds, pests and diseases
Weeds have been tolerated more in grassland than in arable crops. Traditionally, less resort has been made to herbicides for weed control, but their effects on grassland and, hence, animal productivity and economic impact can be appreciable (Doyle, 1982). A vast array of approved herbicides and formulated herbicide mixtures has been introduced over the past fifty years ranging from selective to non-selective, soil- to foliage-applied and contact to translocation in action, while the time of application may be pre-sowing, pre-emergence, post-emergence or combinations of these. Some notable introductions for commercial use were MCPA and 2,4-D in 1945, MCPB, dalapon and mecoprop in the 1950s,

paraquat, linuron and asulam in the 1960s, ioxynil, bromoxynil, glyphosate, ethofumesate and clopyralid in the 1970s and triclopyr and fluroxypyr in the 1980s. These were accompanied by bi- and multi-component formulations particularly from the 1960s onwards and, in fact, most herbicides are now sold as mixed formulations to widen the weed spectrum controlled (Lockhart *et al.*, 1990).

Guidelines for herbicide use are now well documented as a result of evaluation prior to commercial release, subsequent experimentation and advisory literature. Strategies which integrate herbicide use with the older cultural and mechanical control methods have also been evolved (Williams, 1984). Following the Food and Environment Protection Act of 1985 herbicides must be used according to the manufacturers' label recommendations. There have also been concomitant improvements in application technology in relation to volume of spray, pressure of application and safety to operator and surrounding vegetation. Innovative equipment includes controlled droplet applicators, mistblowers, rope-wick applicators for weed plants standing above the level of the sward and spraying asulam by helicopter onto bracken-infested land.

Unless there are dramatic and noticeable attacks by pests and diseases on grassland, their insidious damage to shoots and roots may go unobserved or even ignored. As a result interest and work in the early years was more *ad hoc* and less intensive than in other grassland management factors. The greatest steps forward have been in assessing and recognizing the extent and effects of the major pests and diseases, their biology and population dynamics (Clements, 1995a). Control or alleviation involving cultural, mechanical and chemical methods, or integrated programmes involving these, are available in some instances, but, for many, plant breeding represents the best long term solution.

Surveys and experimental work have shown the substantial gains in production, and its financial value, attainable from the suppression of pests and diseases (Henderson and Clements, 1977). Effective commercial fungicide treatment of some seeds has been devised to combat seed-borne fungi, especially *Fusarium culmorum* which attacks germinating seedlings (Lewis, 1988). Work in the 1970s identified frit fly (*Oscinella* spp.) as a major problem of establishing swards, and its biology and epidemiology were studied and control measures developed (Clements *et al.*, 1982). The adverse effects of viral attack on grassland are now fully appreciated but, as yet, no practical or economic methods of control are available. Effective chemical control has been developed to combat leatherjackets, the larvae of crane-flies (*Tipula* spp.) which damage swards, particularly at the seedling establishment stage, and also the netted slug (*Deroceras reticulum*), which is a problem pest in reseeds or swards renovated by direct drilling. The significant damage and decline or disappearance of forage legumes due to pests and diseases are also now more fully realized (Clements, 1995b).

GRAZING

In the first presidential address to the British Grassland Society, Stapledon (1946) stated that "grassland agronomists in this country must admit that they have rather neglected the grazing animal, to cater for whom is the *raison d'etre* of all their endeavours". However, early attempts were made to rectify this situation (Linehan *et al.*, 1952) and grazing animals increasingly became a key feature in grassland experiments, though the extent of their use was limited by the high cost of animal trials. Thus, most advances in our understanding of the complex relationships existing between plant, animals and their managements have taken place in the last fifty years.

Grazing management and stocking rate

Grazing experiments in the 1940s and 1950s focused on the ways in which controlled grazing practices could be used to manipulate the botanical composition of pastures to favour the more productive and nutritious species. Concurrently, ley farming exploited the newly-bred improved varieties of grasses and legumes which had become available. In evaluating these varieties, DM yields were higher as the rest interval between harvests increased and so claims arose, typified in the writings of Voisin (1959), for the superiority of rotational grazing. This was based on the assumption that the effects of frequency and severity of defoliation on cut swards would pertain equally to grazed swards and that the absence of rest periods and the uncontrolled frequency of grazing on pastures stocked continuously would depress herbage production. A number of comparisons were undertaken which confirmed this proposition but only because more stock were allocated to the rotational management in expectation of higher productivity. Although doubts were expressed over the superiority of rotational grazing in the early 1950s, real debate only began when McMeekan (1956) reported almost identical levels of milk yield from comparisons, over a range of stocking rates, between rotational grazing and set-stocking of dairy cows at Ruakura, New Zealand. He concluded that extreme differences in grazing method were associated with only small effects upon utilization efficiency and that the most powerful influence on output per unit area was stocking rate.

A major contribution to this debate was made by Mott (1960) who examined the interrelationship between output per animal and per unit area at different stocking rates. He explained earlier results favouring rotational grazing by showing how output per unit area continued to increase beyond the stocking rate or grazing intensity at which individual animal performance began to decrease. Thus, only comparisons made at the same stocking rates were valid. His work also emphasized the need for more than one stocking rate in treatment comparisons. Since then a number of reviews of experimentally rigorous comparisons have demonstrated that there is no consistent superiority of any single grazing system (Ernst *et al.*, 1980).

Grazing system

Rotational systems were adopted by many farmers in the 1950s and 1960s, particularly milk producers, thinking such systems would be more productive but also because of the apparent ease with which grass supply could be matched to animal needs. This was coupled with the relatively cheap creation of paddocks using barbed wire or electrified fences. The availability of electric fence units was of major importance in improving the utilization of pasture by permitting greater control and flexibility of grazing managements on farms. The very successful development of a system of 18-month-old beef production (Baker *et al.*, 1967) was also based upon paddock grazing and a well integrated programme of conservation and grazing to ensure grazing needs were always met. None of the improvements to planned beef production, which take account of the grazing and forage conservation requirements in relation to breed, slaughter weight and level of supplementary feed, would have been possible without the concurrent rapid advances in forage conservation dealt with below. For the first time the farmer had systems available which permitted surplus growth to be conserved quickly and at any time of the growing season, thus ensuring leafy regrowths for grazing when needed.

Subsequently simpler systems began to emerge, some of which were pioneered by ICI, and were preferred by producers; for example a two field system reported by Hood and Bailie (1973) and later a modified version based on using three fields. The latter approach involved the continuous stocking of one paddock in early season with two paddocks being conserved. In mid season two paddocks were used for grazing and one for conservation while in late season all three paddocks were grazed. Continuous stocking systems with conservation integrated within them have now attained ascendancy, in the UK, over other systems.

In the hills and uplands a two-pasture system was developed (Eadie, 1978) in which there was complementary use of fenced improved areas and unimproved natural pastures. The higher production and better quality of the improved pasture were exploited by grazing it with the ewe flock before and during mating, to enhance ewe condition, and during the first three months after lambing, to improve ewe lactation and lamb performance. This strategy led to increased stocking rate, lambing percentage and weights of weaned lambs, while the higher stocking rate also allowed more efficient utilization of the hill grazings in summer.

The problems of obtaining high levels of animal output from grazed pasture stimulated interest during the 1950s and 1960s in feeding cut herbage indoors, in what became known as zero grazing. In comparisons with conventional grazing, improved outputs were demonstrated but did not prove cost effective in practice. The difficulties and commitment needed to provide a daily supply of high quality forage also proved a deterrent to its widespread adoption. The system is sometimes used for short periods in early or late season to avoid poaching of pastures by stock or on farms with distant scattered fields. Storage feeding in which all the forage is fed in a conserved form, usually as silage, is in effect a variant of zero grazing and mainly suitable for highly mechanized large scale units.

The provision of early spring grazing and extended autumn grazing was frequently undertaken in the early years but these practices were overtaken by the upsurge in silage making. Nevertheless, there has been renewed interest in recent years because of the lower cost of grazing relative to silage. Techniques to utilize pastures at these times of the year have been refined and now include the subdivision of paddocks by electric fence and limited but flexible periods of strip grazing with back fencing.

Questions were also asked about how grazing management could improve animal health. Thus systems were developed with the twin objectives of protecting young stock from worm parasites and improving their nutrition. Forward-creep and sideways-creep systems for breeding ewes were effective in sustaining good lamb performance, even at high stocking rates. Later, a 'clean' grazing system for ewes and lambs evolved in which equal areas of grassland were alternated annually between sheep, cattle and conservation or arable cropping, the critical feature being that ewes and lambs were not grazed in fields which had carried sheep during the previous year. Leader/follower systems were developed for cows and young stock. Although the young stock benefited from these managements they were too complex and demanding to operate so their uptake in practice has not been widespread. In some areas mixed stocking of cattle and sheep has traditionally been practised. While trials have shown benefits from reducing parasitic burdens and from better utilization of pastures (Dickson *et al.*, 1981) the practice has not been significantly adopted in intensive systems of production. Nevertheless it highlighted how grazing management could keep parasitic burdens low and it stimulated a fresh approach to matching the nutritional requirements of different types of livestock to the seasonal pattern of grass growth.

Growth and utilization of grazed swards

The rapid turnover of tissue taking place as new leaves are continually produced and old ones die was well documented by the 1960s (Hunt, 1965) but the significance of these processes for grazing was not appreciated until much later. The stimulus to this was given by grazing ecologists who wanted to establish the extent to which grazing managements influenced the supply of herbage and the amount eaten. Once plant physiologists appreciated that a balance had to be struck under grazing between photosynthesis, gross tissue production, herbage intake and tissue death, rapid progress was made (see Figure 3). Studies of both the carbon balance of swards and the rate of growth of individual tillers provided the information from which a wider understanding could be developed using mathematical modelling techniques (Johnson and Parsons, 1985). It became clear that maximum yield per unit area was obtained when swards were kept at a leaf area index (LAI) below rather than above the maximum for light interception, as was originally suggested, and the best utilization from the compromise between gross tissue production, herbage intake and loss of herbage through death achieved at lower LAI than the maximum. These findings added substantially to the confidence in new recommended approaches to grazing management based on sward height.

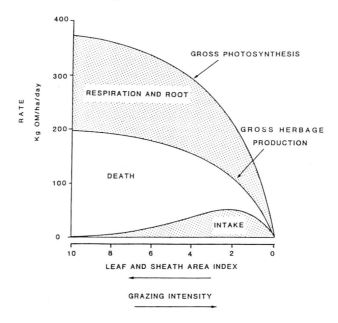

Figure 3. The effects of the intensity of continuous stocking on the balance between photosynthesis, gross tissue production, herbage intake and death (From Parsons *et al.*, 1983).

Herbage intake and grazing behaviour

It was increasingly recognized that the scope for improvements in animal management and production could only be identified if factors influencing grazing behaviour and intake were elucidated. This posed problems not only in developing appropriate techniques (see Leaver, 1982 for a review) but also in presenting the results in terms of practical significance. Early attempts to measure intake from pre- and post-grazing sward measurements proved unsuccessful because of large inherent variability in such measurements. Eventually, intake was estimated from measurements of faecal indicators, initially based upon the faecal N technique (CAB, 1961) and then the use of indigestible markers, particularly chromic oxide (Le Du and Penning, 1982) and more recently n-alkanes (Mayes *et al.*, 1986), to estimate faecal output. As these estimates must be linked to the digestibility of forage consumed to calculate intake, the development in the 1960s of the *in vitro* digestibility technique, using only small quantities of herbage representing the grazed material, was significant.

As adequate equipment became available for recording and processing data, grazing behaviour was studied from recording jaw movements on tape recorders (Penning *et al.*, 1984) and more recently by telemetry coupled with the writing of computer programmes to summarize the electrical wave-forms associated with the different jaw movements in ruminating, prehension and mastication. This opened up the comprehensive study of the grazing process for the first time.

Grazing intensity   The influence of grazing pressure, defined as severity of defoliation or as stocking rate, proved of over-riding importance in determining animal performance. Therefore, considerable attention was devoted to defining grazing pressures that limit production on the farm.

In many experiments an asymptotic relationship was observed between herbage allowance and herbage intake or animal performance but the relationship was only defined in general terms. Allowance was measured as the quantity of herbage available per animal but, because of the difficulties of establishing the quantity per unit area with reasonable accuracy at a point in time and knowing the significance of an allowance to an animal when measured at ground level or some predetermined height above the ground, the findings could only be applied on farms at a superficial level. The digestibility of the herbage grazed contributed little to explaining differences in intake but the weight of herbage present, whether absolute or green material or green leaf, had a major effect.

Sward height, measured by ruler or the HFRO sward stick, either as the stubble height after grazing in rotational systems or as the sward height on pastures stocked continuously, gave a good indication of the intensity of grazing and the likely effects on grassland utilization and animal production (Baker, 1985). The practical sward height guidelines which emerged for the management of pastures in relation to severity of defoliation were summarized by Hodgson *et al.*, (1986). Although they provide an objective method of assessing pasture conditions they are not often used in practice, but the knowledge gained has created confidence in the adoption of efficient grazing managements.

The use of buffers
The use of integrated systems of grazing and conservation overcame many of the problems of sustaining high levels of animal performance and effective utilization throughout the growing season. Nevertheless, temporary shortages of grass inevitably occur and 'buffer' strategies have evolved to maintain intakes by offering hay, silage, or straw mixes or alternatively, there may be a buffer area of grassland which is utilized for grazing or conservation as required and often adjusted in size by moving an electric fence.

In the past, the offering of concentrate supplements to dairy cows at pasture has invariably produced uneconomic results. This outcome was finally explained by the way cows modify their grazing behaviour in response to supplementation (Sarker and Holmes, 1974). They immediately reduce the time devoted to grazing, especially at higher herbage allowances, and as a result a high substitution rate of the supplement for grass occurs. Using forage buffers also has this effect. It is now generally agreed that the most profitable use of supplements is when they act as a buffer to shortages of grazing, when very high grazing pressures are deliberately chosen, when adverse weather conditions reduce intake or when growing animals have not fully adapted to grazing conditions. The offering of restricted quantities of concentrate or forage is also recognized as an effective strategy to maintain optimum sward conditions. The same objective is also achieved by having a buffer area of land which is used in a flexible manner for grazing or conservation. The value of buffering practices is the creation of confidence to stock heavily in early season. This increases sward tiller populations and proportions of live, leafy material; the maintenance of leafy conditions at this time also has beneficial effects on sward density and production later in the season with benefits to animal productivity.

Manipulation of sward conditions

The fuller appreciation of the causative relationships between sward structural characteristics and herbage intake has led to an increased recognition of the mutual benefits of cattle and sheep grazing. Examples are the use of cattle to control the spread of bracken and thistles on pastures grazed by sheep and the use of sheep to remove rejected herbage in late season from swards previously grazed by cattle. The improved understanding of how the severity of grazing alters tiller numbers, the proportion of flowering tillers and the patterns of defoliation of swards by cattle and sheep has emphasized the possibilities for manipulation. The adverse effects of lax grazing in spring on sward structure and on the quality of the diet later in the season are now well recognized. The more uniform patterns of grazing by sheep and the large effect on increasing tiller numbers and sward density when grazed to low levels are being exploited to improve the structure of deteriorating swards.

The quest to improve pasture utilization by the adoption of rotational systems of management focused attention on many other associated topics because of the negative effects that could also arise (McMeekan, 1956). While many paddock-grazed systems maintained vigorous swards, poaching damage was common on wet or poorly drained land, particularly when dairy cows were stocked at high grazing pressures (MAFF, 1970).

Further problems arose because of a failure to match herbage growth with an adequate grazing pressure. This led to under-utilization and herbage rejection at subsequent grazing cycles. In the worst cases of lax grazing, swards of poor density developed which were susceptible to weed ingress, aerial tillering and winter damage. These problems stimulated great interest in the load bearing and drainage properties of soils, the consequences of poaching soils and the effects of dung and urine on plant growth. A suitable grazing system is the answer to most of these problems but a number of strategies exist to prevent or reverse the damaging effects, e.g. effective drainage, use of long term rather than short term swards, renovation, manipulation of type of stock, use of 'sacrifice' areas or fields. Investigation of sward abnormalities in intensive systems showed how swards could be maintained in good condition by close topping or hard grazing provided that the tiller buds at ground level were viable, and highlighted the need for at least one close defoliation of grazed swards during the grazing season (Jackson, 1975).

FORAGE CONSERVATION

Over the past 50 years conservation has become more specialized and highly mechanized, and there is a better understanding of the microbial and chemical processes involved. After the Second World War it was claimed that farmers who overcame the minor difficulties involved in making silage would testify to its high nutritive value (Watson, 1946). The high losses incurred in making hay were recognized and artificial drying was considered, in theory at least, to be the ideal method of grass conservation. Although silage making increased steadily during the 1950s and 1960s it was not until the late 1970s that silage overtook hay as the principal method of crop conservation in the UK (MAFF, 1993) (Figure 4).

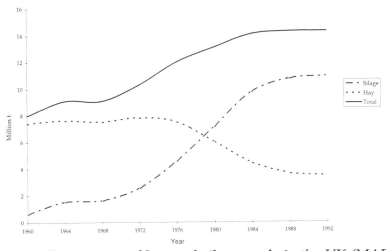

Figure 4. The quantity of hay and silage made in the UK (MAFF, 1993).

Mechanization

Hay In the 1940s hay was built in ricks or heaped onto tripods and after a month or so stored in a stack or a barn. Pick-up balers came into common use in the 1950s. Around 1960 major research began into improved conservation methods (Raymond, 1981). Better mowing machines and conditioners which crushed and bruised grass stems, to speed up the rate of water loss, were designed and the drying of hay in barns introduced. Since the hay had then to be transferred to a shed, the system was too labour intensive and so was replaced by storage hay drying, in which the bales are stacked around wind tunnels in a shed and dried by blowing through a uniform flow of air. Although effective the extra capital and fuel costs incurred have restricted the adoption of this technique, even in wet areas where it is most needed. Field baling became the norm with improved bale handling equipment and increasing bale size.

Mat-making is one of the newer ideas in forage conservation machinery (Bosma, 1991) and is designed to increase the rate of wilting in the field. The cut swath is lifted and fed through a maceration device to remove some of the water and the mashed forage is then squeezed into a thin mat and deposited on the stubble to dry naturally. However, the process has not yet been commercialized.

Silage A notable innovation in the late 1940s was the Paterson Buckrake, a grass pick-up sweep operated by the hydraulic three point linkage on the tractor. With the introduction of forage harvesters in the 1960s and government support for silo construction, silage became increasingly popular (Wilkinson, 1987). Tower, stack, bunker, pit and clamp silos, silos with movable walls and, later, silos with flexible walls have all been effectively used. Early advice to farmers, that grass be allowed to heat up before consolidation, was proved to be wrong and improved mechanization ensured that silos were filled quickly and consolidated well. In the 1970s high-output, wide mowers produced dense swaths which were picked up by large-capacity metered or double chop forage harvesters, some with metal detectors to prevent damage by foreign bodies. Research showed that the use of a shorter chop length than before gave better consolidation, a quicker release of sugars for fermentation and, therefore, a more rapid drop in pH. In addition, precision chopped silage was consumed more readily than long material by ruminants (Dulphy and Demarquilly, 1991). For the upland farmer, the forage wagon, originally designed for hay, was converted for silage making. Around 1970 the Dorset Wedge system of filling a silo was developed and widely adopted; this permitted parts of the silo to be filled to its full depth and sealed quickly. As machines continued to increase in both size and cost, the trend was for farmers to employ contractors to ensile their crops. In the late 1970s tractor-mounted silage cutters revolutionized the cutting and transporting of silage from the silo. Cutting even blocks from the silo face causes less disturbance than other methods of removing silage since less air penetrates the mass and losses due to aerobic deterioration are reduced.

The 1980s saw the introduction of the big round bale (Forster, 1989) and big bale silage, now more commonly wrapped than bagged, accounts for almost one-fifth of silage in the UK. Variable chamber balers give a bale with a more uniform density than fixed chamber balers and now balers with a chopping mechanism have been introduced. Key guidelines for effective baling, storage and feeding have been elucidated. Big bale silage is especially useful when small quantities of silage are to be made, for example, in association with buffer grazing systems and in situations where permanent silos are unaffordable (Eyers, 1989). On a larger scale the Ag-Bag System has been developed in which grass is filled under pressure into a long sausage-shaped plastic bag holding 150-170 t of herbage. Excellent air exclusion is achieved with this system but, because of the good fermentation quality of the silage, it is liable to deteriorate rapidly on exposure to air (Kennedy, 1984).

Dried grass Grass drying advanced rapidly in the late 1940s, but when cereal-based concentrate feeds were derationed in 1952 dried grass, produced by existing technology, could not compete. Conservation by high temperature drying requires about six times the energy used in making hay or silage. This can be reduced by field wilting but, following the energy crisis in 1973, it was obvious that dried forages would only be offered as a supplement to other forages (Raymond, 1974).

Microbiology and biochemistry

Hay Research has shown that if hay is made quickly and baled at a low moisture content and stored or barn dried efficiently, to 20% or less moisture, there will be very little microbial or proteolytic activity on the crop. Conversely, if the moisture content is over 20% moulds develop with the subsequent heating and growth of thermophilic actinomycetes, loss of nutritive value results and the hay will be a health hazard to man and farm animals (Elsässer, 1991).

Silage Silage is the material produced by the controlled fermentation of a crop by lactic acid bacteria (LAB) (McDonald *et al.*, 1991). Interest in the 1950s focused on the sugar contents of crops and the availability of sugars to the LAB. The development of paper chromatography meant that individual sugars could be identified and fructans were found to be responsible for much of the variation in WSC among crops. In temperate grasses, fructans were the most abundant of the WSC but legumes were shown to accumulate starch instead of fructans as their main reserve polysaccharide. In general, ryegrass contains most WSC and cocksfoot least (Waite and Boyd, 1953). Legumes with their low WSC content and high buffering capacity proved to be more difficult to ensile satisfactorily than grasses. The introduction of gas liquid chromatography in the 1960s, and later high performance liquid chromatography, allowed the biochemistry of the ensilage process to be studied in even greater detail.

In the 1950s numbers of LAB on the growing plant were thought to be low and to multiply rapidly when the crop was harvested and ensiled. Microbiologists now believe that techniques used to count the bacteria may have underestimated their numbers (Pahlow, 1991). Clostridia from soil contamination have long been associated with the production of butyric acid and ammonia in silages but since the 1950s other organisms responsible for secondary fermentation in silages have been identified. Certain strains of enterobacteria produce ammonia. Yeasts, even under acid conditions, ferment sugars, and, in the absence of sugars, LAB convert lactic acid to acetic acid. Big bale silage proved particularly prone to the growth of listeria, the bacterial pathogen most frequently associated with silage, but in anaerobic silage listeria die out rapidly if the seal is adequate and oxygen ingress is prevented (Fenlon, 1988). Yeasts, moulds, a proteolytic species of *Bacillus* and LAB have all been implicated in the deterioration of grass silages (Woolford, 1984) and acetic acid bacteria in the deterioration of maize silages (Spoelstra *et al.*, 1988).

Additives

Hay. Research showed that mould growth in stored hay can be modified or prevented by the addition of chemicals at the time of baling. Propionic acid, widely used to prevent moulding in grain, was effective in laboratory studies in the 1970s but was less effective under field conditions, due to evaporation of the acid and/or uneven distribution on the hay. Improved applicators and the use of an ammonium salt of propionic acid, ammonium bispropionate, now allow hay to be baled at higher moisture contents with less risk of moulding but the use of the additive is not widespread because of added cost.

Silage The most important factors affecting fermentation were established as WSC content and buffering capacity. The original objective in applying an additive was to supply additional substrate, usually molasses, for the LAB. Molasses is still used but enzymes are also available to break down the polysaccharides to simple sugars. Added to low DM grass they do produce additional sugar but they also increase the flow of effluent. When an effective additive applicator was designed in the 1960s the range and numbers of additives increased. Formic acid, a by-product of the oil industry, competed for a place on the market with mineral acids and soon attained dominance. The ability of formalin to restrict the fermentation and to protect protein from degradation in the silo and the rumen was recognized. Applied with either formic or sulphuric acid it may improve liveweight gains of cattle and sheep on silage diets and increase milk yields from dairy cows. The Liscombe Star System was introduced to help farmers decide whether or not they should use an additive (ADAS, 1979). In recent years additives containing salts of acids, mainly ammonium salts of formic acid, have been introduced on to the market. These are safer to handle than the free acid and, if applied at a higher rate, will have a similar effect on the fermentation (McGinn *et al.*, 1990).

The application of efficient LAB to improve the fermentation pattern became a viable proposition in the 1980s with the introduction of freeze-drying and encapsulation techniques (Seale, 1986). Initially many products were ineffective since the LAB were not viable and/or application rates were too low. Products have improved gradually and many independent trials have proved that their use can lead to increased liveweight gain (Henderson *et al.*, 1988) and milk production (Gordon, 1989). Unlike acids they are safe to handle, and bacterial inoculants now dominate the additive market (see review by Mayne and Steen, 1990). To aid farmers in their choice of silage additive a UK Forage Additive Approval Scheme has recently been introduced, with categories encompassing all types of silage additive and benefit. Approval depends on the manufacturer providing a dossier containing the results of well designed and analyzed trials.

The increase in silage making, the move towards direct-cut silage in the 1980s and the use of acid and enzyme additives exacerbated the problem of the pollution of watercourses by silage effluent but it was established that materials such as bruised barley, straw (pelleted or alkali-treated) or sugar beet pulp ensiled with the crop reduced effluent flow and DM loss (Offer *et al.*, 1991). However, efficiency of absorption was influenced by the physical characteristics of the crop, method of absorbent application, silo design and drainage.

Nutritive value of conserved forage
Interest in improving the quality of conserved grass was stimulated from the 1960s onwards when the links between digestibility, maturity of herbage at cutting and voluntary intake were clarified. Earlier cutting than previously practised was advocated in order to obtain maximum yields of nutrients, rather than DM, and this ethos eventually led to the dominance of silage over hay. Unless losses were high during ensiling the digestibility of a well preserved silage was shown to be similar to that of the ensiled crop. The toluene distillation technique for determining the true DM of silages (Dewar and McDonald, 1961) led to more accurate measurements of DM losses during ensilage and of the DM intakes of silages. Contamination from soil or slurry has a detrimental effect on fermentation and on losses but is avoidable if the fields are rolled in spring and slurry is applied six weeks or more before harvesting. However, even well preserved silages proved likely to have lower intakes and efficiency of utilization of nutrients than those from the fresh ensiled crops. The relationship between digestibility and intake is frequently very poor as high acidity and high ammonium N are both associated with depression of intake.

In the 1970s the introduction of silage additives encouraged the ensiling of young grass, with its low DM content. Trials throughout Europe showed that, although intakes of wilted silage might be higher than those of direct-cut silage treated with formic acid, low DM silage was used more efficiently for liveweight gain and milk production (Zimmer and Wilkins, 1984). Direct-cut silage produces more effluent and this, if stored, is consumed readily by cattle or pigs (Patterson and Steen, 1982). Nevertheless, the polluting effect of effluent has been increasingly appreciated in recent years so more emphasis is now placed on rapid field wilting whenever possible and on good silo management to curtail DM losses. Effective guidelines developed include reducing swath density to hasten wilting, short chopping to aid crop consolidation, overnight sheeting, airtight sealing and weighting down of the final plastic sheeting.

Studies have shown that the release of amino acids and ammonia in the rumen from many silage diets is not matched by a corresponding supply of available energy and, therefore, protein synthesis by the rumen bacteria is poor (Thomas and Thomas, 1985). The traditional supplementation of silage for dairy cows with low protein, cereal-based diets was challenged in the late 1970s. Protein concentrates, especially those with a source of low degradable protein such as fishmeal, protected amino acids, methionine and lysine, improved milk yield from dairy cows.

Although grass is the principal crop for silage, the ensiling of maize and whole-crop cereals has increased in recent years. The digestibility pattern of cereals proved quite different from that of grasses since the declining quality of the leaf and stem was balanced by an increasing proportion of highly digestible grain. Maize ensiles well but maize silage is prone to aerobic deterioration, as is silage made from whole crop cereals. Investigations of the value of applying alkali to cereal crops have provided methods for improving the feed value of straw and of conferring aerobic stability to very high dry-matter silage by treatment with urea (Wilkinson and Stark, 1990). Legumes, unless wilted or treated with an effective additive, suffer extensive proteolysis during ensilage.

Prediction of nutritive value
The true nutritive value of a conserved forage can only be determined using the type of animals for which it is intended and using techniques which have become more sophisticated over the years. These range from simple intake and digestibility studies to comparative slaughter, animal calorimetry and measurements of energy retention from carbon and nitrogen balance techniques. However, animal trials are expensive and laborious and methods of predicting the nutritive value of forages have been developed. Until recently only DM, pH and ammonia were used to predict silage intake. Now an automated titration of silage juice provides a more detailed analysis of a silage and a better prediction of intake (Offer et al., 1993), both of which are required for accurate ration formulation.

Metabolizable energy prediction from the digestible energy of forage was introduced in the 1960s as there was a good statistical relationship between fibre content and digestibility, the modified acid detergent (MAD) fibre content being used to predict ME. This technique proved suitable for hays but not for silages, especially those which had high fermentation and effluent losses. Recent research has shown that NIRS is more accurate in predicting ME, especially when calibrated directly with measurements made with animals. Interest is now focused on the fermentable ME (FME), that part of the ME which is utilized by the rumen bacteria, and on laboratory techniques for determining this, synchronization of FME with protein degraded in the rumen being of prime importance in maximizing animal production from silage diets (Oldham, 1993).

Traditionally the N content of forage was expressed as CP and converted to digestible crude protein for ration formulation. Now it is more meaningfully expressed as dietary protein degraded or undegraded in the rumen. The artificial fibre bag technique developed in the 1970s (Ørskov and McDonald, 1979), in which forage is incubated in bags in the rumens of sheep or cattle, gives a measure of degradability with time. Research continues into finding a laboratory technique which will predict protein degradability accurately.

SCIENCE INTO PRACTICE
Grasslands, ranging from short term leys to permanent rough grazing, currently comprise about 70% of the UK agricultural land area and provide from two-thirds of the diet of dairy cows to nine-tenths that of sheep. Livestock numbers now total about 12 million cattle and 44 million sheep in contrast to *circa* 9.5 million and 16.5 million, respectively, in the mid-1940s. It has been estimated by Wilkins (1992) that UME output from UK grassland increased from 26 GJ/ha in 1950 to 42 GJ/ha in 1990 as a result of increases of 1.8% annually from 1950 to 1970, 1.4% over the next 15 years but no increases since 1985.

Technology transfer is the bridge across which the results of investigations were translated into uptake by farming practice, and state and commercial advisory services can be proud of their achievements. The synthesis of individual research findings into practical production systems at experimental husbandry and development farms, and evaluation of the systems for input-output interactions and economic viability were invaluable parts of the process. Nationally, the activities of the British Grassland Society, in association with its affiliated local societies, played a leading role in publishing and promoting advances in grassland technology over the years (see Powell *et al.*, 1995, for a review of these activities). Internationally, the European Grassland Federation meetings and International Grassland Congresses must be acknowledged for the interchange of research results which occurs and for the new ideas which are presented.

Clearly, those farmers who apply 'science into practice' are taking advantage of a major resource and are honing their competitive edge, an edge increasingly required in the current climate of changing political and economic pressures and of intensifying competition for agricultural markets. The large variation in UME output between fields, farms or specific stock enterprises demonstrated in various surveys, and the UME levels achieved by leading grassland farmers, indicate the scope for greater uptake of existing technology which in turn would lead to more efficient grassland production and utilization. Furthermore, the rate and degree of technological progress in the next fifty years will, in all likelihood, match or surpass the advances made in the past half century.

ACKNOWLEDGMENTS
Thanks are given to Scott Laidlaw, Gordon Tiley, Graham Swift and Roger Wilkins for constructive comments and suggestions on an earlier draft.

REFERENCES

ADAS (Agricultural Development and Advisory Service) (1979) *Silage. Liscombe Grass Bulletin No. 2.*

ALDRICH D.T.A. (1987) Developments and procedures in the assessment of grass varieties at NIAB 1950-87. *Journal of the national Institute of agricultural Botany*, **17**, 313-327.

ANON (1985) *Advisory Soil Analysis and Interpretation. Bulletin 1.* Aberdeen: MISR/SAC.

ANSLOW R.C. and GREEN R.O. (1967) The seasonal growth of pasture grasses. *Journal of Agricultural Science, Cambridge*, **68**, 109-122.

ARC (Agricultural Research Council) (1965) *The Nutrient Requirements of Farm Livestock*, No. 2. *Ruminants*, London: ARC.

BAKER H.K., BAKER R.D., DEAKINS R.M., GOULD J.L., HODGES J. and POWELL R.A. (1964). Grassland recording v. Recommendations for recording the utilized output of grassland on dairy farms. *Journal of the British Grassland Society*, **19**, 160-168.

BAKER R.D. (1985) Advances in cow grazing systems. In: Frame J. (ed.) *Grazing. Occasional Symposium of the British Grassland Society*, No. 19, 155-166.

BAKER R.D., DOYLE C. and LIDGATE H. (1991) Grass production. In: Thomas C, Reeve A. and Fisher G. E. J. (eds.) *Milk from Grass* (2nd edition). Billingham: ICI/SAC/IGER.

BAKER R.D., KILKENNY J.B., SPEDDING A.W. and TAYLER J.C. (1967) *Beef Production Handbook, No. 1.* Reading: Beef Recording Association (UK) Ltd.

BARKER A.S., CRAY A.S., FOOT A.S. , IVINS J.D., JONES Ll.I. and WILLIAMS T.E. (1955) The assessment and recording of the utilized output of grassland : a report by a Sub-committee of British Grassland Society. *Journal of the British Grassland Society*,10, 67-86.

BAX J. and THOMAS C. (1992) Developments in legume use for milk production. In: Hopkins A. (Ed). *Grass on the Move. Occasional Symposium of the British Grassland Society*, No. 26, 40-53.

BOSMA A.H. (1991) Efficient field treatment for silage and hay. In: Pahlow G. and Honig H.(eds.) *Forage Conservation toward 2000. Landbauforschung Völkenrode*, **123**, 71-85.

CAB (Commonwealth Agricultural Bureaux) (1961) Research techniques in use at the Grassland Research Institute, Hurley. *Bulletin 45, Commonwealth Bureau of Pastures and Field Crops.* Farnham Royal : CAB.

CLEMENTS R.O. (1995a) The importance of pests and diseases to agricultural grassland in England and Wales. A review. North Wyke : IGER.

CLEMENTS R.O. (1995b) The importance of pests and diseases to white clover (*Trifolium repens*) in England and Wales. A review. North Wyke: IGER.

CLEMENTS R.O., FRENCH N., GUILE C.T., GOLIGHTLY W.H., LEWIS S. and SAVAGE M.J. (1982) The effect of pesticides on establishment of grass swards in England and Wales. *Annals of Applied Biology*, **101**, 305-313.

CORRALL A.J. (1984) Grass growth and seasonal pattern of production under varying climatic conditions. *Proceedings of the 10th General Meeting of the European Grassland Federation, Ås, Norway*, 36-45.

COWLING D.W. and KELLY A.F. (1960) Project 210 trials with grass and clover in OEEC countries. *EPA/OEEC Report 23. Grass, Clover and Lucerne Trials in OEEC Countries.*

DAVIES D.A., FOTHERGILL M. and JONES D. (1989) Assessment of contrasting perennial ryegrasses, with and without white clover, under continuous sheep stocking in the uplands. 2. The value of white clover for lamb production. *Grass and Forage Science*, **44**, 441-450.

DEWAR W.A. and McDONALD P. (1961) Determination of dry matter in silage by distillation with toluene. *Journal of the Science of Food and Agriculture*, **12**, 790-795.

DICKSON I.A., FRAME J. and ARNOT D. (1981) Mixed grazing of cattle and sheep versus cattle only in an intensive grassland system. *Animal Production*, **33**, 265-272.

DOUGLAS J.T. (1994) Responses of perennial forage crops to soil compaction. In: Soane B.D. and Ouwerkerk C.(eds). *Soil Compaction in Crop Production*, 343-364. Amsterdam: Elsevier.

DOYLE C.J. (1982) Economic evaluation of weed control in grassland. *Proceedings of the 1982 British Crop Protection Conference - Weeds*, 419-427.

DULPHY J.P. and DEMARQUILLY C. (1991) Digestibility and voluntary intake of conserved forage. In: Pahlow G. and Honig H. (eds.) *Forage Conservation towards 2000. Landbauforschung Völkenrode*, **123**, 140-160.

EADIE J. (1978) Increasing output in hill farming. *Journal of the Royal Agricultural Society of England*, **139**, 103-114.

ELSÄSSER M. (1991) Drying of forage crops. The current practice, future possibilities and research needs. In: Pahlow G. and Honig H. (eds.) *Forage Conservation towards 2000. Landbauforschung Völkenrode*, **123**, 86-115.

ERNST P., LE DU Y.L.P. and CARLIER L. (1980) Animal and sward production under rotational and continuous grazing management - a critical review. *Proceedings of the International Symposium on the Role of Nitrogen in Intensive Grassland Production, Wageningen*, 119-126.

EYERS B. (1989) Place for big bales in current silage scene. *Big Bale Silage. Proceedings of British Grassland Society Conference, February 1989, NAC Stoneleigh*, pp. 1.1 - 1.7.

FENLON D.R. (1988) Listeriosis. In: Stark B.A. and Wilkinson J.M. (eds.) *Silage and Health*, 7-18, Marlow:Chalcombe Publications.

FORBES T.J., DIBB C., GREEN J.O., HOPKINS A. and PEEL S. (1980) *Factors affecting the productivity of Permanent Grassland: A National Farm Study*. Hurley: GRI/ADAS Joint Permanent Pasture Group.

FORSTER L. (1989) Handling and storing of big bales. *Big Bale Silage. Proceedings of British Grassland Society Conference, February 1989, NAC Stoneleigh*, pp. 8.1-8.4.

FRAME J. (1990) The role of red clover in United Kingdom pastures. *Outlook on Agriculture*, **19**, 49-55.

FRAME J. and NEWBOULD P. (1986) Agronomy of white clover. *Advances in Agronomy*, **40**, 1-88.

FRAME J, NEWBOULD P and MUNRO J.M.M. (1985) Herbage production in the hills and uplands. *Occasional Publication of the British Society of Animal Production*, No. 10, 9-37.

GARDNER A.L., HUNT I.V. and MITCHELL I.A. (1954) The 'Muirfad' technique of peatland improvement. *Journal of the British Grassland Society*, **9**, 161-171.

GARWOOD E.A. (1988) Water deficiency and excess in grassland : the implications for grass production and for the efficiency of use of N. *Proceedings of a Colloquium on Nitrogen and Water Use by Grassland*, 24-41, Hurley:IGAP.

GORDON F.J. (1989) An evaluation through lactating cattle of a bacterial inoculant as an additive for grass silage. *Grass and Forage Science*, **44**, 169-179.

GREEN J.O. (1982) *A Sample Survey of Grassland in England and Wales, 1970-72*. Hurley: Grassland Research Institute.

GREEN J.O., CORRALL A.J. and TERRY R.A. (1971) Grass Species and Varieties. *Technical Report 8, Grassland Research Institute*.

HARKESS R.D. and ALEXANDER R.A. (1969) The digestibility and productivity of selected herbage varieties. *Journal of the British Grassland Society*, **24**, 282-289.

HENDERSON A.R., NEILSON D.R. and ANDERSON D.H. (1988). Biological additives for grass silage. In: Frame J. (ed.) *Efficient Beef Production from Grass. Occasional Symposium of the British Grassland Society*, No. 22, 152-157.

HENDERSON I.F. and CLEMENTS R.O. (1977) Grass growth in different parts of England in relation to invertebrate numbers and pesticide treatment. *Journal of the British Grassland Society* 32, 89-98.

HFRO (Hill Farming Research Organisation) (1979) *Science and Hill Farming: HFRO 1954-1979*. Edinburgh: HFRO.

HODGSON J., MACKIE C.K. and PARKER J.W.G. (1986) Sward surface heights for efficient grazing. *Grass Farmer*, **24**, 5-10.

HOOD A.E.M. and BAILIE J.H. (1973) A new grazing system for beef cattle - The two field system. *Journal of the British Grassland Society*, **29**, 101-108.

HOPKINS A., GILBEY J., DIBB C., BOWERING P.J. and MURRAY P.J. (1990) Responses of permanent and reseeded grassland to fertilizer nitrogen. I. Herbage production and herbage quality. *Grass and Forage Science*, **45**, 43-55.

HUNT L.A. (1965) Some implications of death and decay in pasture production. *Journal of the British Grassland Society*, **20**, 27-31.

ICI PLANT PROTECTION (1976) *Handbook of Direct Drilling*. Jealott's Hill : ICI.

JACKSON D.K. (1975) The influence of patterns of defoliation on sward morphology. In: Hodgson J. and Jackson D.K. (eds.) *Pasture Utilization by the Grazing Animal. Occasional Symposium of the British Grassland Society*, No. 8, 119-128.

JARVIS S.C. (1993) Nitrogen cycling and losses from dairy farms. *Soil Use and Management*, **9**, 99-105.

JOHNSON I.R. and PARSONS A.J. (1985) Use of a model to analyse the effects of continuous grazing managements on seasonal patterns of grass production. *Grass and Forage Science*, **40**, 449-458.

JONES D.I.H. and MOSELEY G. (1993) Laboratory methods for estimating nutritive quality. In: Davies A., Baker R.D., Grant S.A. and Laidlaw A.S. (eds.) *Sward Measurement Handbook* (2nd edition), 265-283, Reading: British Grassland Society.

KENNEDY S.J. (1984) Methods of making and feeding silage. *Annual Report on Research and Technical Work of the Department of Agriculture for Northern Ireland 1984*, p. 285.

KILKENNY J.B., HOLMES W., BAKER R.D., WALSH A. and SHAW P.D. (1978) *Grazing Management. Beef Production Handbook*, No. 4. Milton Keynes : Meat and Livestock Commission.

LAZENBY A. (1981) British grasslands; past, present and future. *Grass and Forage Science*, **36**, 243-266.

LEAVER J.D. (ed.) (1982) *Herbage Intake Handbook*, Hurley: British Grassland Society.

LE DU Y.L.P. and PENNING P.D. (1982) Animal based techniques for estimating herbage intake. In: Leaver J.D. (ed.) *Herbage Intake Handbook*, 37-75, Hurley: British Grassland Society.

LINEHAN P.A., LOWE J. and STEWART R.H. (1952) The output of pasture and its measurement. Part III. *Journal of the British Grassland Society*, **7**, 73-98.

LEWIS G.C. (1988) Fungicide seed treatments to improve seedling emergence of perennial ryegrass (*Lolium perenne*) and the effect of different cultivars and soils. *Pesticide Science*, **22**, 179-187.

LOCKHART J.A.R., SAMUEL A. and GREAVES M.P. (1990)   The evolution of weed control in British agriculture. In: Hance R.J. and Holly K. (eds.). *Weed Control Handbook: Principles* (eighth edition). Oxford: Blackwell Scientific Publications.

McDONALD P., HENDERSON A.R. and HERON S.J.E. (1991). *The Biochemistry of Silage.* Marlow: Chalcombe Publications.

McGINN R., KERR W.D. and HINKS S. (1990). The effect of Maxgrass and a range of silage additives on the fermentation of perennial ryegrass in laboratory silos. *Proceedings of the 9th Silage Conference, September 1990, University of Newcastle Upon Tyne*, 89-89.

McMEEKAN C.P. (1956)   Management and animal production. *Proceedings of the 7th International Grassland Congress, Palmerston North, New Zealand*, 146-155.

MAFF (Ministry of Agriculture, Fisheries and Food) (1970). *Modern Farming and the Soil.* Report of Agricultural Advisory Council on Soil Structure and Fertility.London: HMSO

MAFF (Ministry of Agriculture, Fisheries and Food) (1983) *Certification of Seed of Grasses and Herbage Legumes.* London: MAFF/WOAD/DAFS/DANI.

MAFF (Ministry of Agriculture, Fisheries and Food) (1993). *Statistics, Survey of Agriculture, December 1992.*

MAFF (Ministry of Agriculture, Fisheries and Food) (1973) Fertilizer recommendations for Agricultural and Horticultural crops (RB209). Reference Book 209, London: HMSO.

MAYES R.W., LAMB C.S. and COLGROVE P.M. (1986) The use of dosed and herbage n-alkanes as markers for the determination of herbage intake. *Journal of Agricultural Science, Cambridge*, **107**, 161-170.

MAYNE C.S. and STEEN R.W.J. (1990) Recent research on silage additives for milk and beef production. *Annual Report No. 63. Agricultural Research Institute of Northern Ireland 1989/1990*, 31-42.

MEER H.G. VAN DER., UNWIN R.J., DIJK T.A. VAN and ENNIK G.C. (eds.) (1987) *Animal Manure on Grassland and Fodder Crops: Fertiliser or Waste?* Dordrecht: Martinus Nijhoff.

MORRISON J., JACKSON M.V. and SPARROW P.E. (1980) The response of perennial ryegrass to fertilizer nitrogen in relation to climate and soil. *Report of the joint GRI/ADAS Grassland Manuring Trial GM 20. Technical Report*, No. 27 : GRI.

MOTT G. (1960)   Grazing pressure and the measurement of pasture production. *Proceedings of the 8th International Grassland Congress, 1960, Reading, England*, 606-611.

MUDD C.H. and MEADOWCROFT S.C. (1964) Comparison between the improvement of pastures by fertilizing and reseeding. *Experimental Husbandry*, **10**, 66-84.

MURRAY I. (1993) Forage analysis by near infra-red spectroscopy. In: Davies A., Baker R.D., Grant S.A. and Laidlaw A.S. (eds.) *Sward Measurement Handbook* (2nd edition), 285-312. Reading: British Grassland Society.

NAYLOR R.E.C., MARSHALL A.H. and MATTHEWS S. (1983) Seed establishment in directly drilled sowings. *Herbage Abstracts*, **53**, 73-91.

NEWBOULD P. (1974) Improvement of hill pastures for agriculture. A review. Part 1. *Journal of the British Grassland Society*, 29, 241-248.

NEWBOULD P. (1975) Improvement of hill pastures for agriculture. A review. Part 2. *Journal of the British Grassland Society*, 30, 41-44.

NIAB (National Institute of Agricultural Botany) (1977)   Grasses and legumes for conservation. *Technical leaflet*, No. 2.

NIAB (National Institute of Agricultural Botany) (1980) Growing grasses and herbage legumes for seed. *Seed Growers Leaflet*, No. 5.

NIAB (National Institute of Agricultural Botany) (1982) Growing Italian ryegrass and tetraploid hybrid ryegrasses to obtain optimum harvested seed yields and quality. *Seed Growers Leaflet*, No. 8.

OFFER N.W., CHAMBERLAIN D.G. and KELLY M. (1991). Management of silage effluent. In: Pahlow G. and Honig H (eds.) *Forage Conservation towards 2000, Landbauforschung Völkenrode*, 123, 129-139.

OFFER N.W., ROOKE J.A., DEWHURST R.J. and THOMAS C. (1993) Rapid assessment of silage fermentation characteristics by electrometric titration. *Animal Production*,56, 423A.

OLDHAM J.D. (1993) Recent progress towards matching feed quality to the amino acid needs of ruminants. *Animal Feed Science and Technology*, 45, 19-34.

ØRSKOV E.R. and McDONALD I. (1979) The estimation of protein degradability in the rumen from incubation measurements weighted according to rate of passage. *Journal of Agricultural Science, Cambridge*, 92, 499-503.

PAHLOW G. (1991) Role of microflora in forage conservation. In: Pahlow G. and Honig H. (eds.) *Forage Conservation towards 2000, Landbauforschung Völkenrode*, 123, 26-36.

PAIN B. (1991) Improving the utilisation of slurry and farm effluents. In : Mayne C.S. (ed.) *Management Issues for the Grassland Farmer in the 1990's. Occasional Symposium of the British Grassland Society*, No. 25, 121-133.

PARSONS A.J., LEAFE E.L., COLLETT B. and LEWIS J. (1983) The physiology of grass growth under grazing. 2. Photosynthesis, crop growth and animal intake of continuously grazed swards. *Journal of Applied Ecology*, 20, 127-139.

PATTERSON D.C. and STEEN R.W.J. (1982) Studies on the composition of effluent from grass silage and its feeding value for pigs and beef cattle. *Annual Report No 55 of the Agricultural Research Institute of Northern Ireland*, 23-29.

PENNING P.D., STEEL G.W. and JOHNSON R.H. (1984) Further developments and use of an automatic recording system in sheep grazing studies. *Grass and Forage Science*, 39, 345-351.

PHIPPS R.H. and WILKINSON J.M. (1985) *Maize Silage*. Marlow : Chalcombe Publications.

POOLE A.H. (1990) The role of forage crops in UK livestock farming. In: Pollott G.E. (ed.) *Milk and Meat from Forage Crops. Occasional Symposium of the British Grassland Society*, No. 24, 1-8.

POWELL,R.A., CORRALL, A.J. and CORRALL, ROSEMARY, G. (1995) A History of the British Grassland Society, 1945 - 1995. In: Pollott G.E. (ed) Grassland into the 21st Century. *British Grassland Society Occasional Symposium No.29*, 2-30. BGS:Reading.

RAYMOND W.F.(1969) The nutritive value of forage crops.*Advances in Agronomy*,21,1-108.

RAYMOND W.F. (1974) Green crop drying. *World Crops*, 26, 235-237. London, MAFF.

RAYMOND W.F. (1981) Grassland research. In: Cooke, G.W. (ed.) *Agricultural Research 1931-1981*. London: Agricultural Research Council.

REID D. (1978) The effect of frequency of defoliation on the yield response of a perennial ryegrass sward to a wide range of nitrogen application rates. *Journal of Agricultural Science, Cambridge*, 90, 447-457.

REID D. (1982) Conservation of herbage as silage. The sward : its composition and management. In: Rook J.A.F. and Thomas P.C. (eds.) *Silage for Milk Production. Technical Bulletin 2*, 39-62. Reading : NIRD/Ayr:HRI.

RYDEN J.C.. (1984) The flow of nitrogen in grassland. *Proceedings of the Fertiliser Society of London*, No. 229.

SARKER A.W. and HOLMES W. (1974) The influence of supplementary feeding on the herbage intake and grazing behaviour of dairy cows. *Journal of the British Grassland Society*, **29**, 141-143.

SEALE D.R. (1986) Bacterial inoculants as silage additives. *Journal of Applied Bacteriology*, **61** (Supplement), 9S-26S.

SPOELSTRA S.F., COURTIN M.G. and BEERS J.A.C. VAN (1988) Acetic acid bacteria can initiate aerobic deterioration of whole crop maize silage. *Journal of Agricultural Science, Cambridge*, **111**, 127-132.

STAPLEDON R.G. (1946) Presidential address. *Journal of the British Grassland Society*, **1**, 75-81.

STEWART T.A. and HAYCOCK R.E. (1984) Beef production from low N and high N S24 perennial ryegrass/Bianca white clover swards - a six year farmlet. *Research and Development in Agriculture*, **1**, 103-113.

SWIFT G., MACKIE C., HARKESS R.D. and FRANKLIN M.F. (1988) Response of grass in early season to spring-applied phosphate. *Research and Development in Agriculture*, **5**, 49-52.

THOMAS C. and THOMAS P.C. (1985) Factors affecting the nutritive value of grass silages. In: Haresign W. and Cole D.J.A.(eds.) *Recent Advances in Animal Nutrition*,223-256.

THOMSON D.J. (1984) The nutritive value of white clover. In: Thomson D.J. (ed.) *Forage Legumes. Occasional Symposium of the British Grassland Society*, No. 16, 78-92.

TILEY G.E.D. and FRAME J. (1991) Improvements of upland permanent pasture and lowland swards by surface seeding methods. In: *Grassland Renovation and Weed Control in Europe. Proceedings of European Grassland Federation Conference, Graz, Austria*, 89-94.

TILLEY J.M.A. and TERRY R.A. (1963) A two stage technique for the *in vitro* digestion of forage crops. *Journal of the British Grassland Society*, **18**, 104-111.

VOISIN A. (1959) *Grass Productivity*. London: Crosby Lockwood.

WAITE R. and BOYD J. (1953) The water-soluble carbohydrates of grasses. 1. Changes occurring during the normal life cycle. *Journal of Science of Food and Agriculture*,4,197-204.

WATSON S.J. (1946) The role of silage in grassland management. *Journal of the British Grassland Society*, **1**, 36-40.

WHITEHEAD D.C. (1970) *The Role of Nitrogen in Grassland Productivity. Bulletin 48*. Farnham Royal: Commonwealth Bureau of Pastures and Field Crops.

WILKINS R.J. (1992) Grasslands for the future. *Stapledon Memorial Lecture presented at the 3rd Research Conference of the British Grassland Society, Greenmount Agricultural College*.

WILKINSON J..M. (1987) Silage : trends and portents. *Journal of the Royal Agricultural Society of England*, **148**, 158-167.

WILKINSON J.M. and STARK B.A. (1990) *Whole Crop Cereals*. Marlow : Chalcombe.

WILLIAMS R.D. (ed.) (1984) *Crop Protection Handbook - Grass and Clover Swards*. Croydon: British Crop Protection Council Publications.

WILMAN D. and WRIGHT P.T. (1983) Some effects of applied nitrogen on the growth and chemical composition of temperate grasses. *Herbage Abstracts*, **53**, 387-393.

WOOLFORD M.K. (1984) *The Silage Fermentation*, New York : Marcel Dekker.

WPBS (Welsh Plant Breeding Station) (1978) *Principles of Herbage Seed Production*, 2nd edn, rev. Bean E.W. Aberystwyth: WPBS.

ZIMMER E. and WILKINS R.J. (1984) Eurowilt: Efficiency of silage systems : a comparison between unwilted and wilted silages. *Landbauforschung Völkenrade*, **69**, 88pp.

SECTION 1

SOCIO-ECONOMIC FRAMEWORK

The Changing Public Interest in Agriculture: With Specific Reference to Grassland Farming in EU Agri-Environment Policy

P. D. LOWE

Centre for Rural Economy, The University
Newcastle upon Tyne, NE1 7RU

INTRODUCTION

Rural policy is currently a live issue in Britain, and elsewhere in Europe, as governments and societies reassess the role of their rural areas. This paper reviews the shift in the basis of rural policy and what it means for grassland agriculture, focusing in particular on a review of the development of EU Agri-environment Policy.

POST-WAR POLICY AND ITS DEMISE

Nowadays, the period from the 1940s to the early 1980s, from 'dig for victory' to the cold douche of milk quotas, has taken on the glow of a golden age of agricultural prosperity. It certainly now seems a better and simpler world. The essence of the then rural policy was that, in the pursuit of domestic self-sufficiency in food, farming should be supported by the state, and this in turn would ensure the well-being of rural areas. Implicit in this policy were certain fundamental assumptions:

-       that the prosperity of the countryside equated with the prosperity of farming;
-       that the production of food was the overriding purpose of agriculture;
-       that food security equated with increased domestic self-sufficiency.

Thus various meanings elided in the following equation:

THE COUNTRYSIDE = FARMING = FOOD PRODUCTION.

This was an oversimplification, even in the 1950s and 1960s, but it gave a clear sense of purpose to various groups and organisations. Indeed, as the world became more complicated, it still served as the basis of a number of reliable nostrums. Its very straightforwardness was reassuring and helped to define the purpose of a number of different groups and functions.

  For example, the role of official agricultural policy was to increase output while containing costs. The remit of agricultural scientists was to boost yields. The remit of planners was to preserve, as far as possible, every acre of farm land. The remit of agricultural economists was to evaluate the efficiency of these developments in terms of their use of human and capital resources.

Over the past 50 years increased productivity in agriculture has transformed the situation of food supply. Britain has gone from being only about one-third self-sufficient in temperate food before the war to self-sufficiency in most commodities. From being the biggest food importing country in the world, Britain is now part of a trading block which is the second largest food exporting unit in the world.

At the same time, the economy and society of rural areas have changed radically, partly through these policies, but mainly through other changes. In particular, the technologies of transport and communications - the motor car, the telephone, telecommunications - have each successively facilitated the decentering and dispersal of social and economic activity. The rural economy is no longer dependent on primary production but is largely a service economy.Increased mobility and improved rural infrastructure have given most rural families access to a range of services and facilities and have facilitated a middle class influx into rural areas.

Rural areas, their populations and their economic activities have thus undergone profound changes. The consequence has been to undermine the simple post-war equation of the countryside, farming, and food production. For a start, the farming industry has become a victim of its own success. Increased production has led to food surpluses, whose management and disposal have led to mounting budgetary costs, distortions in world trade and international displeasure.

Secondly, farmers' diminishing role in the food chain has led to a diminishing ability to capture added value. Hence, the paradox - which most politicians and members of the public are unable to comprehend - of rising expenditure on agricultural policy but falling farm incomes.

Thirdly, the tremendous increase in farm labour productivity has detached agriculture from the rural economy. Even in the most rural of areas, agriculture and related industries rarely account for more than 1 in 7 of the employed population.

Fourthly, social change in the countryside has transformed rural society. The influx of an articulate middle-class population has displaced farmers and landowners from positions of social leadership. New demands have arisen, particularly for urban levels of service provision and for a protected countryside.

Fifthly, the intensification of agricultural production has diminished the variety of rural landscapes and wildlife habitats and led to an increase in farm pollution, as farmers have treated the countryside as their factory floor. These pressures on the rural environment have become a focus of concern for new middle-class inhabitants.

Sixthly, the broad post-war political settlement between farmers and urban consumers has been undermined by changes in food demand. With food in surfeit, there has been a shift to a more discerning and a more capricious consumer. Food is no longer seen as basic nutrition but as an aspect of diverse lifestyles or of health-conscious living. A production-oriented agricultural policy has experienced considerable difficulty coming to grips with this fragmentation and sophistication of food markets.

Taken together, these developments have eroded the basis for post-war agricultural policy. No longer with any clear sense of purpose or long term objectives, contemporary agricultural policy has become a succession of crises -of food surpluses; of budgetary excesses; of environmental problems; of health scares; and of animal welfare concerns. Policy making is not so much the art of muddling through as perpetual crisis management. There is a clear need for a new strategy for rural areas.

A NEW STRATEGY FOR RURAL AREAS

Social and economic change in the countryside calls for a rethink of policies for rural areas. Only recently has policy making begun to catch up with the fact that the contemporary rural economy and society are very diverse. While this has led to questioning of the dominance of agriculture in rural policy making, it is not yet clear what principles, other than efficient food production, should guide rural management, although environmental protection and the social and economic development of rural areas are receiving greater acknowledgement.

What is apparent is the need to integrate a diversity of objectives. People want a plentiful supply of food *and* an attractive countryside. Rural communities need adequate services and facilities *and* sources of employment.

There may be some contradictory demands, for example, for pest-free food from a pesticide-free environment; for the countryside to be a source of adventure but not of hazards. But these should stimulate the ingenuity of biotechnologists and leisure providers respectively. The greater irrationality would be to continue to view the functions of the countryside through the prism of agriculture and food production.

Recently, there have been some promising political developments. Agriculturalists and environmentalists have moved beyond their earlier polarised politics to a recognition of mutual dependency through realisation of the countryside as a managed environment. It has also become accepted that the desired diversification of farming incomes depends upon the strength of the rural economy. Finally, there is a slow dawning that the maintenance of the rural environment and economic activity depend on the viability of rural communities. Surely, this is the nub of the notion of rural sustainability.

Recognising these dependencies takes us beyond the post-war equation of the countryside, farming and food production, and refocuses our attention on a different set of relationships:

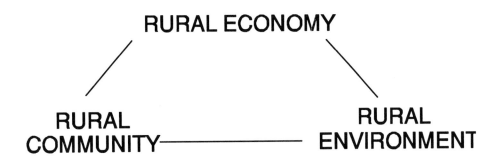

Currently there is a period of transition from an over-arching agricultural policy to a multi-faceted rural policy.

There is obviously a need, therefore, to reformulate the justification and objectives for state intervention in rural areas. It is suggested that the following should be the key objectives:-

- to help ensure the competitiveness of rural economies;
- to overcome the specific disadvantages of rural living;
- to safeguard the public interest in the countryside, particularly those public goods which cannot be left to market forces or civil society to protect or supply.

THE IMPLICATIONS FOR AGRICULTURE

The 1992 reform of the CAP must be seen as a partial and interim step (Harvey, 1994). Important adjustments were made and new principles introduced, but the incompleteness of the reform has destabilised the policy regime, making further reform not only desirable but inevitable. Participation in international negotiations on farm policy reflected and reinforced an understanding that escalating costs could not be contained purely through internal measures and isolation from world markets. The partial opening up to world markets and decoupling of support entitlements from production have established a trajectory for reform which must be carried through.

In the medium and long term European farm prosperity cannot be sustained through market price support but by its own competitiveness. EU agricultural policy will increasingly be subject to international rule under the auspices of the World Trade Organisation. The EU is also preparing to open up its agricultural market to the countries of Central and Eastern Europe, which have been undergoing their own painful transitions to market conditions. Under these circumstances, the extension of the current panoply of production controls is unthinkable, and the only viable course is the adjustment of CAP support levels to world market prices and the abandonment of supply controls.

Inevitably, such a transition will have short-term consequences for farm incomes. To overcome the resistance of farming groups, compensation payments may be needed for price reductions but these should be limited, of finite duration and decoupled from output levels. There will be implications for rural employment and countryside management. To tackle these issues social and environmental support programmes need to be developed separately from farm production policy. Given the geographic variability and the different aspirations and interests of the Member States in rural development and countryside management, the principle of subsidiarity should be applied and the financing, design and implementation of such programmes should be the responsibility of Member States.

The rural economy in Britain is diverse and no longer so dependent on agriculture (Tarling *et al.*, 1993). In Britain, too, agricultural support has not been, and is not, an effective means of maintaining rural employment, either directly or indirectly. Indeed, it has been associated with a sharp decline in the farm workforce. Inevitably, with the workforce now so diminished the absolute rate of decline has tailed off considerably, but the proportional rate has also reduced as the workforce has become concentrated on a core of mainly farm family members (Whitby and Powe, 1995).

Declining farm incomes are encouraging farm families to look for additional income sources, and so-called pluriactivity (multiple job holding) is seen as an important means of maintaining the farming population. The opportunities to diversify farm incomes depend crucially upon the strength and diversity of the local and regional economy. In other words, the prosperity of farm families increasingly depends on the rural economy, which in turn depends less and less on the performance of the agricultural sector (Lowe *et al.*, 1993). Hence, the focus of intervention to promote rural development and employment should be the rural and regional economy and not the agricultural sector.

Turning to the final strand of rural policy: what is the overriding public interest in rural areas? Society looks to the countryside as a reservoir of environmental and cultural resources and values. Some of these may be critical to our survival. In the past, the preoccupation was with food security, but the debate on sustainability has widened the focus of interest.

Firstly, concern has spread to other resources. In recent years, for example, society has been threatened by water shortages, not by food shortages (one of the sources of those shortages has been the growing abstraction demands and pollution from agriculture). A move toward a more resource-conserving society emphasises the role of rural areas as sites for the supply and replenishment of renewable resources (plants, animals, the soil, air and fresh water) and continuing resources (wind, solar energy, water power).

Secondly, the emphasis has shifted to environmental capacities rather than resource flows; to the amount of natural capital rather than the current rate of consumption, which may be unsustainable. In certain cases the pursuit of food self-sufficiency is depleting the productive resource. The classic example is the Fens, as well as other drained organic soils, where current high productivity, brought about through drainage, is wasting the soil resource and will inevitably lead to impoverished mineral soils.

Some of the environmental and cultural resources and values lodged in rural areas are not critical to our survival but are part of our cultural or natural heritage or are considered key components of the good life. Society would be immeasurably impoverished by their loss - rural landscapes, habitats, the natural fauna and flora, the cultural heritage of villages, market towns and historic houses.

The overriding public interest in rural areas is in safeguarding, managing and enhancing their function as an environmental reservoir. This is classically a public good and cannot be left to market forces. The safeguarding of this environmental reservoir must be the chief purpose and justification of rural planning. The maintenance of the reservoir, and society's access to it, depend upon those who own and manage rural land. This must be the prime justification for any long-term continuation of state intervention in, or support for, agriculture. Of course many of these functions of rural areas, as an environmental reservoir, are fulfilled by grassland agriculture. The European Union has begun to address these issues in the recent reforms of the CAP and the development of EU agri-environment policy will now be considered.

THE ROOTS OF EUROPEAN AGRI-ENVIRONMENT POLICY

The first agri-environment measure at the European level is generally taken to be Article 19 of Council Regulation 797/85 on *Improving the Efficiency of Agricultural Structures*. This authorised Member States to introduce "special national schemes in environmentally sensitive areas" to subsidise farming practices favourable to the environment. This amendment to the EC's Structures Directive was promoted by the British Government and initially it found little favour with other Member States or the European Commission. Indeed, the new Article 19 merely permitted governments to introduce environmental incentive schemes without providing any aid from the Community budget.

However, two years later, in Regulation 1760/87, it was agreed that, up to a certain ceiling, ESA payment schemes could be eligible for a maximum of 25% reimbursement from the European Agricultural Guidance and Guarantee Fund (EAGGF=FEOGA). This development must be seen in the context of the mounting budgetary crisis of the CAP, caused through overproduction. It marked the initial acceptance that supporting farmers to conserve the countryside might also help, albeit in a modest way, to curb overproduction. The 1987 change brought Article 19 into line with other elements of Regulation 797/85, concerned with extensification and set aside, introduced at the initiative of the German government, to help reduce market surpluses.

Regulation 1760/87 formally required the Agricultural Council to re-examine the extensification and ESA schemes within 3 years. The Commission took the opportunity to review the three measures (including the voluntary arable set-aside provision) and came up with proposals for "reinforcing the relationship between agriculture and the environment" (European Commission, 1990) which led to a proposed regulation "on the introduction and the maintenance of agricultural production methods compatible with the requirements of the protection of the environment and the maintenance of the countryside" (European Commission, 1990). This eventually became the core of the agri-environment regulation that accompanied the 'MacSharry reforms' of the CAP (European Commission, 1992).

A number of considerations seem to have influenced the Agricultural Directorate of the Commission (Interview with Bertrand Delpeuch, 26 June 1995; Com (90) 366). The first of these was the need to give some substance to the formal commitments made in various policy documents to integrate environmental considerations into agricultural policy. The 1985 Green Paper *Perspectives for the CAP* (European Commission, 1985) had recognised that the role of agriculture is not only to produce food but also that it has an important contribution as the main economic activity required for the management of the countryside and conservation of the environment. With its 1988 statement on *The Future of Rural Society* (European Commission, 1988a) and on *Environment and Agriculture* (European Commission, 1988b) the Commission conceded the need to adapt agriculture to the requirements of protecting the environment and maintenance of the countryside. At the very least this suggested adjustments to the extensification and voluntary set-aside schemes in order to make them environmentally beneficial.

A second and related consideration was the need to respond to specific problems emerging from the implementation of EU environmental policy. The most pressing of these concerned agricultural pollution, which came to public recognition in many parts of the European Community in the late 1980s, in part through the implementation of the Drinking Water Directive. Although this directive did not entail specific restrictions on agriculture, they were envisaged in the proposed Nitrates Directive which was intended to address one of the most serious problems thrown up by the Drinking Water Directive - nitrate pollution from agricultural sources. The Nitrate Directive was intended to promote a preventative approach by reducing leaching from farm land. The Agricultural Directorate was concerned over the consequences for farmers' livelihoods.

A third consideration was the very limited scope and impact of the three existing measures. In part this was seen to be due to inadequacies in their design and in the incentives available. More generally, the Commission felt that such schemes were oriented too narrowly, reflecting specific national concerns rather than Community-wide problems. The extensification scheme had only been taken up by four countries (Germany, Belgium, France and Italy) and the rules were considered difficult to apply and excessively complex. Article 19 also was implemented only by four countries (UK, Germany, the Netherlands and Denmark). It, in particular, was seen to suffer from a northern European bias and in its existing form was thought to be of little relevance to the rural problems of southern Europe. The voluntary arable set-aside scheme was likewise seen to neglect French and southern European worries over desertification (i.e. dereliction of the countryside through land abandonment).

Ever since the instigation of LFA policy, the Agricultural Directorate had shown itself sensitive to this more socially- and agrarian-oriented definition of the rural environment problem. But the Commission is also driven by an integrationist logic, and, while it was evident that some Member States (notably the UK) were pushing rural environmental concerns as part of their general opposition to the CAP, the Commission was keen to see the development of agri-environment policy within a strong, Community-wide framework. It was important therefore in devising the agri-environment regulation to address specifically French and southern European concerns.

Some Member States had simply ignored the 1985 measures. The Portuguese version of Regulation 797/85 did not even include Article 19 (Vieira, 1992). In general, the southern Member States and Ireland had shown little interest in the three measures. Essentially, in these countries the major concern was support for farming populations on social, not environmental, grounds and there was only limited public pressure for an environmental scheme. Southern European governments saw the priority as further intensification, to close the gap with northern Europe, rather than environmental enhancement.

A final consideration for the Agricultural Directorate was the market situation facing farmers. In devising an agri-environment regulation, that consideration could not be put to one side. A necessary condition of any initiative was that it should help to ease overproduction. On the one hand, this meant that the Commission wished to see Article-19 schemes of a kind which contributed not only to conservation but also to the reduction of surpluses; on the other hand, it impelled the Commission to look at a considerably expanded agri-environment programme that might make a significant contribution to the control of surpluses. Insofar as the new agri-environmental schemes would provide an additional source of income for farmers in an era of price restraint, this would complement the new compensatory payments being introduced within the 'MacSharry package'.

THE AGRI-ENVIRONMENT REGULATION 2078/92
This regulation, as one of the 'accompanying measures' to the principal CAP

reform, was agreed in May 1992. It is not surprising that one of the most contentious issues during the debate in the Agricultural Council was over the decision to provide the FEOGA funding through the Guarantee, rather than the Guidance, Fund. Since the Guarantee Fund is the mechanism for supporting the CAP market measures, such as export refunds and intervention purchase, this signalled the incorporation of the agri-environment measures within the core of the CAP. More significantly, perhaps, the Guarantee Fund is not subject to the same budgetary restrictions as the Guidance Fund. Whereas the European Commission had dispensed 10 million ECU co-financing agri-environmental payments in 1990, it was expected that the budget would reach 1.3 billion by 1997, under the new CAP (Delpeuch, 1992; European Commission, 1992).

Member States are able to reclaim 50 per cent of the eligible cost from the Community budget or 75 per cent of the cost in Objective 1 regions - those officially designated as lagging behind in economic terms. Most of the Mediterranean countries, Ireland, the Eastern Länder of Germany and the Highlands of Scotland currently are designated as Objective 1 regions.

It is obligatory on Member States to implement a national agri-environment programme and to include within it all the individual categories of measures listed in Article 2, unless there is a clear reason why these should not apply. Thus, Member States which had not taken any agri-environmental initiatives were to be obliged not only to do so for the first time, but also to develop a programme with a variety of different objectives. By making implementation of the Regulation obligatory, it was hoped to prevent a repetition of experience with Article 19, which was implemented only by a few Member States in Northern Europe. Furthermore, it was hoped that implementation of the regulation might lead to a reduction in the intensity of agriculture over a significant area of land and help, thereby, to stabilise or reduce production and contribute to the wider goals of the 'MacSharry reforms'.

The types of voluntary incentive scheme which Member States may introduce under the Regulation are set out in the box below. Measures (a), (b) and (c) are all concerned with reducing the intensity of agriculture. Taken as a group, they cover both the crop and livestock sectors and make explicit reference to the conversion of arable land to extensive grassland.

Measure (a) is concerned directly with reducing inputs of fertilisers and pesticides and could be seen as a means of reducing pollution arising from agriculture, as well as promoting extensification. There has been some debate about whether incentive payments should be made to farmers who reduce their inputs of fertilisers and pesticides in order to meet pollution control targets, since this can be construed as a breach of the 'polluter pays' principle. In this sense, Measure (a) can be distinguished from Measures (d) to (g) where farmers are being offered incentives to undertake activities which maintain or enhance the countryside. Nonetheless, Measure (a) is popular with several Member States.

The second set of measures, (d) to (g), are concerned primarily with the landscape, nature conservation and public access to the countryside, as well as a rather vague reference to "protection of the environment and natural resources" in measure (d). These measures are rather broadly framed and cover a potentially large range of different schemes, an impression confirmed by the plethora of proposals transmitted to the Commission since 1992 (most of them, though, concerned with pastoral agriculture).

Measure (d) is a development of the wording in Article 19, later Article 21. It also includes the option of providing farmers with incentives to rear breeds of livestock "in danger of extinction". The intention is to preserve a genetic inheritance in the European Community which is in danger of being eroded as certain breeds disappear. Although aid for such breeds already existed on a modest scale in Portugal and Germany, the initiative to include it in the agri-environment regulation arose from Commission staff who felt that rare local breeds could be a focus, especially in the southern Member States, for the public recognition of the regional distinctiveness of traditional farming systems that also conserve wildlife and the landscape.

Measure (e), paying farmers for maintaining abandoned farmland or woodland, is a significant addition and permits aids of the kind put forward by the French government under the old Article 19 scheme but rejected because they fell outside the scope of the scheme, which was confined exclusively to existing farmland. There has been continued sensitivity about this option because it allows stock to be reintroduced into areas from where they have been withdrawn and some officials in the Commission have been concerned that this may be an invitation to allow increases in production, rather than to limit it.

Measure (g) was introduced on a proposal from the British government. It reflects a concern to be able to pay farmers and other landowners for making land available for walking and other forms of public access in return for payment. Few other Member States have been interested in this option.

The measures in Article 2 should be presented within "multi-annual zonal programmes" with a duration of at least five years. The programmes are to "reflect the diversity of environmental priorities". This underlines the intention that Member States should generate schemes which are sensitive to local circumstances, rather than simply introducing standard national schemes. The reference to environmental priorities presumably refers to Community measures such as the nitrates, birds and habitats directives. In practice, a number of Member States have designated areas affected by these directives for incentive schemes introduced in response to the Regulation.

The schemes submitted do not have to be new. However, they do have to respect a number of rules and there is a maximum payment per hectare which is eligible for Community reimbursement, e.g. there is a limit of 250 ECU/hectare on schemes applying to pasture. Many Member States have put forward programmes which contain a mixture of both old and new measures. Arguably, some of the countries that have come to the matter for the first time, such as Ireland, Spain and Portugal, have made more ambitious, if less precisely targeted, use of the Regulation than countries, such as the UK and the Netherlands, with established agri-environmental programmes.

Following on what was initially a German idea, the Regulation suggests that Member States should put forward zonal programmes covering areas reasonably homogeneous in environmental terms. This suggests a series of small-scale programmes tailored to local conditions. There is no requirement that these programmes address specific local objectives or be administered by local or regional authorities. Furthermore, there is the option of establishing a "general regulatory framework" instead of a series of independent zonal programmes. In practice, many Member States have developed national programmes or frameworks complemented by schemes focused on individual areas of high environmental priority. In others, regional authorities have taken the lead in putting forward programmes (Baldock and Mitchell, 1995). The tendency has been to fall back on administrative units rather than to tailor schemes to coherent geographical areas. The option of presenting a cluster of local schemes with no over-arching national element has not been popular.

The timetable for implementation was extended further than originally intended. Member States were to have submitted their proposals by the end of July 1993 for approval by the Commission on the advice of the 'STAR' Committee composed of Member State representatives. Some programmes were ready on time but many trickled in after the deadline, several had to be revised following negotiations with the Commission, and the new Member States also joined the process. In consequence, the approval process continued into 1995. By May, the Commission had approved at least 140 programmes for co-financing and more were to follow (de Putter, 1995). Initially, 2.16 billion ECU had been earmarked for the agri-environment Regulation over five years. However, as national schemes were proposed it was necessary to revise expenditure requirements upwards. A more recent estimate suggests that 3.16 billion ECU is a more likely total for the period up to 1997 (de Putter, 1995).

EVALUATION

A preliminary review of the programmes put forward by the Member States raises a number of strategic issues as follows:

*   The predecessor of Regulation 2078/92 was Regulation 797/85 which, under Article 19 had provided for the establishment of environmentally sensitive areas. That had limited impact and was only taken up by northern Member States. Regulation 2078/92, with its much greater resources, its range of conservation options, and its obligatory requirements on Member States, is having a much wider impact. In consequence, some states are introducing agri-environment policies for

the first time; others have been using such policies for a number of years
and have adapted and expanded them to the present Regulation. 2078/92
does provide for the first time a common European framework for
national policies in the agri-environment field.

AID SCHEMES POSSIBLE UNDER REGULATION 2078/92, ARTICLE 2

Subject to positive effects on the environment and the countryside, the
scheme may include aid for farmers who undertake:

a)   to reduce substantially their use of fertilisers and/or plant
       protection products, or to keep the reductions already made, or
       to introduce or continue with organic farming methods

b)   to change, by means other than those referred to in (a), to more
       extensive forms of crop, including forage, production, or to
       maintain extensive production methods introduced in the past, or
       to convert arable land into extensive grassland

c)   to reduce the proportion of sheep and cattle per forage area

d)   to use other farming practices compatible with the requirements
       of protection of the environment and natural resources, as well
       as maintenance of the countryside and the landscape, or to rear
       animals of local breeds in danger of extinction

e)   to ensure the upkeep of abandoned farmland or woodlands

f)   to set aside farmland for at least 20 years with a view to its use
       for purposes connected with the environment, in particular for
       the establishment of biotope reserves or natural parks or for the
       protection of hydrological systems

g)   to manage land for public access and leisure activities

---

*   Regulation 2078/92 sets certain precedents for agricultural policy which
       may have long-term consequences. It has established the principle that
       farmers, for both environmental and production control benefits, should
       be paid to de-intensify production and to manage the countryside. The
       regulation thus legitimises non-productivist agriculture, particularly low
       intensity pastoral farming. In certain regions and farming systems, it also

brings small-scale and/or part-time farmers within the scope of agricultural support policies. These are potentially major shifts which challenge the hegemony of organisations that represent large-scale productivist agriculture.

* The regulation introduces *subsidiarity* into agricultural policy to a substantial extent. Inevitably, this is leading to considerable variation in national and regional responses to the regulation. To the extent that this reflects the varied nature of European rural environments and the social values attached to them, this is a desirable outcome. But it also seems to reflect variations in resources and capacities both regionally and nationally. For example, within Germany, it is the richer, southern Länder that have put through the biggest agri-environment programmes.

* The differential capability of different regions to co-finance the agri-environmental measures is off-set by the much greater levels of EU assistance available for Objective 1 regions. However, in such regions, the limited organisational and administrative capacity may be a more significant barrier to full involvement in the agri-environment regulation.

* Member States vary in the extent to which they have devolved responsibility sub-nationally for preparing schemes under the agri-environment regulation. In Germany, responsibility rests with the individual Länder, within an agreed national framework. In the UK, marginally different schemes have been introduced for England, Wales, Scotland and Northern Ireland. In preparing zonal programmes Member States have fallen back on administrative units rather than seek to tailor their schemes to coherent geographical areas.

* There is a steady advance of Environmentally Sensitive Areas. Article 19 covered a range of agricultural practices in specific 'sensitive' and important areas for landscape or wildlife. This focus on specific zones has tended to continue even under Regulation 2078/92: in Spain's national and regional parks; special habitats in Portugal; 'operations locales' in France; British ESAs and Natural Heritage Areas in Ireland.

* All types of incentive have been used but their distribution is uneven. For example, the provision for public access has mainly been used by the UK. Maintenance of abandoned land has, not surprisingly, been a priority for Mediterranean countries. There has been strong interest in endangered breeds from Germany, Spain and Portugal. Incentives for organic farming are available to both existing producers and new entrants in Germany, the Netherlands, Denmark and Spain, but in the UK it is restricted only to

those converting to organic farming, and in France the national scheme covers only new entrants, but certain regional programmes are offering payments to existing organic producers.

* The variety of national and regional responses has already thrown up some anomalies. The very different levels and types of support for organic farmers in different regions may well raise questions of unfair competition and market distortion. Other variations raise questions about the equity and effectiveness of the payments being made. For example, the Bavarian extensification programme pays farmers up to a stocking density of 2.5 livestock units per hectare; this compares with lower ceilings elsewhere including in other German Länder. Certain variations of this kind might be desirable in relation to different local environmental conditions, but the Bavarian ceiling might be considered unacceptably high in relation to any environmental benefits it might possibly achieve. The French approach has been to adopt a single national ceiling of 1.4 livestock units per hectare, but the problem here may be a lack of sensitivity towards localised conservation needs; for example, the ceiling is too low to support the management of important Alpine meadows in the French Jura. This national 'prime a l'herbe', or 'grassland premium', will absorb almost two-thirds of the total budget for French agri-environment measures. An EC official has commented:

> "Dreamed up at the very moment when CAP reform was adopted, this premium is designed to encourage livestock farmers to maintain their extensive pastures in the face of competition from very generous area payments for maize silage under the arable regime. But given the very low level of the premium and the fairly wide conditions for eligibility (1.4 LU/ha and 70 kg of nitrogen per hectare) its real usefulness has been questioned - will it really dissuade farmers in western France from cultivating their pasture land, or encourage the continued grazing of distant meadows in mountainous areas?" (Delpeuch, 1994).

It is safe to predict that, not only in France, but in other countries too, tensions between environmental and income support objectives will be a recurring theme in the implementation of the Regulation.

Although the Regulation includes a diversity of conservation options, it adopts a common means to achieve them, namely payments to farmers and their voluntary involvement in agri-environment schemes. Implicitly or explicitly, therefore, it promotes a particular model for resolving the tensions between agriculture and the environment and of the property rights that should regulate the matter. There are already signs that this nascent European model is challenging other approaches, including those traditionally pursued at the national level. In certain circumstances, it may undermine the 'polluter pays' principle. Also it challenges national systems where, in the past, the maintenance of low-intensity farming systems was ensured by restrictions on property rights (for example, through zoning or land use planning restrictions). In addition, it may challenge the rationality of traditional approaches to the resolution of agriculture-environment tensions pursued through the sharp geographical segregation of agricultural and environmental functions (farm land versus natural areas).

Incentives are being deployed on a large scale to address environmental issues, which have been defined partly at a European level and partly by local administrations, particularly agriculture ministries. The standard procedure of offering farmers a form of management agreement for a fixed period may not be the most appropriate response to some of these issues and there are already questions about whether some schemes will generate any significant environmental benefit. Other questions are also emerging. What will happen after the management agreements expire? How far are national and regional administrations becoming committed to incentive payments as a permanent feature of rural policy?

Monitoring and evaluation of this policy will prove complex because of the extremely diverse agendas of individual Member States. This is not simply a matter of Member States positions *vis à vis* the EU but also of the fact that states have very diverse administrative structures internally with the consequence that consistency of policy implementation across the EU will be very difficult to achieve or judge.

In terms of expenditure, the agri-environment Regulation remains a minor element in the CAP. There are conflicts with the major commodity regimes, not least when farmers are eligible for larger payments for arable set-aside than for entering environmental schemes. The organisations which represent large-scale productivist agriculture continue to be a powerful force in directing the CAP and there is a widespread perception that the Regulation is an adornment to the CAP rather than a more far-reaching attempt to integrate environmental concerns into the heart of the policy. Environmental interests may still find it difficult to penetrate the fabric of European agricultural decision making but they can no longer be marginalised entirely. The architecture of the CAP is changing, not only through the incorporation of environmental objectives but also because of the proliferation of regional and local schemes which it now embodies.

The CAP is in the process of what may prove to be a long drawn out transformation from an agri-food policy to a rural environment and rural development policy. This calls for clear thinking and a long term strategy to influence these changes. In the medium term much attention will be devoted to monitoring the impact and improving the effectiveness of new instruments such as the agri-environment Regulation. However, with the prospect of significant sums going to these new fields, there are larger issues at stake which demand attention to basic institutional and accountability questions. There is a pressing need to explore the institutional mechanisms that would help satisfy the following criteria in the deployment of agri-environment resources: that payments are targeted to ensure cost effectiveness; that the level and targeting of funds are responsive to public demand; that the public benefit is clear and proportionate; that tangible and long-lasting environment benefits result.

REFERENCES

ALLANSON, P., HARVEY, D.R., LOWE, P., MURDOCH, J., WARD, N. and WHITBY, M.C. (1995) *The CRE's Comments for the White Paper on Rural Areas*. Centre for Rural Economy Working Paper 14, University of Newcastle upon Tyne.

BALDOCK, D., BEAUFOY, G., HAIGH, N., HEWETT, J., WILKINSON, D. and WENNING, M. (1992) *The Integration of Environmental Protection Requirements into the Definition and Implementation of Other EC Policies*. Institute for European Environmental Policy, London, 42pp.

BALDOCK, D. and BEAUFOY, G. (1993) *Plough On! An Environmental Appraisal of the CAP*, a report to WWF UK. Institute for European Environmental Policy, London, 65pp.

BALDOCK, D. and MITCHELL, K. (1995) *Local Influence - Increasing Local Involvement in the Development of Green Farming Schemes*. Council for the Protection of Rural England, London.

BEAUFOY, G., BALDOCK, D. and CLARK, J. (eds) (1995) *The Nature of Farming: Low Intensity Farming Systems in Nine European Countries*. Institute for European Environmental Policy, London, 66pp.

DELPEUCH, B. (1994) Ireland's Agri-Environmental Programme in the European Context In: Maloney, M. (ed.) *Agriculture and the Environment : proceedings of a Conference on the integration of EC environmental objectives with agricultural policy*, held in the Royal Dublin Society from March 9-11, 1994,. Dublin: Royal Dublin Society.

DELPEUCH, B. (1991) Politique agricole européenne et environnement: une intégration croissante. *Eau et Rivières* 78 (August), 11-17.

DELPEUCH, B. (1992) PAC et environnement. *Perspectives*, 1, 17-19.

DE PUTTER, J. (1995) *The Greening of Europe's Agricultural Policy: the Agri-environmental Regulation of the McSharry Reform*. Ministry of Agriculture, Nature Management and Fisheries, The Hague, The Netherlands.

DIXON J. (ed.) (1992) *A Future for Europe's Farmed Countryside*. RSPB:Sandy, UK.

EUROPEAN COMMISSION (1985) *Perspectives for the Common Agricultural Policy*. Com (85) 333.

EUROPEAN COMMISSION (1988a) *The Future of Rural Society*. Com (88) 501.

EUROPEAN COMMISSION (1988b) *Environment and Agriculture*. Com (88) 338.

EUROPEAN COMMISSION (1990) *Proposal for a Council Regulation on the introduction and the maintenance of agricultural production methods compatible with the requirements of the protection of the environment and the maintenance of the countryside*. Com (90) 366.

EUROPEAN COMMISSION (1991) *The development and future of the Common Agricultural*

Policy - Reflections paper of the Commission. Com (91) 100.

EUROPEAN COMMISSION (1992) *Council Regulation on Agricultural Methods Compatible with the Requirements of the Protection of the Environment and the Maintenance of the Countryside.* EC 2078/92.

HARVEY, D.R. (1994) Policy reform after the Uruguay Round. In: K. Ingerset *et al.*, (eds.) *Agriculture in the Uruguay Round.* London: Macmillan.

LOWE, P. *et al* (1993) *Countryside Change : A Synopsis,* Centre for Rural Economy Research Report RR93/1, University of Newcastle upon Tyne.

LOWE, P. and MURDOCH, J. (1993) *Rural Sustainable Development.* London : Rural Development Commission.

LOWE, P.D., COX, G., MACEWEN, M., O'RIORDAN, T. and WINTER, P.(1986) *Countryside Conflicts: the Politics of Farming, Forestry and Conservation.* Gower: Aldershot.

LOWE, P.D., MARSDEN, T. and WHATMORE, S. (eds) (1994) *Regulating Agriculture.* Wiley: Chichester, UK.

MARSH, J. (1991) *The Changing Role of the Common Agricultural Policy.* Belhaven, London.

TARLING, R., RHODES, J., NORTH, J. and BROOM, G. (1993) *The Economy and Rural England* Salisbury: Rural Development Commission.

VIEIRA, M. (1992) Environmentally sensitive areas in Portugal. In: Dixon, J. (ed.) *A Future for Europe's Farmed Countryside.* RSPB, Sandy, UK, pp. 149-155.

WHITBY, M.C. (ed.) (1994) *Incentives for Countryside Management: the Case of Environmentally Sensitive Areas,* CAB International: Wallingford.

WHITBY, M.C. and POWE, N. (1995) Some British experiences of promoting rural development through rural employment projects and policies. In: Marr, P. (ed.) *Rural Realities* (forthcoming) Aberdeen.

WHITBY, M. and WARD, N. (eds.) (1994) *The UK Strategy for Sustainable Agriculture : A Critical Analysis.* Centre for Rural Economy Research Report RR94/5, University of Newcastle upon Tyne.

Demand for Animal Products from Grassland

V. WHEELOCK
Verner Wheelock Associates Ltd
10 Hey Street, BRADFORD, West Yorkshire BD7 1DQ

ABSTRACT

The changes in food consumption patterns since 1950 are examined in detail and related to some of the important developments within society and the economy. The evolving role of the multiple retailers is described and explained. Looking to the future, it is virtually certain that demand for food will continue to change quite rapidly. To be successful with consumers, new products will have to be tasty and good to eat, safe, produced in an acceptable fashion, healthy and convenient. It is strongly advocated that primary producers should work in close collaboration with other sectors of the food production system if they are to prosper and survive in a market which is extremely volatile.

INTRODUCTION

Food is big business. In 1983, consumers in the UK spent £46.0 billion on household food. In addition, they spent £25.7 billion on alcoholic drink and £35.7 billion on catering in the form of meals and accommodation. The total represents over a quarter of all consumer expenditure and is about £2,000 for every man, woman and child.

The food chain is a highly complex system, which is subject to a variety of different pressures. In order to understand the future role of grassland and indicate how those involved can cope, it is essential to have an appreciation of the key driving forces within the food chain and the impact they are likely to have.

This paper has three objectives. First, it will examine some of the major changes in food consumption patterns since 1950 and relate them to developments within society. Second, it will consider how the food chain has been evolving with particular reference to the role of the multiple retailers. Finally, it will suggest how those in primary production can respond if they are to survive and prosper.

FOOD CONSUMPTION PATTERNS SINCE 1950

The National Food Survey (NFS) provides data on food purchased for use in the home. This information has been used to prepared a series of graphs showing how patterns of purchasing have changed since 1950. Although the NFS does not include food bought and consumed outside the home, it nevertheless measures about 90% of the food that is eaten and gives a reliable picture of the trends.

Figure 1 shows how the proportion of total food expenditure on different food groups has varied between 1950 and 1990. From this perspective, the meat and meat products group is clearly the most important. As living standards improved after the Second World War, the proportion of expenditure increased steadily until 1980. Since then there has been a progressive decline, which roughly corresponds to an increase in the proportion of food expenditure spent on fruit and vegetables.

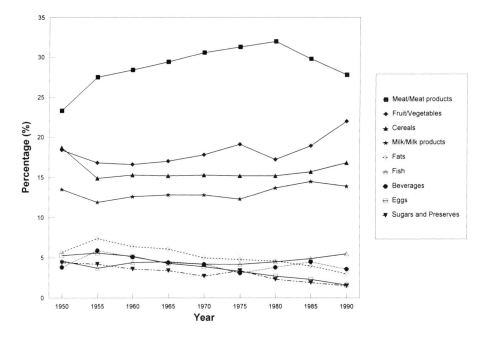

Figure 1.   Changes in the proportion of total food expenditure on individual food groups 1950 - 1990.

Expenditure on milk and milk products has remained reasonably steady with a small increase in recent years, largely due to a growth in demand for cheese. Similarly, expenditure on cereals has been maintained. Of the remaining categories, fish is the only one to show an increase in recent years. Expenditure on beverages - mainly tea and coffee - has fluctuated, while the values for fats, sugars and preserves and eggs have all fallen steadily since the 1950s.

A rather different perspective with more detail can be obtained from data on the actual amounts of food purchased. Demand for milk remained steady until 1975 (Figure 2). Since then it has fallen by about 30%, but the most significant feature has been the growth in demand for low fat milks over the past 15 years. On the other hand, there has been steady growth in the demand for cheese, although a small reduction has occurred in the last few years. Demand for eggs has slumped since the peak observed in 1965.

There has been a fall in demand for bacon and ham while demand for pork has remained fairly constant except for a surge in the early 1980s (Figure 3). Demands for both beef/veal and mutton/lamb have fallen steadily in recent years. By contrast, demand for poultry has expanded rapidly.

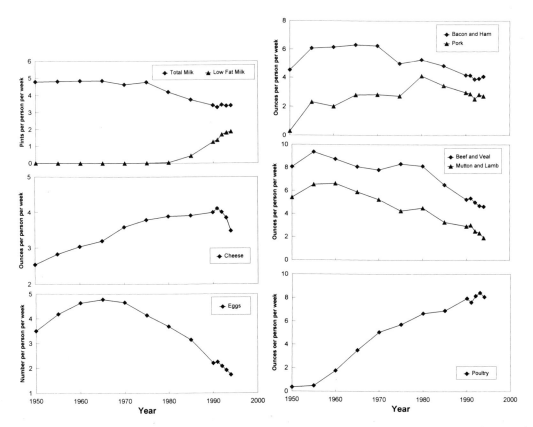

Figure 2. Changes in demand for total milk, low fat milk, cheese and eggs since 1950.

Figure 3. Changes in demand for pork, bacon and ham, beef and veal, mutton and lamb, and poultry since 1950.

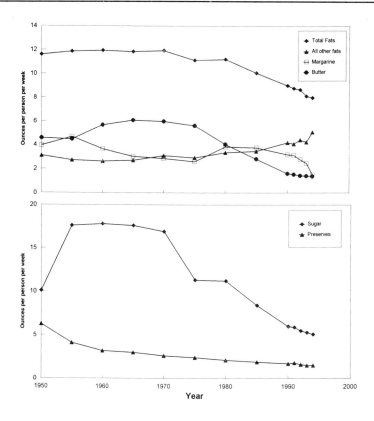

Figure 4. Changes in demand for total fat, all other fats, margarine, butter, sugar and preserves.

Demand for total fats has fallen steadily over the past 15 years (Figure 4). In the early 1980s, margarine became more popular than butter although in the last few years the demand for margarine has also fallen, while that for other fats has been growing. In the 1950s and 1960s, the 'other fats' consisted mainly of lard. However, since then demand for lard has almost disappeared and most of the 'other fats' are cooking oils and low fat spreads.

Demand for sugar expanded markedly in the 1950s and remained virtually constant until 1970. Since then it has fallen by well over 50%. Demand for preserves has fallen steadily since 1950.

It is clear from these data that many of the staples such as bread, sugar, potatoes, beef, mutton and eggs have experienced big decreases in the amounts consumed. To some extent, these have been balanced by growth in the markets for cheese, poultry, breakfast cereals and fruit.

However, it is important to appreciate that total energy consumption, as measured by the NFS, has fallen (Figure 7). Average energy consumption has fallen from over 2,600 kilocalories per head per day in the 1950s to under 1,900 in the 1990s. Intake of total fat and of saturated fat has also fallen substantially in the last 25 years. To some extent, the decrease may be an overestimate because the NFS does not include food prepared and eaten away from home. Eating out in cafes and restaurants certainly has increased but the growth in this activity is partially off-set by the decline in 'industrial catering' ie, the provision of meals at the place of employment. It follows, therefore, that the reductions in consumption which have occurred are largely because people are eating less food.

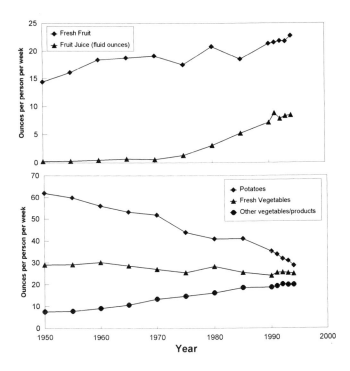

Figure 5. Changes in demand for fresh fruit, fruit juice, potatoes, fresh vegetables and other vegetables or products since 1950

On the other hand, several categories have shown big increases in demand. There is no doubt that convenience is an important factor influencing choice of food. The driving force has obviously been the growth in the proportion of married women at work. Between 1971 and 1993, the percentage of women aged 25-34 in employment increased from 45.5 to 70.7. This means that the number of full-time housewives has declined and so the time available for the usual household chores, including meal preparation, has been reduced substantially. Women who spend a substantial proportion of their day at work want to buy food which can be served quickly and easily. There is much less home baking carried out now, which to some extent is the reason why the demand for sugar, fats and eggs has fallen.

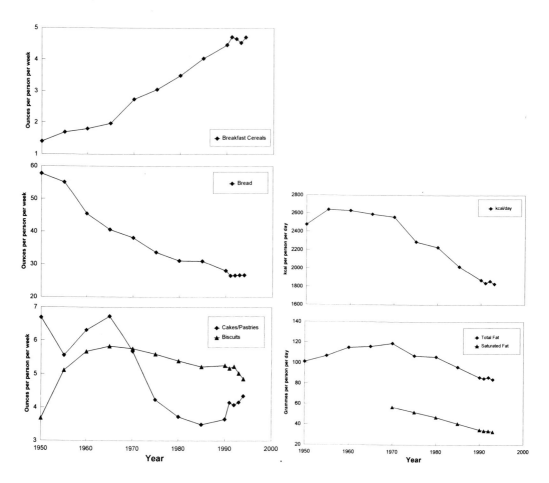

Figure 6. Changes in demand for breakfast cereals, bread, cakes, pastries and biscuits

Figure 7. Changes in the intake of energy, total fat and saturated fat.

Data on the changes in consumption of convenience vegetable products (Table 1) and convenience meat products (Table 2) show that the demand for frozen foods has increased between 1983 and 1993. However, there has been a decline in demand for certain other types of convenience foods, particularly those in cans.

Snacks such as potato crisps are also exhibiting growth. Rising incomes are clearly having an impact. Table 3 shows that households with the highest incomes (Group A) spend about 3 times as much as those without an earner on meat-based ready meals - a growing sector of the market.

Table 1. Consumption of convenience vegetable products (g/person/week).

	1983	1993
Crisps, potato snacks and other potato products	26.3	43.9
Canned vegetables	274.5	239.7
Chips excluding frozen	25.5	27.5
Frozen chips and other frozen convenience potato products	49.5	97.4
Frozen vegetables exluding potatoes	89.7	105.6
Other vegetable convenience	15.3	40.8
Total	480.8	554.7

Source : National Food Survey Committee (1994)

Table 2. Consumption of convenience meat products (g/person/week).

	1983	1993
Bacon and ham	30.9	34.5
Meat pies and sausage rolls, ready to eat	21.5	16.1
Meat pies, pasties and puddings	37.1	32.8
Ready meals, not frozen	17.3	32.5
Canned meat	59.4	50.9
Frozen meat products	44.7	73.9
Other convenience meals	50.4	63.4
Total	261.2	304.2

Source : National Food Survey Committee (1994)

Table 3. Expenditure on meat based ready meals, 1993 (p/person/week).

Income Group	Expenditure
A	44.0
B	30.0
C	33.5
D	27.5
E_1	16.0
E_2	15.5
OAP	3.0

Source : National Food Survey Committee (1994)

Changes in personal circumstances obviously have a major impact on choice of food and so it is instructive to consider some of the changes in society and in the economy during the last 40 years. Here are a few examples :

*   Manufacturing industry is no longer the most important source of employment. With men, the proportion of the workforce in manufacturing declined from 41% in 1971 to 28% in 1994. Over the same period, employment for women declined from 29% to 12%

*   Part-time employment for men has almost doubled in the last 10 years from 570,000 in 1984 to 998,000 in 1994

*   Holidays abroad now make up over 40% of all holidays taken. In 1993, 23.5 million holidays abroad were taken by British residents - more than 3 times as many as in 1971

*   In 1993, 90% of households had a telephone, compared with 42% in 1972

*   Expenditure on clothes and footwear more than doubled in real terms between 1971 and 1993

*   In 1971, 8% of families with dependent children were headed by a lone mother, but by 1992 this had increased to 21%

*   The average family size fell from 3.1 in 1961 to 2.4 in 1993

*   The percentage of 18 year olds in full-time education increased from 2.3 in 1981 to 4.4 in 1992

*   In 1993, over 20% of the UK population were aged 60+

*   At the end of June 1994, 153,000 mortgages were 6-12 months in arrears

It is self-evident that these developments influence people's attitudes and positions, which in turn may be reflected in the foods that are demanded. Since 1950, the average household expenditure on food has fallen from 35% to 12% of income. This factor alone has created considerable potential for products which are relatively expensive, provided they match up to expectations. This has certainly been the main reason for the success of Marks & Spencer in food retailing.

On the other hand, at the lower end of the market, there is a sizeable sector with low incomes. For these people, the price of food is still the dominant factor and this has contributed to the success of discounters such as Netto and Aldi, which have moved into this country recently. There has also been a huge growth in the number of people in higher and further education. Many of these move away from home and, as a consequence, make changes in their regular patterns of food habits. They are also exposed to new attitudes and outlooks, which can induce a willingness to try innovative foods.

Concern about diet and health is probably a key factor which contributes to the growth in demand for low fat milks, fruit juices, fruit and vegetables, cooking oils, breakfast cereals and poultry. The most striking change is undoubtedly the increase in the proportion of semi-skimmed milk, which has grown from virtually zero in 1986 to about 50% of the total liquid milk market today. Switching from whole milk to semi-skimmed milk is an effective way to reduce fat intake because the change is easy to make. Semi-skimmed milk is purchased and used in exactly the same as whole milk. The price is about the same and the difference in taste is relatively small. In fact, after a period of adjustment, whole milk can taste rather fatty.

THE RETAIL SCENE

Hundreds of thousands of small shops selling food have ceased trading, while the multiple retailers have emerged as the dominant force. 'The Big Five', Sainsbury, Tesco, Safeway, Asda and Gateway now sell over 50% of all the food purchased in Great Britain. It is self-evident that these businesses have an important influence on the changes in food consumption patterns outlined above. Therefore, it is worth considering some of their characteristics and the ways in which they operate :

* The stores are large - many are over 20,000 m² and, therefore, can provide a much more extensive product-range than a typical corner shop; 15,000-20,000 food lines are not an exceptional number. As a result, shoppers have access to food products that would not be available in smaller shops.

* Most of the multiple retailers have developed their 'own label' product range. In some cases, this can account for up to 60% of the food items available. The recent introduction of the Sainsbury Cola shows that it is possible to challenge such well established brands as Coca Cola. In 1993, Sainsbury spent a total of over £23 million on advertising. As this was to support the entire operation, it is obviously highly effective when compared with what is spent on individual products such as Heinz Baked Beans (£4.6 million), Anchor Butter (£3.5 million), PG Tips (£9.5 million) or Kellogg's All Bran (£5.8 million).

* The major retailers employ food scientists and technologists to devise the specifications for new products and to improve existing products. Because they have little capital tied up in production and manufacturing plant, it is relatively easy for them to alter the range of products available to customers. Since the big retailers control such a high proportion of the food market, there are numerous suppliers who are keen to do business with them.

* The buying power of the retailers enables them to dictate terms to the suppliers with respect to quality of food and standards of manufacturing. Furthermore, the economies of scale mean that it is feasible to deal directly with suppliers from overseas and to work collaboratively with them to provide products specially tailored for the UK market. For example, this approach has been used very effectively to obtain a variety of good quality wines at reasonable prices. Anecdotal evidence indicates

that it was the threat to import semi-skimmed milk from Europe that eventually persuaded a rather reluctant industry in this country to make the product available.

*   As the retailers are close to the ultimate consumers, they rapidly detect emerging concerns. The introduction of electronic scanners at the check-outs provides high quality information on changes in purchasing patterns. For example, this technology makes it very easy to study impact of promotion campaigns on demand of individual items.

LOOKING AHEAD

Pressures for change

There is no doubt that food consumption patterns will continue to change - almost certainly at an increasing rate. Modern consumers are much more imaginative and adventurous in their choice of food than their parents were. Pressure from the media and from advertising will generate interest in new food products and stimulate sales. Concerns will be raised about some existing foods that could result in a decline in sales. Science and technology will create virtually unlimited scope for sourcing and developing new products. Tough competition between businesses at all points in the food chain will force the pace of change

The Office of Science and Technology has recently conducted a series of exercises as part of 'Technology Foresight' to identify opportunities in markets and technologies likely to emerge during the next 10-20 years. Some of the features which relate to the food chain have been selected and used to give an indication of what may materialise.

Table 4.   Selected features likely to emerge in the next 10 - 20 years that will have an impact on the choice of food (Technology Foresight - Delphi Study)

---

*   Most consumers order routine staple items of food from home to be delivered to the doorstep.
*   Widespread acceptance of the consumer of food or drink produced from a genetically modified organism.
*   50% of the population no longer eat red meat.
*   Causal links between diet and cancer are sufficiently understood to cause widespread changes in people's eating habits.
*   Elucidation of individual human genetic profiles so that dietary advice can be targeted.
*   Tailor requirements of a healthy diet includes studies of how to maximise micro-nutrients (eg, vitamins) and minimise anti-nutrient content (eg, allergies).

Source : Office of Science and Technology (1995)

From the consumer perspective (Table 4) the shift towards home delivery is likely to extend the range of products, since there will be no need to display foods prior to purchase. With the efficiency of information technology, it could well be that tailor-made products are actually made to order. Concerns about avoiding disease and achieving optimum health will continue to grow as factors which affect the choice of food. The existence of structures such as the Committee on Medical Aspects of Food Policy (COMA) will facilitate the interpretation of scientific data for the food industry and for consumers.

Table 5.   Selected features likely to emerge in the next 10 - 20 years that will have an impact on the *production* of food (Technology Foresight - Delphi Study).

---

* Widespread availability of an extensive variety of freshly cooked meals for rapid home delivery.
* 90% of all manufactured food products carry a retailers' own label.
* Practical use of foods which require no additional preservatives.
* Functional effects of fat in food are satisfied in other ways, so that current fat intakes can be reduced by about a third.
* Hydroponically grown muscle, based on selective gene expression, allows a substantial shift from animal husbandry to industrially produced meat.
* Climatic changes require an alteration in a quarter of the UK's agriculture and food production.

Source : Office of Science and Technology (1995)

From the production perspective (Table 5) the position of the retailers is likely to become even more powerful. Even if home shopping becomes established, the retailers are expected to retain a key role here. If new methods for the production of meat-like products can be successfully developed, then the reduction in demand for conventionally produced meat will continue.

One does not necessarily have to agree with the view expressed in 'Technology Foresight' reports to appreciate that the food chain will continue to be very dynamic. In fact, the technology has provided an enormous number of possibilities and it must be appreciated that many potential developments will not be acceptable. Products which are technologically feasible are not necessarily socially desirable or economically successful as BST, for example, has demonstrated.

Coping with the changes

Grassland production is a long way from the consumer end of the food chain. It really is impossible for those in farming to predict precisely how food markets will evolve. Agriculture can no longer remain isolated from the rest of the food chain. Producing a crop in the hope of finding a market is an approach which is doomed to failure. Hence, the only realistic way to cope is to ensure that a market is in place before making a commitment to produce. This means linking in with the rest of the food chain.

Although it is clear that the retailers have major advantages, their success is critically dependent on a regular reliable supply of high quality goods. Failure to maintain this, places the retailers in a very vulnerable position. Modern successful businesses have recognised that it is absolutely vital to have a close working relationship between retailer and supplier. Exactly the same principle should apply to the relationship between food manufacturers and farmers, especially as agricultural produce is increasingly used as an ingredient for subsequent processing. This will become even more important with the growing sophistication of the market, which is likely to demand products tailored to suit the requirements of individual consumers. The specifications for commodities such as milk, beef and potatoes are becoming extremely critical in order to ensure the quality of the final product and the efficiency of the process.

This is exactly how it is done in the McDonald's system. Suppliers to the restaurants work closely with those responsible for purchasing and quality assurance in McDonald's. The company has been operating in the British Isles for the past 21 years. During this period, a number of food companies which supply McDonald's has grown steadily as the number of restaurants has increased.

The french fries are produced by McCain's, which has growers contracted to supply potatoes. These are grown in accordance with specifications formulated by McDonald's working in co-operation with McCain's. Specifications are designed to ensure that there is a high yield of french fries which reach the quality standards demanded by McDonald's. The potato growers know they are assured of a market and price which depends on how successful they are in meeting the specifications. Consequently, they operate in a reasonably stable business environment. Under present arrangements, occasionally growers on the open market can obtain higher prices than those under contract. However, over a period, there is no doubt that those with contracts are economically successful.

This example is part of an inexorable trend. Farmers, growers, manufacturers and retailers must all be prepared to co-operate to provide the consumers with what they want. The issues are complex and it will be difficult to decide exactly what will be required. The products likely to be successful are those which meet the following characteristics :

*   tasty and good to eat
*   safe
*   produced in an acceptable fashion
*   healthy
*   convenient

By working together, it should be possible to harness the new technologies effectively in order to meet the demands of the market and, perhaps, even exercise some control over events. This is really no different from the challenges faced by any type of business. Finally, remember that although it may be a difficult market to satisfy, there will always be a demand for food.

REFERENCES

NATIONAL FOOD SURVEY COMMITTEE (various years) *Household Food Consumption and Expenditure.* London : HMSO.

OFFICE OF SCIENCE AND TECHNOLOGY (1995) *Technology Foresight Progress Through Partnership : Food and Drink.* London : HMSO.

The Economic Context for Grassland Farming

J. P. McINERNEY

Agricultural Economics Unit, University of Exeter, Lafrowda House,
St German's Road, EXETER EX4 6TL

ABSTRACT

This paper takes two different views of the economic context for grassland farming. One looks at the grassland farming specifically as an economic activity and examines it using an economist's definitions and perceptions - in effect, analysing it from the standpoint of an economic model. The second approach considers the wider economic context within which grassland farming takes place and the role it plays in the agricultural economy as a whole.

Grassland farming should be viewed in its dual context of food production and as part of the countryside resource use system, and its efficiency defined with respect to both roles. Consumer food preferences are changing and encompass many factors, of which conventional production efficiency (reflected in product cost) is only one. Animal welfare, protection of the environment, reduction of pollution, maintenance of species diversity and the preservation of traditional farming images are all valid demands which society also places on livestock producers. The relevant definition of 'efficient grassland farming', therefore, must recognise these changing requirements in food production along with the developing demands for other uses of rural land. Apart from the commercial value of its products, an increasing economic value is being attached to other products of grassland. This in turn requires a wider definition of economic efficiency which diverges from the more conventional (technical) notions of efficiency in grassland farming.

Grassland covers two thirds of the UK land area, and products from it contribute substantially to the agricultural economy, with 32% of UK agricultural output being attributable to grass. The value of grassland to particular geographic areas and farm-size groups in the UK is considerable. This applies particularly to the Less Favoured Areas and to small family farms. With the growing polarisation of farms into fully commercial full-time units and smaller part-time holdings, the socio-economic importance of grassland is emphasised by its particular relevance to the growing proportion of people who rely on farming for only part of their income.

INTRODUCTION

There seem to be two interpretations of the title I have been given for this paper. One is to look at grassland farming specifically as an *economic* activity and examine it in the context of an economist's definitions and perceptions - in short, to analyse grassland farming from the standpoint of an economic model. The second interpretation is to view the wider economic context within which grassland farming takes place and the role it plays in the operation of the agricultural economy as a whole. The distinction between the two approaches, although perhaps a bit subtle for the untrained eye, is a potentially helpful one and I will attempt to develop the two viewpoints separately in what follows. If they appear to merge in places, it suggests the distinction is too subtle even for me.

GRASSLAND FARMING AS AN ECONOMIC ACTIVITY

From an everyday point of view we all have an image of grassland farming. It means keeping cows and sheep, making silage, walking across fields with a dog, going to market, looking out on a world of green and not disturbing the soil surface as much as an arable farmer does. If we wish to analyse the processes that take place however, we each adopt our own disciplinary viewpoints and redefine grassland farming in more narrowly rigorous terms. To the agricultural scientist it means fostering photosynthetic processes within particular herbage

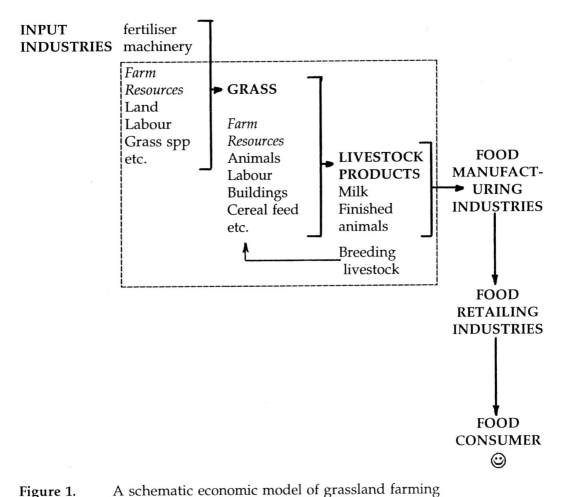

Figure 1.   A schematic economic model of grassland farming

species to create plant material and then transforming it, via the metabolic processes of farm livestock, into saleable animal products. To an economist, however, that same technical process is characterised as a two-stage value-creating activity based around distinctive resources - particularly land, grass species and ruminant livestock - to generate goods and services as part of a wider process designed to enhance human benefit. While this may appear to be merely arcane semantics, it highlights the features of all economic activity and hence the structure of the basic analytical model of economics.

All economic activity, whether to produce fertiliser, food, Ford Fiestas or financial services, is a process (or chain of processes) to transform initial entities (resources) into different, higher value commodities specifically for the benefit of the people who constitute society (note, *not* for the benefit of 'the producers'). In this sense, there is nothing special about any particular sector or industry other than that its technical processes, or what it produces, are identifiably distinct. Grassland farming can be defined in this context as a two-stage resource transformation process embedded in a much more extended set of such processes which together constitute the human food chain (Figure 1).

The sequence within the dotted box represents the two distinct economic processes of grassland farming; first producing grass as an output and then using it as a resource for livestock production. Both add value to a starting set of resources and pass the product on to a further value-adding stage in the food chain. There are distinctive economic issues relating to each of these processes which can be examined separately, as, indeed, from a technical point of view they are separate, both in time and in biological terms. However, given that the concerns of economic analysis and the criteria for success are centred on the far end of the chain - i.e. the benefit created for people - it is ultimately necessary to consider the performance of grassland farming integrally with the rest of the food-production and countryside-resource-use system, of which it is a part. If we lose sight of this wider context, there is a danger of ending up defining how to do an impressive job of the wrong thing!

DEFINING EFFICIENCY

The issue of primary analytical concern - in grassland farming as elsewhere - is that of efficiency. The economist's definition of this tends to be conceptually different from that of the agricultural scientist because it is broader based and focuses on *value* measures rather than on specific *technical* ratios. Because the objective of economic activity is to generate human benefit, an efficient process is simply one that provides what people want (not something else) at the lowest cost in terms of all the resources used (not just one particular resource). This places the emphasis squarely on demand-side considerations, and requires reference to the pattern of products and quality characteristics that society seeks, rather than simply quantitative measures of some physical output. Defining the objective in terms of satisfying demands is more relevant than the alternative supply-side approach, which starts with a given set of resources and characterises efficiency in terms of gaining maximum output from them. However, resources are not fixed in availability, do not always have to be used, are not all equally scarce and can be used to produce a number of different outputs. Consequently the 'maximise output' criterion can be misleading.

Thus, objectives of maximum yield per cow, maximum ME per hectare, high rates of liveweight gain or maximum output per man are not sufficient guides to efficiency achievement because they ignore the other components of the production set, and carry no indication about which are the most important ('scarcest') resources to use to maximum effect. Appreciation of this distinction is crucial in the search for efficiency in grassland farming. The evidence of recent years is that demand patterns for ruminant livestock products are undergoing distinctive changes. In consequence, established definitions of good (technical) achievement are being forced to change because the value assigned to output increasingly relates to qualitative characteristics (its provenance, the conditions under which the animals were kept, the 'naturalness' or intensity of the husbandry systems and the particular inputs that have been used) rather than simply to the level of product availability and its money price. Similarly, the costs to be minimised in production are being progressively widened to include costs to the animal (its 'welfare'), environmental and pollution costs of resource use, reduction in species diversity and loss of traditional farming images. Together, these are leading towards a new definition of what efficient grassland farming will mean in the 21st Century, based far more on human valuations of acceptability than on conventional measures of technical performance.

EFFICIENT GRASSLAND FARMING

As an integrated two-stage process, the success of grassland farming is based on efficiency in both producing grass and in utilising it. Producing grass generates no direct economic benefit in itself, of course, its value being created by the subsequent process of livestock production. From the economy's standpoint, therefore, efficiency in grassland farming is dependent on producing the particular level, mix and nature of livestock products that satisfies the real demands of society. The emphasis on 'real demands' is crucial, because the tendency in all countries has been to obscure these economic realities, at various times, by administrative policies which distort values and artificially adjust demands. For example, supported prices for livestock products overstate their real economic value and, while this may serve social objectives of enhancing producers' incomes (though it rarely does) or political objectives of increasing domestic self-sufficiency, it diverts livestock farming away from the path of genuine economic efficiency. However, in the post-GATT world of market liberalisation and evolving reform of the CAP towards demand-based product pricing, the signals to which livestock producers will have to respond imply some significant adjustments to the mode and activities of grassland farming.

The previous paper has considered the changing demands for animal products from grassland, and to which the evolving economic environment will give greater prominence. The conventional economic theory of food demand would say that, because livestock products have a relatively high income elasticity of demand, an increasingly affluent society will seek to expand its aggregate consumption of them. Coupled with availability at progressively lower unit costs, because of continuing advances in production technology, the prospects would seem to be for expanded demand for animal production and for the grassland resources from which they are derived.

However, it appears that cultural changes are taking place in the consuming public. Preferences are turning against red meat and animal fats for dietary reasons. Attitudes are growing in opposition to 'efficient' husbandry systems which exploit the animal's technical production potential in pursuit of cheap product prices and secure supplies. Concerns over health and perceived product quality, coupled with reasons of lifestyle, ethical and personal preferences of individuals, are suppressing the normal income-related growth in demand for livestock products.

All this holds the prospect of the proverbial double whammy for ruminant livestock producers over the next 20 years. Reduction in the artificially supported market demands that policy has created will be exacerbated by diversion of consumer preferences away from the traditional expansionary developments for more and cheaper supplies of milk and meat. More subtle requirements in terms of perceived quality characteristics of animal products will increasingly affect the economic value they are seen to represent, and hence how livestock farmers will be expected to meet the needs of the food economy. The terms 'wholesome', 'natural', 'traditional', 'extensive', 'farm-based', 'organic', etc., while subject to no rigorous specification in scientific or technological terms, have a powerful influence on what food consumers may define as desired animal products. These attitude and valuation changes are not restricted to ruminant livestock production, of course, but they will nevertheless have unavoidable direct and indirect effects on the economic value of the grassland production systems upon which they are based.

FUTURE DIRECTIONS FOR EFFICIENCY
All this has major implications for the definition of efficiency in grassland farming and the direction that developments may take in pursuit of this aim. If efficiency means first providing what people want, then the redefinition must start at the livestock production stage of the system, where economic value is most obviously identified and where society's demands impinge most directly. Values placed on livestock output now increasingly relate not only to the final products but also to the conditions under which they are produced. If the efficiency target is to maximise the value gained by society, the question as to which sources of value to consider becomes more complex. The calculation includes not only the commercial/saleable value of products going into the food

chain, but also various unpriced values (so-called 'externality values' because they are external to market processes). In particular, the welfare of the animals concerned - or, at least, human perceptions of that welfare, which may be very different from what the animals themselves would choose - is becoming considered as a significant quality characteristic of the final food product. The more consumers are prepared to pay a higher price for welfare-friendly products, the greater this aspect becomes a component of economic value. Further perceptions of product quality, related to the flavour of meats or the absence of 'unnatural' inputs or practices in the production process, seem likely to exercise an increasing influence on consumer valuations. These aspects may appear to be undefinable - or even empty - in technical scientific terms, but the realities of economic systems are what the decision-making public define them to be, not necessarily what scientific method can identify. As Oliver Wendell Holmes asserted, "the truth is what people can't help believing is true".

As a result, many of the technical developments which offer increased production efficiency according to our long-established image of progress will, in fact, be seen as *inefficiencies* because they detract from the value society gains from its livestock processes. For example, the use of BST, growth hormones, genetic manipulation and embryo transfer are considered by many as representing net *costs,* not benefits. The inevitable accompaniment to high-input/high-output livestock systems - the production of comparable levels of animal waste - is being increasingly viewed as a major reduction in output value rather than simply the issue of a by-product. Nutritionally efficient high-energy diets, intensive housing systems and meticulous disease management will be less applauded as the benchmarks of good livestock farming. Animal products derived from grazing-based rather than housed systems of husbandry will offer more value to more people, and the output of low-productivity obsolete livestock types (under the caché of 'minority breeds') and production methods will be increasingly valued for its apparently more preferred flavour and other qualitative characteristics. There will still be a substantial core demand for standard cheap food products, of course, because substantial numbers of households cannot afford to indulge these quality preferences or do not hold the newer perceptions about food and farming. Even so, the growing diversity of the food market inevitably means larger sections of grassland farming will need to be responsive to these widening market demands.

Economic axioms assert that productivity growth (which is not the same as *production* growth) is always a valid aim, but research into livestock production technology will need to reconsider what this term now means (milk and slurry are different outputs of a dairy cow, but enhancing its productivity of both is not unquestionably a good thing!). Since market prices frequently fail to reflect true economic values (because of externality effects), increasing commercially valuable output may not represent a genuine productivity improvement. Similarly, it is becoming less clear for which resources high productivity should be sought.

High output per unit of land has been a traditionally applauded target - but is irrelevant if agriculture faces a surplus of land. Increased labour productivity is good for farmers if it relates to their own labour or that of their hired workers- but not for an agricultural economy where excess labour is available anyway. Conceivably it is maximum productivity to fertiliser or chemical inputs - the use of which is necessary, but is increasingly considered as 'bad' -that should become the primary target in order to minimise their use in achieving the output levels required. The maximisation of *all* resource productivities has always been conceptually impossible, of course, but until now the question of choosing the appropriate target variable has not been confronted.

EFFICIENT GRASS PRODUCTION

These valuation changes in society will generate similar pressures to hold back from exploiting the full technical potential of resource use in grass growing as well. In the economic model of Figure 1 grass is simply one of the inputs in the value-creating livestock production sector of food supply. All that seems necessary for economic efficiency is for grass (or, more correctly, the relevant nutrients embodied in grass) to be made available at the point of use in the required quantities at the lowest possible cost. The 'required quantities' of grass nutrients will be determined by the demand for ruminant livestock products and the costs of alternative nutrient sources, such as cereals, which might be used instead. Defining "the lowest possible cost", however, is becoming more complex. It is typically calculated from the value of the land used and the financial expenditures on fertiliser, labour, machinery, etc., and the reduction of these costs per unit of grass output is the conventional measure of success in the long term drive for greater grassland productivity. However, the growing awareness in society of the environmental side effects of intensive plant growth practices has not only introduced into the calculation all the non-price externality costs already referred to, but is increasingly assigning a rising economic value to them. A dramatic fall in the numbers of skylarks and other ground-nesting birds is now recognised as an economic cost of forage conservation based on silage, and could encourage some moves back to haymaking. Dismay at nitrogen leaking into water courses and groundwaters could lead to images of 'efficient' grassland farming based more on minimising nitrogen inputs per unit of grass output than maximising output per unit of land. As a result, significant available responses to nitrogen applications may be eschewed as 'not worth it', despite the conventional farm financial accounting processes.

Furthermore, those same evolving public preferences seem to be attaching a *direct* value to grassland *per se*, in addition to its indirect value as a source of inputs to livestock production. Certain areas of grassland have always had a direct economic value, of course; they are called lawns, sports fields, parks and golf courses, and competitive prices have been paid to draw them into these uses. But more and more people are valuing grassland specifically for its *countryside* value - they want to look at green fields and hillsides carrying grazing animals, rather than yellow fields and cultivated hillsides. These preferences imply not only a lower agricultural productivity of land use relative to arable cropping, but also in many cases a demand for lower productivity grassland farming. Mixed swards - often containing lots of pretty weed species - are considered in some sense better than vast expanses and the boring uniformity of the latest Italian ryegrass variety. Ill-drained pastures, buttercup meadows, wetlands and 'natural' grassland (as long as they are not *too* scruffy) are valued for their intrinsic characteristics as well as for their contribution to the food supply system.

There may not be very effective mechanisms for people to express these preferences, or in any manner comparable to the way they can indicate their demand for food products. But this is a failing in our institutional structures and one which applies in countless areas of economic activity: it does not undermine the authenticity of the economic value that is derived from these (technically) 'less efficient' modes of grassland farming. Indeed, to the extent that they are more preferred systems, they represent by definition (economically) *more* efficient grassland farming.

THE NEW ECONOMIC CONTEXT

Many of these new ideas and perceptions are difficult to accept as other than way-out, minority viewpoints. People who have grown up with the post-war outlook, in which expansion of food supplies was a self-evident objective and productivity growth through science-based technological development the essential strategy, cannot easily relearn their priorities and presumptions. But, in the industrialised/western world at least, food sufficiency is no longer a problem. Our technological capability to extract food raw materials from our landbase is already reassuringly adequate, with further developments available on the shelf which could rapidly be exploited should the need arise. Population levels are stable, everyone is tolerably well fed, and further income growth will lead to almost no expansion in the aggregate demand for agricultural products. People, therefore, want to direct their consumption to other things. New economic values are being created to accompany these new demands. In the food system, those new valuations are associated with convenience and quality of food, and more psychological (as opposed to nutritional or appetite-satisfying) attributes of the products consumed. In its perception of how farm-based resources can best generate further economic value, contemporary society is seeking the benefits of countryside, visual amenity, environmental features, biological diversity, the creation or maintenance of traditional rural structures and comfortable images of a farming industry that are inconsistent with charmless, hard-nosed science and industrial processes. These are all genuine economic commodities because they are derived as benefits from using resources in a particular way; the fact that they are not *commercial* commodities does not negate this fact - it just makes it more difficult to organise and deliver their supply.

As stated at the outset, this is a decidedly demand-driven concept of developments in agriculture, but that is the only valid viewpoint. It was the great 18th Century economist, Adam Smith, who recognised that "the object of economic activity is not production; it is consumption". There is no point, therefore, in scientists or technologists protesting that they can produce more and cheaper agricultural products from the nation's available resources. The rest of society is saying "we don't want any more of the bloody stuff, thank you; we now want more of something else". Nor is it relevant to point out that these environmental/welfare-friendly/feel-good attributes of livestock products will cost more, or that potential cost reductions will have to be foregone. If having the more expensive product is preferred to having the money that could be saved, then by definition it means it yields greater economic value. (No-one would expect to be deterred from buying a colour TV rather than a black and white one simply because it costs more). Our starting economic model emphasised exactly this point; it is what people actually want that defines efficiency, not what they could get if only they took advantage of some impressive supply process.

It is true that there remains a need for higher food production on a global scale if people in the poorer nations are to be better fed. But this has little relevance to western agriculture and does not provide an economic context for grassland farming in Europe. The technical possibility of producing more and low cost agricultural output here does not change the fact that consumers there have insufficient income to buy it. The food *needs* in poor countries do not translate into effective food *demands* on the world markets which European agriculture has the undoubted technical capability to supply. It is demand forces, not supply capabilities, that are the ultimate determinant of resource use. Since there is no evidence (or likelihood) of dramatic political initiatives to transfer benefit from rich to poor nations, world agriculture will continue to function as essentially an economic system. And in this context, land use in Europe (and especially in the UK) will remain primarily responsive to domestic demands.

One should not belittle the changing preferences of society nor underestimate their impact on our economic processes - for they are the inherent forces that drive these processes. Nor is there any basis for judging whether the new land use and production patterns are 'sensible' or not, whether on scientific or other grounds. (Why should so many people spend so much money to buy water in bottles from the supermarket, when virtually the same stuff comes out of the tap at zero cost? Why will individuals seriously choose a particular brand of soap powder/coffee/car/insurance policy/etc. when it is effectively identical to the others?) A society that is well-fed, has never experienced food shortage and never expects to, for whom food expenditures are not a major proportion of the household budget is now expressing strong and enforceable preferences for different types of land use and farming processes from those which have characterised the last half century. And since supply is the servant of demand, not the other way round, those of us who have influence over developments in supply capability must respond to these new preferences, not our own assumptions about what is or always has been important.

It is this economic context which will increasingly determine the adjustments that will be made to grassland farming. Food production will still be the dominant role for rural land. But problems relate to making changes, not maintaining the core activities, and so it is the 'new' ways of using grassland to meet society's needs that will demand increasing emphasis by researchers and grassland operators. Not all grassland will need to adapt to the new demands but an increasing proportion of it will. There will still be merit in finding ways of raising grassland productivity as conventionally measured, but this will mean less land is needed in the food production chain and allow more to be employed in other uses. At some stage it will be recognised that research into how best to produce amenity or habitat grassland, how to utilise grass most efficiently in producing the newer style of livestock products, or how to farm grassland jointly for people and ruminant livestock, are becoming important research areas in the pursuit of greater economic efficiency.

GRASSLAND IN THE AGRICULTURAL ECONOMY

We now turn to the second interpretation of the title - the economic role that grassland plays. Two characteristics give grass a special place in the farming economy of a country like the UK. First, it covers over two thirds of the agricultural area and in that sense is by far the most important crop in British

Table 1.   Utilisation of UK agricultural land, 1994.

	Area '000 ha	% of total
Grass < 5 years	1,436	7.8
> 5 years	5,322	28.8
Rough grazing	4,551	24.6
Common land	1,224	6.6
Total grass	12,533	67.8
Cereals	3,042	16.5
Other arable	1,471	8.0
Other land	1,436	7.8
Total agricultural area	18,482	100

Source: Agricultural Census.

105

farming (see Table 1). Second, nearly half this grassland is the naturally-occurring and original (in farming terms) vegetation type which, in economic terms, classifies it as a natural resource. Natural resources have a particular economic significance because - unlike man-made capital and labour, the other two primary resource types - they are the original, God-given 'free' resources (like oil, minerals, wildlife, climate) which underlie the inherent wealth of an economy. The productivity of this natural grassland (mostly defined as rough grazing and common land) may not be very high in an agricultural sense but, having virtually no alternative use beyond livestock keep, it effectively comes free to the agricultural economy. (Technically speaking all plant species are natural resources, but modern grass varieties have been subject to so much constructive development through plant breeding programmes that they are probably more correctly considered now as man-made capital resources.)

Because of the dominance of this resource base the UK agricultural economy is essentially - and in western regions it is almost exclusively - based on grassland farming, for this is where its comparative advantage lies. As a result, the product base of agriculture is heavily weighted towards ruminant livestock which, give or take a few deer, rabbits and horses, is the only economically effective way of exploiting grass growth. Ruminants dominate the farmed animal population, accounting for 85% of the total livestock units in 1994. Furthermore, the production from these livestock, valued at farmgate prices, amounts to almost three quarters of the value of all livestock output, and approaching half of the total value of UK agricultural output (Table 2).

Applying to Table 2 the estimates (by Lazenby and Doyle, 1981) that grass provides 60% of the energy requirements in dairying, 80% in beef production and 90% in sheep production, yields a crude calculation that 52% of all livestock output, or some 32.2% of total UK agricultural output, is specifically attributable to grass. One way of stating the economic context of grassland farming, therefore, is to say it constitutes fully one half of the farm livestock economy and contributes a third of UK farming.

The livestock output from grassland not only generates substantial economic value but has beneficial trade effects too. This is of some benefit for a food importing nation like the UK which, even for the temperate agricultural products that could be produced domestically, is only 70% self-sufficient. In 1994 there was a generally positive trade balance for ruminant livestock products, with exports exceeding imports by 83% for beef and veal, 45% for sheepmeat, and only in deficit of 18% for milk products. (This does not, of course, account for the net imports of feedstuffs utilised in producing those exports.)

However, remember Adam Smith's dictum and consider the economic contribution of grass-based livestock to consumers. About 25% of the average person's expenditure on food is for products that derive from ruminant livestock (calculated from National Food Survey, 1993). This amounts in total to some £11 billion annually, or about 3% of all consumers' expenditure. Stated like that it may not sound a large proportion. But considered in the context of the vast array of things that people spend their money on to enhance their well-being, there will be few other single components within any industry in the economy that can claim to make a contribution to society's benefit of similar magnitude to grassland farming.

Table 2.   Livestock output in UK agriculture, 1994.

	Output value (£ million)	% of total agricultural output
Finished cattle	2,396	15.4
Finished sheep	1,212	7.8
Milk	3,266	21.0
Wool	44	0.3
Total grass-based livestock	6,918	44.4
Other livestock	2,634	16.9

Source: Agriculture in the UK, 1994

SOCIO-ECONOMIC ASPECTS OF GRASSLAND FARMING

Farming's dependence on its landbase makes it not only unique as an economic activity but, more than any other industry, gives it an unavoidable social and political dimension. The spatial distribution of agriculture across regions represents a distribution also across populations and communities; variation in farming conditions, therefore, reflects as differences in the well-being of identifiable groups in society. The role of grassland in this context is considerable.

For example, the natural climatic advantages for grass growth (or relative lack of advantage for arable crops) on the western side of the UK determines the economic lives of farmers in that half of the country. Perhaps more importantly, in the hill and upland areas virtually the only viable form of agriculture has to be based around grassland and livestock production, for the land has no other commercial use. It is mostly unsuited for arable cropping, and while trees may grow satisfactorily they cannot provide a return comparable with livestock - even with substantial state aids. It is no overstatement to assert that grassland farming is the central feature of the rural economies in these areas, which lack the resources and the locational advantages for economic activity based on industrial production or service provision. The regions are 'less favoured' in the literal as well as in the institutional sense.

Without grassland farming the Less Favoured Areas would have little basis for economic activity or community. As shown in Table 3, this designation covers a substantial proportion of UK agriculture with some 80,000 farm holdings and almost 45% of the land area located in these disadvantaged regions. The socio-political significance is, in fact, even greater for being 'less favoured' seems to mean being a Welsh, Scottish or Northern Ireland farmer! Some two-thirds of farms in these countries are so designated, and if grassland is the basis of agriculture in the LFAs then it underpins the well-being of some very distinctive rural populations. In many respects the explicit policy support for farming in the uplands is unconnected with food supply (and in the limit not a lot to do with environmental management either); it is effectively a political recognition of the economic vulnerability of particular national and cultural groups in UK society.

Table 3.   Less Favoured Areas (LFA) in UK agriculture.

			LFA		LFA as % of total	
	Number of holdings ('000)	Area ('000 ha)	Number of holdings ('000)	Area ('000 ha)	Holdings	Area
England	153.4	9,354	19.0	1,371	12.4	14.7
Wales	29.9	1,490	20.0	1,115	66.9	74.8
Scotland	32.5	525	21.0	4,394	64.6	83.6
N Ireland	28.4	1,007	19.2	686	67.6	68.1
UK	244.2	17,109	79.2	7,567	32.4	44.4

From an overall standpoint, the importance of grassland to the incomes of people in farming is comparable with the relative magnitudes already quoted for the nation's agriculture. The most recent report on *Farm Incomes in the UK (1993/94)* indicates that six out of every ten full-time farms are classified as either dairy or cattle and sheep farms, and hence are rooted in grassland farming. The dairy farms have the highest incomes in this group and the lowland livestock farms the smallest, but together they earn some £1.28 billion, fully one half of all the net farm income from agriculture. The fact that subsidies constitute a large proportion of this, particularly for the hill livestock farms, does not alter the fact that control over grassland is a substantial route to farming income.

Grassland has an added importance in the agricultural economy because of its association with the structure of farming and the pattern of farm sizes. In an agriculture still characterised by small family businesses (well over half of all full-time farms in the UK) the grassland resource provides the essential basis for their endurance. The possibilities for intensive land use, which allows a viable business to be sustained on a relatively small land area, are substantial with modern grass production methods. Dairying, for example, represents an important means of commercial survival for small farms and has been traditionally considered 'the sheet anchor of the small farmer'. Economies of scale will always tend to give larger units an economic advantage in all types of farming, but the capital requirements for machinery and the discontinuous nature of production operations can make small-scale arable farming far less feasible than small-scale livestock farming. In its socio-economic context, grassland is important not just because it figures large in the national farm, but also because it sustains an even larger proportion of the farming population.

Its importance could conceivably become even greater in this respect with the way agriculture is changing towards a structure of increasingly part-time participants. It has become evident over recent years that a clear 'duality' is emerging in UK farming (McInerney, 1994), which current policy adjustments towards more market-oriented product pricing, coupled with social changes in the countryside and preferences for rural living, will cause to increase. These developments mean that agriculture is characterised by two distinct sub-populations of farms. One group consists of full-time, progressive, 'efficient', relatively large-scale units potentially well able to survive through an exclusive dependence on the commercial production of agricultural products at free market prices. Although their numbers will continue to decline over the coming years, those units and their operators typify the conventional image of the modern farmer. In contrast, there is a second sub-population of part-time farm units whose economic survival is jointly dependent on the generation of income from non-farm employment or business sources, as well as from farming. Already, 45% of all agricultural holdings in the UK have output levels insufficient to constitute a full-time occupation, and 40% of all those who identify themselves as 'farmers' in the annual Agricultural Census are part-time. The numerical importance of this group will increase in the future for entirely understandable economic and social reasons.

The relevance of this in the present context is that, arguably, it is grassland which provides the bedrock for part-time farming systems. The selling of grasskeep is possibly the most convenient way of generating an income from a landholding without getting too involved with its use and management. It is far easier to keep a few sheep or cattle as an accessory activity than to grow a small area of cereals or other crops. Contract services can be readily employed for the major operations in grass production, limiting the needs for labour inputs or capital stock. Added to this, the increasingly important personal 'consumption' reasons for operating an agricultural holding - i.e. as a preferred living environment, which people are choosing if they have adequate additional income sources to supplement their farming operations - are probably more satisfied by land in grass than by an arable area, and enhanced more by keeping livestock than by crop production. These attitudes are not to be belittled, or dismissed as self-indulgent 'hobby' farming. For many people (including established small farmers struggling to keep their holdings going) part-time farming is the only way they can retain a desired connection with country living; the operation of their farm holding is an entirely serious activity, but just happens to be insufficient on its own to provide a full household income. This kind of part-time involvement in farming is becoming an expanding feature of the rural scene, and with it the socio-economic role of grassland becomes more prominent in modern society.

GRASSLAND, RECREATION AND THE ENVIRONMENT

Finally, the distinctive non-agricultural role that grassland plays in society must be recognised. Rural land is not only a key resource in the food supply system; it is also space, location and visual features from which people derive considerable economic benefit through recreational uses - and it is almost exclusively grassland which provides these benefits. For example, more than 400,000 hectares of grass (3.3% of the total area) is given over just to keeping the 550,000 horses and ponies in the UK (Peat Marwick McLintock, 1988). A grass covering to the surface is the essential characteristic of golf courses, sports fields, parkland, race courses, banger racing tracks, airfields, picnic sites, campsites, caravan parks and countless other areas of agricultural land designated for specific sporting and recreational uses. The culture and management of the sward, while directed towards different notions of fitness for purpose, are just as important for those uses as they are for supporting livestock production. And even for people whose rural leisure preferences are less associated with a particular use of land but more with simply walking in, driving through, sitting in or looking at the countryside, it is a grassed environment rather than an arable one which best meets those needs.

As we become a more affluent and mobile society, with virtually no demands for additional food products, the contribution of grassland to these more diverse dimensions of economic well-being will receive increasing recognition. Already in the UK about 14% of consumer expenditures are devoted to leisure goods and services - not a lot less than the 18% of the household budget which goes on food. Leisure expenditures are almost double their level of 20 years ago, indicating how rapidly this area of economic activity is growing; and while rural recreation is not the greatest component it is a major area of development for meeting new demands in contemporary society. Some of these demands can be met by grassland farmers on a purely commercial - and highly profitable - basis, renting out land for recreational use or establishing farm enterprises which cater specifically for this leisure market. In other cases it is likely that the provision of a grassed landscape to satisfy more general scenic and walking preferences may require specific public sector payments to landowners to maintain these characteristics of their land. The interesting possibilities for the modern farmer are to work out the most efficient stocking rates and complementary utilisation patterns for joint exploitation of grassland through people and livestock!

The one remaining role for grassland that must be noted is in the production of 'pure' environmental goods and services - either exclusively, dominantly, or in an accessory manner with farming. The increasing clamour over 'the environment' in contemporary society is not necessarily well informed, rarely distinguishes between conservation and preservation, is frequently based on speculative fears about what might be lost, and usually seems to presume that all environmental goods and features are valuable and costless to retain. Nevertheless, it is a reality with particular economic implications that people are increasingly placing an explicit value on rural wildlife, diversity of fauna and flora, distinctive biological habitats and what are considered as desirable visual features of the countryside. In effect society is declaring them to be economic commodities, because it recognises the benefit gained from their existence (or at least perceive a cost should they be lost) and are prepared to see resources allocated to their retention. Grassland has an important place in this context, because it is the provider of many of these special environmental characteristics. In that sense, much grassland is particularly valued as a biological and countryside environment in itself, regardless of (or possibly in negative relation to) its agricultural productivity - the Somerset Levels, chalk downland, the Yorkshire Dales, wilderness areas, the field patterned Blackdown Hills, etc. It is evident that, if faced with the choice, more and more people would accept the higher economic costs of the more varied sward and colour of traditional permanent pasture (the return of Cockle Park mixture?), the assorted vegetation patterns of 'natural' grassland, the more diverse wildlife populations, and the more extensive livestock farming practices that go with it.

Again this emphasises the duality of the economic context of grassland if it is to be responsive to the actual land use demands of society rather than some presumed continuing imperatives for more and cheaper food. Whether or not intensity will have to be reduced on *all* grassland to meet these demands remains to be seen - but it is highly doubtful. More likely, particular areas and sites will be drawn into serving specific defined 'environmental' requirements on the basis of special payments for this purpose. Their extent and location will depend on the inherent characteristics and hence capability to meet these needs, and on the level of demand for them - which in turn determines how much public money will be diverted to pay the necessary price, that necessary price being simply whatever is sufficient to draw the land out of commercial grassland farming. In many cases no payment will be necessary at all, because the environmental characteristics under 'normal' farming conditions will be judged as entirely acceptable; in these circumstances farmers cannot help producing a desirable countryside as a by-product of their work and so have no basis for extracting a special additional payment from the public. (This could apply to large areas of the West Country, for example.)

The likelihood is that, while distinctive, important and of genuine economic significance in the economy of grassland farming, environmental uses will be far less extensive than many of its lobbyists presume. The value of many environmental components is more associated with what in economics is identified as *existence value* (as opposed to *use value*). This means that, while a considerable loss would be felt if they were to disappear completely, the total value they provide is not simply a function of their availability. Beyond a certain threshold, further hedgerows, wetlands, wilderness areas, natural moorlands, old pastures, etc. would be considered to add nothing to overall benefit; they would not be worth the cost in terms of the other uses foregone, whether for food, or recreation, or just to lie idle, and so would not justify the diversion of public resources to their further provision or protection. Furthermore, these thresholds of public demand are probably very much lower than one would guess from the publicity and political emphasis given to conservation and the environment. It is the major role of economists, working in association with other scientists in the rural domain, to identify just where they are likely to lie so that policy measures to guide land use can be more rationally established.

REFERENCES

JOLLANS J.L. (ed.) (1981) *Grassland in the British Economy*, CAS Paper 10, Centre for Agricultural Strategy, University of Reading.

LAZENBY, A. and DOYLE, C.J. (1981) Grassland in the British Economy - some problems, possibilities and speculations. In: Jollans, J.L. (ed.), *Grassland in the British Economy*, CAS Paper 10, Centre for Agricultural Strategy, University of Reading. 14-50.

MAFF. (1994) *National Food Survey 1993*. London, HMSO.

MAFF. (1995) *Agriculture in the United Kingdom 1994*. London, HMSO.

MAFF (1995) *Farm Incomes in the United Kingdom 1993/94*. London, HMSO.

MCINERNEY, J.P. (1994) Duality - the future face of farming. *Journal of the Royal Agricultural Society of England*, **155**, 25-33.

PEAT MARWICK MCLINTOCK .(1988) *The Economic Contribution of the British Equine Industry*. British Horse Society, Stoneleigh, Warwickshire.

Economic and Social Changes in Slovak Co-operative Farms in the Period of Transition

M. ZIMKOVÁ

Grassland and Mountain Agriculture Research Institute,
Mládežnícka 36, 974 21 Banská Bystrica, Slovakia

INTRODUCTION

After the 'velvet revolution' in 1989 somewhat harsher changes in Slovak agriculture have now begun. For more than 40 years only co-operative farms were found in Slovakia but now new private farms have started to be created and new agricultural laws established. Nevertheless many co-operative farms still represent a unique source of employment and income for villagers and a food supply for the nation.

RESULTS AND DISCUSSION

The main changes in structure, crop production, animal husbandry and employee's income of three co-operative farms are given in Table 1. All three co-operative farms are in Central Slovakia: Zaježová and Očová are in the mountain region, Sebechleby in the lowlands. Although the climatic conditions for agricultural production are more favourable in Sebechleby, Očová also shows good results in cereal and forage crop production. Zaježová is smaller (1185 ha of agricultural land) and produces mainly forages.

In 1994 only a few hectares were excluded from the co-operative and used as private farms (Sebechleby 7 ha, Očová 80 ha, Zaježová 100 ha). The population in Zaježová live in hamlets around the village and the development of family farms is more natural and sometimes inevitable there.

Cereal yields have increased in Zaježová and Očová (1989-94) and decreased in Sebechleby in 1992. In contrast grassland production has increased (1989-94) and the highest yields were achieved in Sebechleby and Zaježová (4-5 t DM/ha). Očová specializes in cereal production. Animal numbers declined over this period. Cattle numbers decreased in both big co-operative farms because beef and milk became less profitable, or even unprofitable, since 1991. There was less demand for milk and beef from consumers because the prices of all foodstuffs increased by several hundred per cent (e.g. a litre of milk cost 2 crowns in 1990; now it costs 12 crowns). Better development of agricultural policy is still needed although the economic situation of co-operative farms seems have stabilized now. Annual turnover was the highest in 1994. The difficult task for co-operative farms is to invest while the interest rate increases from 5-6 % to 18-22 %. The system of subsidies is still working and helping but not enough and it cannot be the only solution. Annual milk production is quite low (3600 - 3782 l/cow) in all co-operative farms in comparison with family dairy-farms in Western Europe. Milk yield declined in 1991-92 but recently has stopped declining. The period of transition has brought many problems for the social life of villagers

113

(unemployment, high prices, low income, etc.). The development of salaries shows an increase (Očová: 2807 - 5272 Sk) although it is less than in other Slovak industries. The influence of the market economy is rather hard.

Table 1.		Agricultural characteristics of co-operative farms Očová, Sebechleby and Zaježová in 1989, 1992 and 1994.

Agricultural characteristics	Očová			Sebechleby			Zaježová		
	1989	1992	1994	1989	1992	1994	1989	1992	1994
Climatic conditions									
Altitude (masl)	350-460			230-310			500-850		
Mean annual temp. (⁰C)	7.8	7.6	7.9	9.0			10.8		
During growth period (⁰C)	14.4	15.4	15.5	16.0			15.0		
Mean annual rainfall (mm)		640		600	615	570	612	630	510
During growth period	477	219	522	300	320	255	300	380	230
Land (ha)									
Agricultural land, total	4373	4294	4293	1767	1767	1760	1285	1185	1185
Arable land	2110	2028	2077	1241	1241	1056	170	170	150
Grassland	2263	2266	2116	428	428	612	1115	1015	1035
Cereals, total	1020	1207	1290	489	533	515	84	50	60
Forages on arable land	670	545	527	418	204	154	86	100	90
Yields (t/ha)									
Cereals	5.0	5.08	5.12	4.8	3.7	3.9	3.4	3.8	3.8
Grass/clover mixtures	9.1	3.1	6.5	6.9	7.0	10.3	-	10.0	12.0
Grassland (DM)	2.5	2.0	2.2	2.1	2.3	4.0	3.0	4.0	5.0
Livestock (head)									
Cattle	3461	2909	1773	1212	1015	731	340	434	420
of which dairy cows	1122	1041	905	417	322	331	150	150	150
heifers	1025	776	595	234	186	132	100	90	70
Sheep	806	707	512	0	0	0	300	250	250
Pigs	6878	6157	6349	2766	2283	2547	0	0	0
Milk prodn. (l/cow/ann)	3850	3298	3782	3713	2664	3734	3000	3400	3600
Labour force and income									
Total number of employees	490	330	315	180	158	118	30	36	45
of which graduates	17	17	17	9	7	3	3	3	1
Average salary (monthly)	2807	3563	5272	3100	3800	4400	2890	3680	4440
Annual turnover (million Sk)	106	88	119	24	27	30	2.9	4.3	6.5
Interest rate (%)	5	14	18	6	18.5	22.5	0	0	0
Subsidies (Sk/ha)	6417	3267	5445	2400	1600	1570	4300	2965	3210

Sk = Slovak crown. 1 £ = 47 Sk

CONCLUSIONS

The period of transition has brought new opportunities for private and co-operative farming. Co-operative farms are still the main source of agricultural production because only a small amount of land was taken over by the owners. After 1992 the situation in agriculture is more stable although the need of agricultural policy and strategy still exists. Prosperity and an improvement of the social life in the villages can be achieved also by co-operative farming.

SECTION 2

THE ENVIRONMENTAL FRAMEWORK

Reduction of Nutrient Emissions from Ruminant Livestock Farms

H. G. VAN DER MEER AND A. H. J. VAN DER PUTTEN
Research Institute for Agrobiology and Soil Fertility,
(AB-DLO), Wageningen, The Netherlands

ABSTRACT

Inorganic nitrogenous fertilizers and concentrates strongly contribute to the high level of forage and ruminant livestock production in Western Europe. Liberal use of these relatively cheap production inputs has resulted in large N losses and P accumulation in soils and consequently pollution of ground and surface waters and eutrophication of forests and nutrient-poor natural ecosystems. Environmental legislation increasingly aims at a reduction of these effects to ecologically acceptable levels. The purpose of this paper is to assess which adaptations of farm management are necessary to reduce ammonia volatilization, nitrate leaching and P accumulation on intensive grassland-based dairy farms to acceptable levels. Results of field experiments are used to show that Dutch regulations on rate, timing and technique of slurry application bring about a large improvement in the utilization of slurry N and simultaneous reduction of losses. In addition, these regulations make slurry a reliable source of N. However, calculations with the model FARM-MIN indicate that in addition to these regulations a strong reduction of the total rate of N application and, hence of fertilizer N, is necessary. For different grassland management systems, the target-value for the surplus on the N balance-sheet of the farm is about 180 kg/ha/year. This is less than 50 % of the surplus in recent years.

INTRODUCTION

Inorganic nitrogenous fertilizers and concentrate feeds have significantly contributed to the increase of forage and ruminant production in Western Europe. Relatively low prices have stimulated a liberal use of these production inputs. Besides, inorganic fertilizers are a more reliable source of N than legumes or surface-spread animal slurries, and concentrates are important to correct deficiencies in forage supply and quality for productive ruminant livestock. The use of fertilizer N on grassland in The Netherlands is the highest in Europe; it increased from 50 kg/ha in 1950 to 315 kg/ha in 1985 (Van der Meer, 1991). In the same period, consumption of concentrates increased from 450 to about 2250 kg/cow/year (Korevaar *et al.*, 1988). Although average figures for fertilizer N and concentrate consumption are much lower in other countries, many individual farms attain comparable levels.

In many European countries there is much concern about nutrient losses to the environment from intensive ruminant production systems. Until now, the pollution of water resources by leaching and run-off of N, P and organic matter has received most attention. In addition, ammonia volatilization receives increasing attention, particularly in areas with high livestock densities where it contributes considerably to the high levels of atmospheric N deposition (The United Kingdom Review Group on Impacts of Atmospheric Nitrogen, 1994; Heij and Schneider, 1995). This causes eutrophication of terrestrial ecosystems, increased susceptibility of trees to stress, soil acidification, and, in some cases, even too much nitrate leaching from affected ecosystems (Heij and Schneider, 1995). Finally, emissions of greenhouse gases (NO_2, CH_4, and CO_2) and pesticides, and accumulation of heavy metals in the soil play a part in the environmental debate. However, these problems have received less attention, and, so far, hardly affect farm management.

This paper presents information about emissions of nitrates, ammonia and P from intensive ruminant production systems. Measures taken to reduce these emissions will be discussed. Model calculations will be used to illustrate the impact of these measures on the whole production system and to assess which additional measures are required to reduce losses to ecologically acceptable levels.

NUTRIENT BALANCE-SHEETS

Van der Meer (1982) proposed the use of nutrient balance-sheets to assess the efficiency of nutrient use on dairy farms. A nutrient balance-sheet compares the total input of a nutrient on a farm with its output in products, both expressed in kg/ha/year. The difference between inputs and outputs is an estimate of potential losses to the environment. The N balance-sheets presented in 1982 illustrated the poor utilization of N on intensively managed dairy farms.

At present, nutrient balances play an important part in the agriculture/environment issue in The Netherlands. They are drawn up on many farms, e.g. on the specialized dairy farms included in the Farm Accountancy Data Network (Poppe et al., 1994). Table 1 presents the average nutrient balance-sheets of these farms in 1992/1993. It is evident that artificial fertilizers contribute most to the surplus on the N balance, and purchased feeds to the surpluses of P and K. The nutrient outputs presented in Table 1 relate to a production of about 12000 kg milk and 1000 kg liveweight/ha. Although beef and lamb production has increased on Dutch dairy farms since the introduction of milk quotas, the latter figure appears unrealistically high.

The data in Table 1 are averages of a large number of dairy farms. Amongst the farms included in this study there was a large variation in nutrient surpluses. The 20% of farms with the lowest or highest N surpluses had average surpluses of 247 and 555 kg N/ha/year, respectively. For the P surplus, these figures were 6 and 55 kg P/ha/year, and for K 17 and 191 kg K/ha/year (Poppe et al., 1994).

Comparison of the balances presented in Table 1 with balances of a similar group of farms in 1983-1986 (Aarts et al., 1992) shows that the surpluses of N, P and K decreased by about 20%. This is mainly caused by a reduction in the use of artificial fertilizers, indicating both improved utilization of nutrients in animal slurry and a better awareness amongst farmers of the problems associated with a too liberal use of fertilizers.

Table 1.   Average N, P and K balance-sheets in 1992/1993 of the specialized dairy farms included in the Farm Accountancy Data Network in The Netherlands (calculated from Poppe *et al.*, 1994).

	N	P	K
		Element (kg/ha/year)	
Inputs:			
artificial fertilizers	257	12	10
animal manure	18	5	12
purchased feeds	168	29	90
animal products	5	1	0
sundries	56[1]	1	6
Total	504	48	118
Outputs:			
milk	62	10	17
animals sold	29	7	2
crops	3	1	3
animal manure	12	2	8
sundries	5	1	5
Total	111	21	35
Surplus (inputs-outputs)	393	27	83

[1] including atmospheric deposition of 45 kg/ha/year

There is little information about nutrient balances of ruminant livestock farms in other European countries. Based on information from the Farm Accountancy Data Network of the EC, Brouwer *et al.* (1995) calculated net N surpluses for different types of farms in the EC12. They defined net N surplus as: total supply of N from atmospheric deposition, inorganic fertilizers, and purchased and produced manures, minus ammonia-N losses from manures and N yield in the harvested crops (all in kg/ha/year). In fact, this is an N balance-sheet of the farm land and the surpluses calculated in this way should not differ from the surpluses calculated by the method in Table 1 ('farm-gate balance') by more than the ammonia losses from manure. These authors estimate that a good 10% of the dairy farms in the EC12 have an N surplus of more than 300 kg/ha/year. However, the official figures used in this study for N excretion by dairy cows in some countries (85 kg N/cow/year) and for N uptake by crops (86 kg N/ha/year) are unrealistically low, particularly for grassland-based production systems. As these values will vary from farm to farm depending on forage species, rate of N application and milk production level of the cows, it is not clear how these assumptions affect the calculated surpluses. Nevertheless, statistical information on livestock densities and production on the 25% of dairy farms with the highest calculated net N surplus in different countries, or regions, suggest that many of these farms will have high N and P surpluses (Brouwer *et al.*, 1995).

The surplus on a nutrient balance-sheet equals the sum of losses and change of the content in the soil. In particular for N, it is impossible to estimate the different forms of emission from the surplus on the balance-sheet of a farm. For this, quantification of the different flows and losses is necessary. However, the nutrient balance-sheets of farms can be used to monitor the effectiveness of measures to improve nutrient management and reduce losses. For instance, measures to improve utilization of slurry nutrients affecting rate, time and technique of application, should result in lower inputs of artificial fertilizers and lower nutrient surpluses. Recently, much attention has been paid in The Netherlands to establish relationships between ecologically acceptable losses of N and P and surpluses on the N and P balance-sheets of different types of farms (Van der Putten and Van der Meer, 1995). Possibly, a gradual decrease of acceptable N and P surpluses will be included in future legislation.

ECOLOGICALLY ACCEPTABLE NUTRIENT LOSSES
Pollution of drinking water sources by N is of serious concern in most Member States of the European Union. According to the EU drinking water standards, nitrate concentration in ground and surface water that can be used for preparation of drinking water should not exceed 50 mg/l, i.e. 11.3 mg nitrate-N/l. In addition, a target concentration of 25 mg nitrate/l has been established. If the nitrate content exceeds 50 mg/l, nitrates have to be removed, which is a very costly process (Van der Meer and Wedin, 1989). The critical nitrate concentration of 50 mg/l is a difficult target for farms in areas with a small precipitation surplus and freely drained soils with a limited denitrification capacity. For instance, in regions with a precipitation surplus of 300 mm/year, acceptable nitrate leaching losses may be as low as 34 kg N/ha/year.

In The Netherlands, the critical value of 50 mg nitrate/l applies to all groundwater resources that potentially can be used for drinking water, i.e. water with less than 150 mg Cl⁻/l. Moreover, critical values have been defined for average N and P contents in stagnant surface waters in summer. These are 2.2 and 0.15 mg/l, respectively. However, knowledge on the effects of land use and farm management on these quality traits is still too limited to formulate relevant practices (Goossensen and Meeuwissen, 1990). Finally, international agreements on a reduction of total N and P emissions to the North Sea have to be observed. For both elements, this reduction amounts to 50% of the 1985 level in 1995.

Ammonia volatilization contributes considerably to the high rate of atmospheric N deposition in The Netherlands and other western European countries (Van

Breemen *et al.*, 1982; Ap Simon *et al.*, 1987; Berendse *et al.*, 1988). On average, N deposition in The Netherlands amounted to 38 kg/ha in 1993, of which about 72% was as ammonia or ammonium salts, together indicated as NH_x (Lekkerkerk *et al.*, 1995). In some areas with high livestock densities, average NH_x deposition was as high as 70 kg N/ha. Similar values have been reported in the United Kingdom (The United Kingdom Review Group on Impacts of Atmospheric Nitrogen, 1994). After volatilization, about 30% of the ammonia returns as wet or dry deposition to soils and vegetations within 5 km of the source. A large part of the remaining 70% reacts in the atmosphere with SO_2 and NO_x and is transported over a distance of 5 to about 1000 km (Lekkerkerk *et al.*, 1995). High rates of N deposition cause ecological damage to forests and nutrient-poor natural ecosystems. These vegetations absorb and accumulate this N very effectively (Heij and Schneider, 1995). The resulting increase of N supply causes undesirable floristic changes, loss of biodiversity and physiological problems to trees, such as increased susceptibility to abiotic and biotic stress (drought, frost, herbivory, fungal diseases) and deficiencies of other nutrients. Besides, deposition of NH_x potentially contributes to soil acidification which may also affect vegetation. This acidifying effect only occurs after nitrification of NH_x in the soil, particularly when part of the nitrates produced is lost by leaching because the vegetation was not able to absorb all (United Kingdom Terrestrial Effects Review Group, 1988; Lekkerkerk *et al.*, 1995).

Based on an assessment of ecologically acceptable values for acid and N deposition in different natural ecosystems, the Dutch government aims at a reduction of the average acid deposition from 4280 mol H^+/ha in 1993 to 2400 mol/ha in 2000 and 1400 mol/ha in 2010. Simultaneously, average atmospheric N deposition should be reduced from 38 kg/ha in 1993 to 22 kg/ha in 2000 and 14 kg/ha in 2010 (VROM *et al.*, 1993; Lekkerkerk *et al.*, 1995). Related to this, ammonia volatilization from the animal production sector has to decrease gradually, and in the year 2000 it should be at least 50% but preferably 70% less than in 1980. A further reduction is envisaged for 2010.

In the United Kingdom, agricultural emissions of ammonia contribute as much to total N deposition throughout the country as NO_x emissions from industry and vehicles. Thus emission control to reduce problems of total N deposition must address emissions from industry, vehicles and agriculture (The United Kingdom Review Group on Impacts of Atmospheric Nitrogen, 1994).

ENVIRONMENTAL LEGISLATION

Many European countries have legislation to reduce nutrient losses from livestock farms. This legislation is often focused on the rate and timing of animal manure application. Accepted rates differ widely among countries and regions (Schröder, 1992; Brouwer and Godeschalk, 1995) and in many cases the main objective of these regulations seems to be the avoidance of excesses rather than to fully protect the environment.

The *Nitrate Directive* (91/676/EEC) issued by the EU in 1991, is a first step towards a more common approach concerning the protection of waters against pollution by nitrates from agricultural sources (CEC, 1991). This Directive invites the national governments to identify zones which are vulnerable to nitrate leaching, and to establish regulations on handling and application of animal manures and artificial fertilizers for these areas in accordance with general instructions. One of the main elements of the Directive is that the rate of application of animal manure, including faeces and urine of grazing animals, should not exceed 170 kg N/ha/year in the vulnerable zones. This standard has to be met in 1999 unless the goals formulated in the Directive can be achieved by other means. Several Member States, *viz.* Denmark, Germany, The Netherlands and Luxembourg consider the whole country to be vulnerable to nitrate leaching. Approximately 650,000 ha in 72 zones of England and Wales are identified as vulnerable, which is less than 10% of the agricultural land (Brouwer and Hellegers, 1995).

In The Netherlands, the targets for environmental quality mentioned in the preceding paragraph have led to a comprehensive system of restrictions regarding production, handling and application of animal manure (Misset, 1994). The most important restrictions are:

- Farms with an annual 'P production' in manure of more than 55 kg/ha are not allowed to increase livestock density.
- Annual application rates of manure on grassland, maize and other arable crops are restricted to 65, 48 and 48 kg P/ha, respectively. On grassland, this rate includes excreted P by grazing animals.
- On most soils, slurry application is not allowed in the period between 16 September and 31 January. Besides, it is forbidden on all soils when the soil is frozen or covered with snow. This means that all farms need to have slurry storage capacity for at least 5 months.
- Since 1995, low-emission slurry application techniques are compulsory on grassland and arable land on almost all soil types. On grassland, deep injection, shallow injection, shallow injection with open slits, and application by trailing-feet machines are officially accepted as low-emission techniques. On arable land, direct incorporation of slurry into the soil is compulsory.
- Slurry storage facilities have to be covered.

These regulations determine rate, period and technique of slurry application. The allowed rates of application still lead to P accumulation in the soil, and are too high from this point of view. Therefore, the Government plans a further reduction towards P equilibrium, where the rate of P application equals P yield in harvested products plus some ecologically acceptable losses. However, farmers' organizations strongly oppose this intention because it will result in a manure surplus on many farms with a high livestock density. Nevertheless, existing legislation has already resulted in an improvement in the utilization of slurry nutrients and a corresponding reduction of nutrient losses if the rates of application of artificial fertilizers are adjusted properly to the increased availability of slurry nutrients. These aspects will be discussed in the next section.

EFFECTIVE USE OF ANIMAL SLURRY NUTRIENTS

Up to now, most European livestock farmers dispose of slurry as cheaply as possible whilst avoiding damage to grassland and crops. Common practices in the framework of this farm management policy, such as (1) over-dosing of slurry on part of the land, particularly on maize land, (2) land-application of slurry in late summer, autumn and winter, and (3) surface spreading, are linked with large losses of N, and result in a low and unpredictable N value of the slurry applied. Consequently, farmers often do not make allowance for slurry nutrients. In general, there is little incentive to improve this situation.

Environmental legislation in The Netherlands requires investments for slurry storage and slurry application equipment and generally increases the cost of slurry handling and application. Improved utilization of slurry nutrients will not pay for these extra costs. In fact, it is cheaper to buy chemical fertilizers than to make provisions for effective recycling of nutrients in animal waste. Therefore, without legislation, farmers will be reluctant to adopt better slurry management techniques. However, if there is a strong public pressure to reduce nutrient emissions from agriculture, these techniques are cost-effective, i.e. they give a large reduction of emissions per unit of money spent (Mandersloot and Van Scheppingen, 1994). In addition, these techniques make slurry a reliable source of nutrients.

This can be illustrated with the results of two field experiments on grassland on a sandy soil. In the first experiment the effects of slurry injection at different times in winter and addition of the nitrification inhibitor dicyandiamide (DCD) on the apparent recovery of N (ANR) by grass were studied (Figure 1; Geurink and Van der Meer, 1996). This experiment comprised 3 periods of injection: in the first two experimental years, these were late October, early December and in Spring at the moment of the first application of fertilizer N (between late February and early April). In the last two experimental years slurry was injected in early December, mid January, and again in Spring. Slurry was injected at a rate of 60 t/ha using the equipment described by Van der Meer et al. (1987). On average, it contained 5.1 kg total N/t and 2.5 kg inorganic N/t. On the relevant experimental plots, DCD was mixed with the slurry at a rate of 25 kg/ha in October and 15 kg/ha in the other periods of application. Effects on grass yield and composition were assessed in 6 or 7 cuts taken in the growing season after injection.

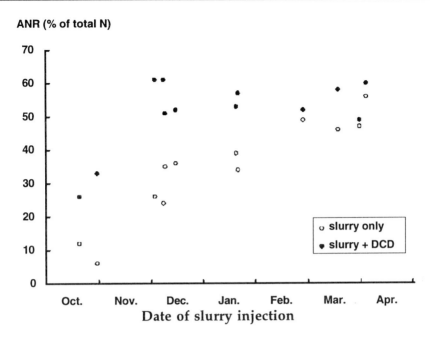

ANR (% of total N)

Figure 1.   Effects of date of slurry injection and addition of the nitrification inhibitor DCD on the apparent recovery of slurry N (ANR) in the herbage harvested in the growing season after injection (Geurink and Van der Meer, 1996).

Figure 1 shows a large effect of the date of injection on ANR, particularly on the experimental plots without DCD. On these plots, ANR varied from less than 10% after injection in October to about 50% after injection in Spring. Addition of the nitrification inhibitor increased ANR in all cases, even on the plots where slurry had been injected in Spring. As deep injection almost completely prevents N losses by ammonia volatilization, differences in ANR in this experiment reflect differences in N losses by denitrification and nitrate leaching. Taking into account that maximum ANR values of slurry varied between 50 and 60% in this experiment, losses by these processes amounted to over 40% of total slurry N after injection of slurry only in October, and on average about 25% after injection of slurry only in December. Estimated N losses by denitrification during 18 weeks after injection in December of the last experimental year were 0.9 (untreated plot), 4.1 (slurry + DCD), and 13.7 kg N/ha (slurry only). On the injected plots this was 0.9 and 3.5% of total N applied (De Klein *et al.*, 1994). These results suggest large nitrate leaching losses. Unfortunately, measurements of nitrate leaching did not give reliable results because of the complicated hydrological situation of this experimental field. Apparent recoveries of the lowest rate of fertilizer N in this experiment (200 kg/ha/year) were 89, 88, 91 and 74% in the four experimental years. This indicates effective N use by the sward.

Table 2.   Effects of slurry application techniques on ANR (% of total N) from different types of slurry by grass. Averages of 2 years (Geurink and Van der Meer, 1995).

Application technique	Cattle slurry	Pig slurry	Liquid fraction pig slurry
Deep injection	47	52	72
Injection with open slits	42	50	56
Surface spreading of diluted slurry	34	41	37
Surface spreading of untreated slurry	19	26	32

In the second field experiment the effects of four slurry application techniques on ANR from three types of animal slurry by grass were studied (Table 2; Geurink and Van der Meer, 1995). Slurry application techniques were: deep injection, injection with open slits, surface spreading of untreated slurry and of diluted slurry (diluted to about 25 kg DM/t of slurry). Types of slurry were: cattle slurry (101 kg DM and 5.5 kg total N/t; inorganic N 48% of total N), pig slurry (111 kg DM and 8.5 kg total N/t; inorganic N 57% of total N), and the liquid fraction of pig slurry from a slurry processing plant (46 kg DM and 7.2 kg total N/t; inorganic N 65% of total N). Slurry was applied to the first and second cut at a total rate of application of about 100 kg inorganic N/ha. Effects on grass yield and composition were assessed in 3 or 4 cuts after slurry application.

The slurry application techniques had a large effect on ANR from all types of slurry (Table 2). This reflects differences in ammonia volatilization. Differences between types of slurry probably were related to the proportion of inorganic N in total slurry N. Also in this experiment apparent recoveries of fertilizer N in the harvested herbage of about 90% were found, which indicates that other N losses were insignificant.

The results of these experiments illustrate the importance of both period and technique of slurry application to effective utilization of slurry N. Both experiments confirmed earlier results that the 'efficiency index' of cattle slurry N on grassland is about 60% when slurry is applied in spring or early summer by injection techniques (Van der Meer *et al.*, 1987). This means that 100 kg of total N from slurry has the same effect on herbage N yield as 60 kg fertilizer N. If this 'efficiency index' is taken into account when fertilizer N is replaced by injected slurry N, nitrate leaching losses even tend to decrease (Jarvis *et al.*, 1987; Geurink and Van der Meer, 1996). The difference in effect between slurry N and fertilizer

N is probably caused by the rather stable organic N fraction in the slurry which is added to the soil organic N pool (Van der Meer *et al.*, 1987; Schröder and Dilz, 1987). This organic N is likely to become available in the long term. From this it can be concluded that a large part of the N from injected slurry can be utilized for grass growth, particularly when the residual long-term effect is also taken into account.

FURTHER ADJUSTMENTS OF FARM MANAGEMENT TO DECREASE NUTRIENT EMISSIONS

Although present-day Dutch legislation related to rate, timing and technique of slurry application strongly reduces N losses by ammonia volatilization and nitrate leaching, and P accumulation, it is not yet sufficient to reduce these losses to ecologically acceptable levels. This will be illustrated using calculations with the computer model FARM-MIN. This is a simulation model of the production process and related N flows and losses on dairy farms. FARM-MIN also calculates a P balance-sheet of the farm. Description of herbage production and utilization, animal production, and N flows and losses in FARM-MIN is very similar to that in GRASMOD (Van de Ven, 1992). However, FARM-MIN has been developed and structured to be used on commercial farms to explore which adjustments of farm management are required to reduce ammonia volatilization and nitrate leaching to the levels laid down in regulations (Van der Putten and Van der Meer, 1995). Here, only a brief description of FARM-MIN will be given. Detailed information has been published elsewhere (Van de Ven, 1992; Van der Putten and Van der Meer, 1995).

FARM-MIN applies to dairy farms on freely drained sandy soils with a good water supply. Land can be used for production of grass and maize. FARM-MIN is a static model based on empirical relationships. Relationships and assumptions have been derived from the literature (e.g. Van der Meer, 1991), consultation with experts and standards used by the Dutch extension service. For grassland, FARM-MIN contains relationships between rate of N application, N yield in the harvested herbage, and dry matter yield and quality for three grassland utilization systems, *viz.* day-and-night grazing, daytime grazing only and zero-grazing. Based on the rate of N application, the grassland utilization system, and the composition and productivity of the herd, the model calculates the intake of fresh grass and the amount available for conservation. The stage at which the herbage is harvested depends on the utilization method (grazing, zero-grazing and cutting for conservation) and is in accordance with current practices in The Netherlands.

The diet of the animals may consist of fresh and conserved grass, maize silage, maize-cob silage and concentrates. If roughages have to be bought, they are of the same quality as those produced on the farm. The cows calve on 1 February and produce between 5000 and 9000 kg milk per 305-day lactation. Diet calculations are based on the Dutch Feeding Standards (Rompelberg *et al.*, 1984;

Pelser, 1988; Tamminga *et al.*, 1995). Feed intake and composition, together with animal production, determine N retention in animal products and N excretion in faeces and urine. FARM-MIN calculates N excretion in faeces and urine in the livestock buildings and pastures. In the grazed fields, it quantifies the distribution of faeces and urine and the effects of faecal and urinary N on ammonia volatilization, N yield in the herbage, herbage yield, and nitrate leaching (Vertregt and Rutgers, 1988; Van der Meer and Whitehead, 1990). In the model, only urinary N affects N yield in the herbage and nitrate leaching. In the part of the field that is not affected by urine, the model calculates N yield in the herbage and nitrate leaching from the relationships presented in Table 3. In the urine-affected part of the field, it applies the same relationships, adding 60% of urinary N to the rate of N application and assuming that this N has the same effect on N yield and nitrate leaching as additional fertilizer N (Van der Meer and Meeuwissen, 1989).

Table 3. The relationships between rate of N application, N yield in the harvested herbage, and leaching of nitrates (kg N/ha/year) as used in FARM-MIN.

Rate of N application	N yield in the herbage	Leaching of nitrate-N
0	122	16
100	207	17
200	292	21
300	362	28
400	432	56
500	482	104
600	522	166
900[1]	572	376

[1] included to quantify effects of urinary N.

FARM-MIN calculates ammonia volatilization as follows: barns and slurry storage: 13.2% of excreted N; surface-spread slurry: 60% of inorganic N in slurry; slurry injected with open slits: 8% of inorganic N in slurry; faeces and urine in grazed fields: 13% of excreted N; herbage residues: 3% of N content. These assumptions imply that the fraction of excreted N lost by ammonia volatilization is constant and not affected by N content and other characteristics of the diet. In fact, there is no clear information on this point and consequently there is a strong need for systematic research on this subject.

FARM-MIN was used to quantify the production and N cycle of a current intensively managed dairy farm and subsequently the effects of different management variants to reduce emissions. The farm in question is a pure grassland farm and has 2 dairy cows plus additional young stock/ha (0.4 head of <1 year and 0.3 head between 1 and 2 years per cow). Milk production is 7000 kg/cow per 305-day lactation. The farm has sufficient slurry storage capacity and applies all the slurry in spring and early summer. The effects of the following farm management variants have been quantified in Table 4:

1. Starting situation. Day-and-night grazing, rate of N application in accordance with the recommendations for intensively managed dairy farms (about 400 kg/ha/year fertilizer N + available slurry N), surface spreading of slurry.
2. The same as 1, except slurry application by injection with open slits (Figure 2).
3. The same as 2 but reduction of the rate of N application to restrict N losses by ammonia volatilization and nitrate leaching to 50 and 34 kg/ha/year, respectively.
4. The same as 3 but restriction of grazing to daytime grazing only.
5. The same as 3 but zero-grazing.
6. The same as 5 and adaptations in livestock buildings to reduce ammonia volatilization from them by 50 %.

Comparison of the data in Table 4 and Figure 2 with those in Table 1 indicates that the N balance-sheets of the Management Variants 1 and 2 correspond rather well with that of the average specialized dairy farm in the Dutch Farm Accountancy Data Network. Minor differences emanate form the higher livestock density, a higher proportion of liveweight gain in farm output, and some maize production on the commercial farms. The P surpluses calculated by FARM-MIN are much lower than on the farms, because the model did not allow the use of fertilizer P, as in most farm management variants P inputs in purchased feeds exceed P outputs in milk and liveweight gain.

Despite improvements of animal slurry management in the Farm Management Variants 1 and 2, N losses remain far too high (Table 4). This is strongly related to the high total N supply to the fields from mineralization of soil organic N, atmospheric deposition, faeces and urine from grazing cattle, applied slurry and chemical fertilizers (Figure 2). Hence, reduction of the rate of application of fertilizer N appears a logical next step to reduce N losses to ecologically acceptable levels (Management Variant 3). However, because of the large contribution of urine N to nitrate leaching under day-and-night grazing (Van der Meer and Meeuwissen, 1989), a drastic reduction of N application is required to attain the nitrate leaching target (Table 4). As a consequence, net herbage yield decreases sharply and more roughage and concentrates have to be bought to maintain herd size and production. This causes a strong increase in the P surplus. Restriction of grazing allows a higher rate of N application within the nitrate leaching target (Management Variants 4 and 5; Table 4). However, this results in higher ammonia volatilization losses, because the fraction lost from N excreted in the barn is higher than from N excreted in grazed grassland. In this situation specific techniques to reduce ammonia volatilization from the buildings will be useful (Management Variant 6). It should be mentioned that in addition to fertilizer N, all farm management variants have a considerable supply of slurry N. In the Variants 1, 2, 3, 4, 5 and 6 the amount of slurry N available for application is 202, 202 (Figure 2), 172, 218, 258 and 324 kg/ha/year. The high net herbage yields under zero-grazing (Table 4) are caused by higher gross yields due to the lower harvesting frequency and to lower herbage losses.

Table 4.   Effects of different management variants for a dairy farm on the rate of application of fertilizer N, net herbage yield, N losses by ammonia volatilization and nitrate leaching and surpluses on the N and P balance-sheets of the farm. Data derived from calculations with the model FARM-MIN. A description of farm structure and management variants is given in the text. All results are in kg DM, N or P/ha/year.

Management variant	Rate of fertilizer N	Net herbage DM yield	N losses NH_3-N	NO_3^--N	Surplus of N	P
1	326	9561	125	118	427	6.8
2	271	9561	125	64	372	6.8
3	7	7108	34	46	166	17.2
4	69	9203	34	48	168	6.6
5	33	11736	22	50	123	5.0
6	129	13013	34	36	184	-0.3

Table 4 shows that in addition to measures related to period and technique of slurry application (farm Management Variants 1 and 2, respectively), total rate of N application has to be cut down considerably to reduce ammonia volatilization and nitrate leaching to the target values (Variants 3, 4, 5 and 6). In this case it is not sufficient to consider only N in animal excreta. Nevertheless, it should be taken into account that ammonia losses originate almost completely from excreted N, whereas urinary N strongly contributes to nitrate leaching from grazed grassland. A reduction of the rate of N application affects these processes mainly indirectly by reducing N excretion. Research is needed to determine whether it is also possible to reduce the proportion of excreted N getting lost by volatilization or leaching. The large reduction of herbage yield caused by Farm Management Variant 3, and high costs of a restriction of grazing (Variants 4, 5 and 6) indicate the importance of this.

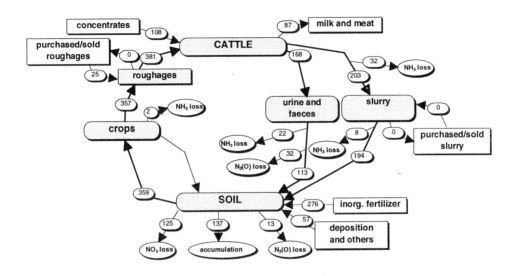

Figure 2. Nitrogen flow diagram of Dairy Farm Management Variant 2. Data (kg N/ha/year) calculated with the model FARM-MIN. A description of farm structure and management variant is given in the text.

In addition, it is necessary to assess the technical and economic consequences of decreasing livestock densities. Obviously, politicians are more interested in this option than farmers.

As a result of the reduction of the rate of fertilizer N, required to attain environmental targets, the surplus on the N balance-sheet of the farm decreases to about 180 kg N/ha per year (Table 4). This applies to a pure grassland farm. If part of the land is used for maize production, the acceptable N surplus is much lower (Van der Putten and Van der Meer, 1995). This is caused by the lower N requirement of maize and relatively high nitrate leaching losses.

REFERENCES
AARTS H.F.M., BIEWINGA E.E. and VAN KEULEN H. (1992) Dairy farming systems based on efficient nutrient management. *Netherlands Journal of Agricultural Science*, 40, 285-290.
APSIMON H.M., KRUSE M. and BELL J.N.B. (1987) Ammonia emissions and their role in acid deposition. *Atmospheric Environment*, 21, 1939-1946.
BERENDSE F., LAURIJSEN C. and OKKERMAN P. (1988) The acidifying effect of ammonia volatilized from farm-manure on forest soils. *Ecological Bulletins*, 39, 136-138.
BROUWER F.M. and GODESCHALK F.E. (1995) Mineral surplus in EU agriculture: Economic implications of environmental measures to pig farming. *Cahiers d'Economie et Sociologie Rurales* (in press).
BROUWER F.M., GODESCHALK F.E., HELLEGERS P.J.G.J. and KELHOLT H.J. (1995) Mineral balances at farm level in the European Union. *Research Report 137, Agricultural Economics Research Institute (LEI-DLO)*, The Hague, The Netherlands.

BROUWER F.M. and HELLEGERS P.J.G.J. (1995) The Nitrate Directive and Farming Practice in the European Union. *European Environment* (in press).

CEC (1991) Council directive of 12 December 1991 concerning the protection of waters against pollution caused by nitrates from agricultural sources (91/676/EEC). *Official Journal of the European Communities*, Nr. L 375 (31.12.91), 1-8.

DE KLEIN C.A.M., VAN LOGTESTIJN R.S.P., VAN DER MEER H.G. and GEURINK J.H. (1995) N-losses due to denitrification from cattle slurry injected into grassland soil with and without a nitrification inhibitor. In: De Klein, C.A.M.: *Denitrification in grazed grasslands in The Netherlands*, pp. 65-78, PhD Thesis, University of Utrecht, Utrecht, The Netherlands.

GEURINK J.H. and VAN DER MEER H.G. (1995) De stikstofwerking van verschillende soorten dunne mest bij verschillende toedieningstechnieken op grassland [Effects of slurry application techniques on the nitrogen value of different types of animal slurry on grassland]. *Rapport 42, Research Institute for Agrobiology and Soil Fertility (AB-DLO)*. Wageningen: The Netherlands.

GEURINK J.H. and VAN DER MEER H.G. (1996) De invloed van de nitrificatieremmer DCD op de stikstofwerking van in het winterhalfjaar op grasland geïnjecteerde dunne rundermest [The effect of the nitrification inhibitor DCD on the utilization of nitrogen by grass from cattle slurry injected in different periods of the winter season]. *Rapport xxx, Research Institute for Agrobiology and Soil Fertility (AB-DLO)*, Wageningen, The Netherlands (in press).

GOOSSENSEN F.R. and MEEUWISSEN P.C. (1990) *Advies van de Commissie Stikstof* [Advice of the Commission Nitrogen]. Agricultural Research Department, Wageningen, The Netherlands.

HEIJ G.J. and SCHNEIDER T. (eds.) (1995) *Eindrapport Additioneel Programma Verzuringsonderzoek, derde fase (1991-1994) [Final Report Dutch Priority Programme on Acidification, third phase (1991-1994)]*. Rapport nr. 300-05, Dutch Priority Programme on Acidification, State Institute for Public Health and Environment, Bilthoven, The Netherlands.

JARVIS S.C., SHERWOOD M. and STEENVOORDEN J.H.A.M. (1987) Nitrogen losses from animal manures: from grazed pastures and from applied slurry. In: Van der Meer, H.G., Unwin, R.J., Van Dijk, T.A. and Ennik, G.C. (eds.) *Animal manure on grassland and forage crops. Fertilizer or waste? Developments in Plant and Soil Sciences*, Vol. 30, pp. 195-212, Martinus Nijhoff Publishers, Dordrecht, The Netherlands.

KOREVAAR H., DEN BOER D.J. and VELLINGA TH.V. (1988) Intensive and extensive grassland systems: implications of restrictions. *Proceedings of the 12th General Meeting of the European Grassland Federation*, Dublin, Ireland, pp. 98-115.

LEKKERKERK L.J.A., HEIJ G.J. and HOOTSMANS M.J.M. (eds.) (1995) *Ammoniak: de feiten [Ammonia: The Facts]*. Rapport nr. 300-06, Dutch Priority Programme on Acidification, State Institute for Public Health and Environment, Bilthoven, The Netherlands.

MANDERSLOOT F. and VAN SCHEPPINGEN A.T.J. (1994) Mineralenmanagement op bedrijfsniveau [Nutrient management at farm level]. In: De Haan, M.H.A. and Ogink, N.W.M. (eds.) *Naar veehouderij en milieu in balans, 10 jaar FOMA onderzoek*. Onderzoek inzake de mest- en ammoniakproblematiek in de veehouderij 19 (Rundvee), pp. 125-140. Agricultural Research Department, Wageningen, The Netherlands.

MISSET (1994) Mestwijzer [Manure regulations]. *Boerderij*, 22, bijlage. Misset Uitgeverij,

Doetinchem, The Netherlands.

PELSER L. (ed.) (1988) *Handboek voor de Rundveehouderij [Manual for Cattle Husbandry]*. Proefstation voor de Rundveehouderij, Lelystad, The Netherlands.

POPPE K.J., BROUWER F.M., WELTEN J.P.P.J. and WIJNANDS J.H.M. (eds.) (1994) *Landbouw, milieu en economie, Editie 1994 [Agriculture, Environment and Economy, Edition 1994]*. Periodieke Rapportage 68-92, Agricultural Economics Research Institute (LEI-DLO), The Hague, The Netherlands.

ROMPELBERG L.E.M., WIELING H. and OVERVEST J. (1984) Normen voor de Voedervoorziening [Standards for Feed Supply]. *Publikatie 23, Research Station for Cattle Husbandry (PR)*, Lelystad, The Netherlands.

SCHRÖDER J. (1992) Legislation on animal manure in Europe. *Meststoffen*, 1992, 69-74

SCHRÖDER J. and DILZ K. (1987) Cattle slurry and farmyard manure as fertilizers for forage maize. In: Van der Meer, H.G., Unwin, R.J., Van Dijk, T.A. and Ennik, G.C. (eds.) *Animal manure on grassland and forage crops. Fertilizer or waste? Developments in Plant and Soil Sciences*, Vol. 30, pp. 137-156, Martinus Nijhoff Publishers, Dordrecht, The Netherlands.

TAMMINGA S., VAN STRAALEN W.M., SUBNEL A.P.J., MEIJER R.G.M., STEG A., WEVER C.J.G. and BLOK M.C. (1994) The Dutch protein evaluation system: the DVE/OEB-system. *Livestock Production Science*.

THE UNITED KINGDOM REVIEW GROUP ON IMPACTS OF ATMOSPHERIC NITROGEN (1994) *Impacts of nitrogen deposition on terrestrial ecosystems*. Department of the Environment, London, United Kingdom.

UNITED KINGDOM TERRESTRIAL EFFECTS REVIEW GROUP (1988) *The effects of Acid Deposition on the Terrestrial Environment in the United Kingdom*. First report, HMSO Publications Centre, London, United Kingdom.

VAN BREEMEN N., BURROUGH P.A., VELTHORST E.J., VAN DOBBEN H.F., DE WIT T., RIDDER T.B. and REIJNDERS H.F.R. (1982) Soil acidification from atmospheric ammonium sulphate in forest canopy throughfall. *Nature*, 299, 548-550.

VAN DER MEER H.G. (1982) Effective use of nitrogen on grassland farms. In: Corrall, A.J. (ed.) *Efficient Grassland Farming*, Occasional Symposium of the British Grassland Society, No. 14, Reading, United Kingdom, pp. 61-68.

VAN DER MEER H.G. (ed.) (1991) *Stikstofbenutting en -verliezen van gras- en maïsland [Nitrogen utilization and losses from grassland and maizeland]*. Onderzoek inzake de mest- en ammoniakproblematiek in de veehouderij 10, Agricultural Research Department, Wageningen, The Netherlands.

VAN DER MEER H.G. and MEEUWISSEN P.C. (1989) Emissie van stikstof uit landbouwgronden in relatie tot bemesting en bedrijfsvoering [Emissions of nitrogen from agricultural soils in relation to fertilization and farm management]. *Landschap*, 1989 no. 1, 19-32.

VAN DER MEER H.G. and WEDIN W.F. (1989) Present and future role of grasslands and fodder crops in temperate countries with special reference to over-production and environment. *Proceedings XVI International Grassland Congress*, Nice, France, Vol. III, pp. 1711-1718.

VAN DER MEER H.G. and WHITEHEAD D.C. (1990) The fate of nitrogen in animal excreta applied to grassland. Paper presented at the 13th General Meeting of the European Grassland Federation, Banská Bystrica, Czechoslovakia, *Report 141, Centre for Agrobiological Research (CABO-DLO)*, Wageningen, The Netherlands.

VAN DER MEER H.G., THOMPSON R.B., SNIJDERS P.J.M. and GEURINK J.H. (1987) Utilization of nitrogen from injected and surface-spread cattle slurry applied to grassland. In: Van der Meer, H.G., Unwin, R.J., Van Dijk, T.A. and Ennik, G.C. (eds.) *Animal manure on grassland and forage crops. Fertilizer or waste? Developments in Plant and Soil Sciences*, Vol. 30, pp. 47-71, Martinus Nijhoff Publishers, Dordrecht, The Netherlands.

VAN DER PUTTEN A.H.J. and VAN DER MEER H.G. (1995) Verkenning van streefwaarden voor het overschot op de stikstofbalans van melkveebedrijven [Assessing target values for the surplus on the nitrogen balance-sheet of dairy farms]. *Rapport 45, Research Institute for Agrobiology and Soil Fertility (AB-DLO)*, Wageningen, The Netherlands.

VAN DE VEN G.W.J. (1992) GRASMOD, a grassland management model to calculate nitrogen losses from grassland. *Verslag 158, Centre for Agrobiological Research (CABO-DLO)*, Wageningen, The Netherlands.

VERTREGT N. and RUTGERS B. (1988) Ammonia volatilization from grazed pastures. *Report 84, Centre for Agrobiological Research (CABO-DLO)*, Wageningen, The Netherlands.

VROM, EZ, LNV, V+W and OS (1993) *Tweede Nationaal Milieubeleidsplan [Second National Environmental Policy Plan]*. House of Commons, Proceedings 1993-1994, 23 560, Nrs. 1-2, The Hague, The Netherlands.

Environmental Benefits from Grassland Farming

T. D. ALLEN

Countryside Commission, John Dower House,
Crescent Place, Cheltenham, GL50 3RA

ABSTRACT

This paper reviews how grassland farming can produce environmental benefits and looks at how these can be enhanced further in future. Post-war agricultural policies have improved production and increased UK self-sufficiency in temperate food products. However, one consequence of this process is farming systems that can be damaging to landscapes and their wildlife. Grassland farming has had a key role in the agricultural improvement story. It also plays a key role in conserving and improving what is valued in the countryside.

In general, low input/low output grassland systems are needed to deliver environment benefits. This is not an environmental argument for blanket prescriptions to change all grassland farming systems but for a targeted approach that identifies clear objectives and supports the selective continuation of, or adjustment to, beneficial systems.

For the future the Countryside Commission advocates greater integration of environmental objectives into agricultural support and into systems of farming. This requires a re-appraisal of our definition of agricultural efficiency to reflect the wider costs and benefits of farming systems.

INTRODUCTION

The brief of this paper is to review how grassland farming can produce environmental benefits and to take a forward look at how systems might develop to further do so.

CONTEXT

Post-war agricultural policies have concentrated principally on improving agricultural production with an added concern to sustain farming in marginal upland areas as a socio-economic objective. It is often argued that these policies have been successful in producing a modern, efficient British agriculture and in increasing self-sufficiency in the production of temperate food products. In accepting such arguments some important caveats must be applied. Achieving these objectives has been at substantial cost to the public purse through direct subsidy, tax concessions and government funded advice and research. These policies and associated technological developments have enabled, and sometimes impelled, rapid and far-reaching changes to agricultural systems. One consequence of this process is a well documented loss in the quality of some of our landscapes, their features and their wildlife. For example the DOE Countryside Survey, 1990 identified the following:

- that there were 23% fewer hedges in 1990 than in 1984;

- that between 1978 and 1990 species diversity declined by 22% overall in semi-improved grasslands;
- that there has been a 10% decrease in field boundary walls. Recent Countryside Commission work (National Survey of the State of Repair of Drystone Walls in England, May 1995) shows that 67% of remaining walls are in sufficient disrepair to give cause for concern.

Over the last 40 years agricultural production has been pushed to both physical and economic margins; for example in cultivating steep downland permanent pastures, re-seeding moorlands with productive grasses, introducing lowland breeds and livestock systems into the uplands and in replacing hedgerows and walls with fences. It would be wrong to argue that the process of agricultural development is fundamentally wrong. However, in the current re-appraisal of agricultural policies, society is indicating that environmental loss has gone too far, that steps are needed both to better conserve our countryside and to replace some of what has been lost. Government and the EC recognise this through an increasing shift of emphasis towards integrating environmental concerns into the CAP.

One reflection of this change is the emergence of incentive schemes which initially supported farming practices that conserve what is most valuable in environmental terms in the countryside and latterly also wider and more creative conservation objectives. Expenditure is still modest in comparison with overall agricultural support budgets (currently approximately £100 million/year for environmental schemes against a total agricultural support cost of £2.9 billion), but it is has grown rapidly since their inception in 1985.

There is also a growing recognition of the contradictions in agricultural policies and the conflicting signals that they continue to give farmers. For example, headage premia still encourage levels of grazing that can be damaging in environmental terms. In some instances environmental schemes are simply paying to counteract the adverse impact of agricultural support payments.

THE IMPACT ON GRASSLAND FARMING SYSTEMS

Livestock farming has played a key role in the post war agricultural development story. Changes and developments are well documented and have broadly involved a move to higher input/output systems that rely on increased fertiliser usage, higher stocking densities and the development and use of fewer, more productive breeds.

Whilst physical factors such as rainfall, slope and altitude remain determinants of the individual farm system, locality and local tradition are less important and there is greater standardisation; for example the ubiquitous use of Holstein/Friesians in dairy herds. Overall the environmental impact has been to impose increased uniformity on the countryside with a loss of, what the organisation Common Ground terms, 'local distinctiveness'; those features, habitats and details, both large and small, that convey a sense of place.

However, grassland farming also continues to play a crucial role in conserving much that is valuable in our countryside.

THE POSITIVE CONTRIBUTION GRASSLAND FARMING MAKES TO THE ENVIRONMENT

Grassland farming can contribute in a number of ways to the positive conservation of the countryside.

Landscape quality

It would be wrong to claim that grassland farming is 'good' and cultivation 'bad' in landscape terms. However, in pushing cultivation to the fringes, some of our landscapes have suffered. There is a strong landscape and agricultural argument for continuing, or returning to, pastoral management on a targeted basis; for example on our downlands and wetlands. Pastoral agriculture also provides a practical justification for the continued beneficial management of some of our most important landscape features such as hedgerows and drystone walls, even if public money is needed to assist in their conservation. The adage that form follows function is valid in this context.

Wildlife conservation

Grasslands can be important and diverse habitats. Examples include agriculturally unimproved calcareous grasslands which are one of the most diverse habitats in Western Europe, notable particularly for their floristic interest but also for the invertebrates that they support. Many species of birds rely on grassland for nesting habitat or for feeding. These habitats are highly sensitive to any change in management practice.

History

Grasslands are a key component in some of our historic landscapes; for example designed parklands. More widely, grassland management is an important tool in protecting historic remains. For example, ancient field systems created by cultivation and often visibly evidenced by lynchets are progressively destroyed by modern cultivation techniques. Maintaining carefully grazed permanent grassland is often vital to the protection of these remains.

Pollution control and management

A separate paper reviews the role of grassland farming in relation to pollution. However, appropriate grassland management can make a significant contribution in seeking to protect water courses and water supplies from enrichment or unacceptable levels of pesticide residue.

Soil erosion
Soil erosion is not a major issue in many parts of the UK but on a localised basis the ploughing of permanent pasture or changes in cultivation techniques have led to worrying losses and, in some cases, to public nuisance. There are well documented cases on the South Downs. Grassland management can in some circumstances be a solution to this problem

Public access
Research indicates that there has been no significant increase in the number of visitors to the countryside in recent years (National Survey of Countryside Recreation, 1984-1991). However, there is a powerful demand for more extensive access provision to the countryside as countryside users extend the scope and range of their activities.

The recent House of Commons Environment Committee Report 'The Environmental Impact of Leisure Activities' clearly identified that "access agreements with farmers and landowners are valuable and that these agreements to procure new access should be significantly increased by the year 2000". Coupled with this is a strong argument for making people's local countryside more accessible and, where appropriate, more attractive; for example to reduce reliance on the motor car for leisure. Countryside Commission research indicates a likely increase in car usage in rural areas of approximately 400% over the next 25-30 years.

The use of grasslands, both where they exist and where they might be extended to provide for access, is therefore likely to feature increasingly in farm management as government explores ways to create additional access, for example through incentive scheme payments.

THE PRACTICAL IMPLICATION OF ENVIRONMENTAL IMPROVEMENT FOR GRASSLAND MANAGEMENT
In concluding that grassland farming has many potential benefits for the environment and for public recreation it is important to qualify this by identifying the particular grassland farming techniques that deliver these benefits. In targeting environmental management or improvement, individual farms or areas of land must be taken on their merits. However, there are some general principles for identifying which techniques are necessary.

Low inputs
If there is one general rule, it is that environmental benefits from grassland farming dictate low-input systems. Occasionally, simple objectives such as improving the landscape by increasing the areas of grassland or by protecting historic remains may not require the cessation of fertiliser inputs or a reduction in grazing densities. However, maximising environmental benefits, for example in protecting or enhancing biodiversity, can rarely be achieved without sustaining

or returning to low-input/low-output management. Even modest applications of nitrogen can rapidly and fundamentally alter the sward composition of a species-rich meadow in favour of competitive and more productive grasses. The application of phosphate and potash has even more far-reaching implications. Once levels are built up they can inhibit the long term re-establishment of species diversity.

On a more positive note, conservationists have tended to ignore the potential of agriculturally improved land. Whilst past improvement, and in particular fertiliser applications, may preclude the replication of the most diverse species-rich meadow composition it is still possible to create interesting habitat through some simple techniques. The Countryside Commission's 'Countryside Premium' experiment on set-aside land provided valuable insights. This took former arable land and under one option required the sowing of a 'traditional' mixture of meadow grasses such as Common Bent (*Agrostis capillaris*), Crested Dog's-Tail (*Cynosurus cristatus*) and Sheeps Fescue (*Festuca ovina*). By leaving an area uncut until late in the season many common species of wildlife rapidly returned to areas where previously they were uncommon or absent. The grasses attracted invertebrates, providing a food source and habitat for butterflies, such as the Meadow Brown (*Maniola jurtina*), and cover that encouraged small mammals. In some cases species higher up the food chain also returned; for example Kestrel and Barn Owl who used the meadows as hunting grounds.

Creating a diverse sward

In recent years conservation objectives have become more creative in seeking to combine protective measures with steps to create or recreate diverse grasslands. Conventional wisdom, backed by some research, indicates that the development of a truly species-rich sward can take 50 or 100 years. However, the evidence of the 'Countryside Stewardship' and 'Countryside Premium' experiments indicates that there are conditions where encouraging results can be achieved more rapidly than this 'conventional' wisdom indicates. Suitable areas include land converted to cultivation relatively recently; where soils are thin and relatively nutrient poor e.g. calcareous soils or light sands; where the land is subject to periodic flooding; or where an existing seed source is close by. Careful management, particularly through natural regeneration, can enhance biodiversity, even over a 5-year period, if the land is well chosen.

Country Commission experience in developing environmental schemes has highlighted a debate about whether to sow a sward or to encourage natural regeneration. The latter is being actively encouraged even though many farmers instinctively feel that they should sow. Where a sward is to be sown, biodiversity objectives are generally best achieved by using traditional meadow grass species appropriate to the site and are rarely compatible with the use of ryegrass and clover swards. Seed rates also need to be lower than those typical for a modern grass ley, using a seed rate of 15-20 kg/ha.

Another current debate is about the use of wild flower seeds in grass mixes to accelerate conservation results. On occasion this may be justified but as a principle conservationists are increasingly cautious. Commercially available wildflower seed is sometimes harvested from UK species-rich meadows. However, the techniques concerned mean that this is expensive. The cheaper alternative is to buy imported cultivars. Philosophically some find this unacceptable but, perhaps more importantly, these imported cultivars may not be compatible with the ecology of British grasslands. For example, imported commercial varieties of Birdsfoot Trefoil may not provide a food source for native blue butterflies in the way that their indigenous counterparts do. Also, the seasonal cycle of imported cultivars may not follow that of their indigenous relatives and therefore may not coincide with that of species typically associated with them.

Grazing management

It is beyond the scope of this paper to consider the details of environmentally beneficial grazing management. The precise pattern of grazing will be influenced by the nature of the land concerned and the environmental objectives set for it but will also need to reflect seasonal variations. Different species are supported and encouraged by different types of sward; for example Snipe tend to favour a taller tussocky sward whereas over-wintering migratory wildfowl require a tighter, grazed 'lawn'. The key is to be clear about the environmental purposes of grassland management and that the land is suitable for those purposes. There is little point in converting the Solway Saltmarshes, which are so important to migratory birds, into habitat for Snipe. However, English Nature, RSPB and other organisations have undertaken research work to help; for example, in demonstrating the relationship between grazing density in spring and early summer and the success of ground nesting birds in breeding (higher densities lead to disturbance, the trampling of nests and therefore to reduced success).

Mowing and cutting

Manipulating cutting dates can be crucial in supporting and improving the environmental value of the sward. As a general rule environmental objectives will dictate later cutting and often the preference is management for hay or, in the uplands, late-cut, big-bale silage. Early cutting disturbs the nesting cycle and prevents flowers and grasses from setting seed and regenerating.

Weed control

The first question to be asked from an environmental perspective is whether there is a problem with weeds. Clearly in certain circumstances there is a statutory obligation to control notifiable weeds under the 1958 Weeds Act. Outside this obligation there may be circumstances where a change in management can trigger an initial problem and control may be necessary. After confirming that weed control really is needed, there is one guiding principle; blanket spray treatments are seldom compatible with environmental objectives. The ideal solution is to achieve control by adjustments in grazing practice or by cutting (except where ragwort is involved). The next best option is selective chemical application.

Water level management
Drainage improvements have dramatically changed farming systems in many wetland areas. The selective raising of water levels and, in appropriate circumstances, seasonal inundation can have dramatic environmental benefits. Wetland landscapes are attractive and are important for wildlife. Raising water levels can encourage ground nesting birds, sub-aquatic and wet grassland flora and, in the case of land converted from cultivation or intensive grassland management, can encourage the rapid dispersion of seeds and therefore the re-establishment of biodiversity. The introduction and expansion of funding for this purpose, under some environmental schemes, is beginning to make this reversal a possibility for farmers.

Grassland management and public access
In most cases informal public access through rights of way or provided for under schemes such as 'Countryside Stewardship' and 'Environmentally Sensitive Areas' will not fundamentally affect grassland systems. Generally, when establishing new access under incentive schemes the aim is to make it compatible with the farming system by offering the public clearly waymarked and signed routes or areas. It is only where high levels of use are envisaged, or where more ambitious recreational activities are involved, that land managers may need to consider specifically tailored grassland management; for example more frequent cutting or seeding to create a particularly durable sward or to stabilise erosion.

The final guiding principle when considering environmentally beneficial grassland management is that it should be selective and targeted to appropriate land. There is no universal prescription.

THE FUTURE
UK agriculture is in a period of transition. After a sustained period of relative policy stability with the improvement of production as the core aim, farmers are now in a more uncertain policy framework as the industry grapples with the implications of measures to limit the cost of agricultural support, the possible accession of new member states to the EC, and a move to a freer world market for agricultural commodities.

Whilst acknowledging the challenges and pressures that changes bring, the Countryside Commission sees welcome opportunities in these developments. These include:

- environmental concerns further integrating into agricultural support policies both through the increased availability of incentives, where conservation has a clear cost to the land manager or farmer, but also through the structure and direction of all agricultural support where it affects the management of the land.
- support to positively encourage specific systems of farming that are at least environmentally neutral and hopefully that actively contribute to environmental improvement. Current measures are tentatively moving in this direction; for example by linking headage payments for livestock to stocking levels.
- a re-appraisal of the definition of agricultural efficiency, given increasing concerns to achieve the sometimes illusive concept of sustainable development. Such a re-appraisal needs to reflect the wider costs and benefits of agricultural systems on the environment as a means of orienting support payments and any environmental incentives that are needed to help adjust systems to reflect these wider environmental aspirations for our countryside.
- a continuing and increasing emphasis on combining conservation objectives to protect what is of value with a more creative approach that builds bridges between changing farming systems and opportunities to positively improve landscape through the process of change.
- the exploration of ways in which farm conservation management might generate a positive income without necessarily relying on public funds.

Underlying this both farmers and conservationists need to adjust their thinking. Conservationists must recognise that improving agricultural production as an objective remains important and that it is not possible to turn the clock back to some mythical golden age of traditional farming. In return the farming industry might look again at the definition of the words 'improved' and 'efficiency' so that in producing high quality food it builds on the contribution that farmers already make to the countryside, to enhance it and protect the environment.

The skills of farmers, researchers and agronomists are needed. Their expertise is essential if we are to increase our understanding of how farming can sensibly and practically deliver environmental objectives. The challenge is to find modern systems that may sometimes echo the traditional rhythms of grassland management but which combine environmental and recreational benefits with the best of modern farming practice.

Climate Change and its Implications for Grassland Agriculture in the United Kingdom: A problem of Scale

C. J. POLLOCK, A. DAVIES, JUDITH HARRISON, LESLEY TURNER,
J. GALLAGHER AND M.L. PARRY[1]
IGER, Plas Gogerddan, Aberystwyth, SY23 3EB
[1]Jackson Environment Institute, University College,
26 Bedford Way, London, WC1H 0AP

ABSTRACT

Based upon the improved spatial resolution of current climate change models, the major changes of relevance to UK agriculture are predicted to be increased mean temperatures, altered spatial and temporal distribution of rainfall, changes in summer evapotranspiration and possibly an increased incidence of extreme climatic events. All of these will affect agricultural production, as will the direct effects of elevated carbon dioxide concentration. This review discusses the potential sensitivity of plant processes at the cell, organ, plant and sward level to these environmental changes, emphasising where possible the responses of grassland systems or their components. The problems of integrating responses at one level and applying them to the next one are discussed. Although the broad responses at the lower levels can be described with some confidence, secondary interactions with soils, weeds, pests and diseases are not well understood, and considerable buffering seems likely. There appears to be widespread differences in response to the primary environmental drivers between different crops, and the 'maximal' responses are strongly affected by a range of other inputs. At the highest level, grassland production systems may be more sensitive to global market changes than to perturbations in UK climate, although global climatic changes will themselves influence world markets in agricultural commodities. Predictive modelling generates opportunities to allow higher-level problems to be addressed, but defects in the basis for mechanistic crop growth models need to be overcome before such approaches are of general value.

INTRODUCTION

The magnitude of the problem.

Grassland of different types is the largest component by area of UK agriculture. It provides the major energy and nutrient input into a livestock industry with a current value to the UK economy of approximately £7 billion per annum (HMSO, 1994), and the management of this resource is the major factor shaping the British landscape. Whilst the characteristics and intensity of grassland agriculture have changed markedly this century, in response to social, political and economic pressures, there is a growing awareness that human activity is directly affecting the environment, both nationally and globally. The deleterious consequences of such activity are being felt across a range of industries, of which agriculture is one, and there has been considerable interest in research aimed at predicting the

143

likely effects of anthropogenic climate change. It is the purpose of this review to consider the scientific approaches which have been used in such studies, to outline some of the relevant findings and to consider whether or not this allows realistic predictions of the likely responses, at various levels from single cells through to whole agricultural systems.

The major environmental variables.

Anthropogenic climate changes can usefully be divided into three classes. Climate forcing by increased concentrations of greenhouse gases is globally the most significant (Parry, 1990) and is the main subject of this review. Accumulation of atmospheric pollutants is usually more local but can affect plant performance and may also interact with the environmental effects of greenhouse forcing (Mansfield and Pearson, 1993). Finally, depletion of stratospheric ozone has led to increases in the flux of UVB radiation at the earth's surface. This has both direct and indirect effects on living organisms, the significance of which is, as yet, poorly understood (Cullen and Neale, 1994).

Table 1.   Summary of the key predictions for the UK climate in the 2050s (based upon the information in Hulme, 1996).

Variable	Mean change by 2050	Geographical distribution
Winter temperature	+1.5°	+1.0°in North West to +2.0°in South East
Summer temp	+1.5°	+1.2° in North to +1.6° in South
Winter precipitation	+9%	+3% in Nth. West to +12% in South East
Summer precipitation	zero	+9% in North to -9% in South
Winter windspeed	+6%	+1% in North to +6% in South
Summer RH	zero	+3% in North to -6% in South

To perform both mechanistic and modelling studies on the potential impacts of climate change, it is obviously important to have predictions of both the magnitude and rate of such changes. Such predictions are usually derived from climatic models which, in turn, are driven by estimates of the future pattern of release of greenhouse gases (Parry, 1995). There are limitations to the accuracy and resolution of such models and this has the logical effect of increasing the uncertainty of any second-level predictions. Recently, a series of more detailed predictions has been made, based upon the use of the Meteorological Office UK high resolution model (Hulme, 1996) and Table 1 indicates the likely magnitude and gradient of some of these variables for the decade beginning in 2050, based upon a realistic emission scenario (IS 92a: business as usual; CO_2 at 500 vpm; total greenhouse gases at 690 vpm CO_2 equivalents; Parry, 1995). The predictions in Table 1 are broadly consistent with the temperature changes which have been used by many physiologists and biochemists in order to study the responses of specific organisms or processes within organisms. What is clear, however, is that secondary changes, associated with alterations in the temporal and spatial distribution of factors such as rainfall, windspeed and relative humidity, may have equally marked effects. Thus the range of significant variables and their potential interactions under field conditions are greater than normally studied in the laboratory.

Determining or predicting responses
Research on the responses of agricultural systems has been of two main kinds. Mechanistic studies of response to altered environmental variables have been carried out at a range of scales using a restricted range of treatments (Lawlor and Keys, 1993 and references therein). Such approaches have been valuable in pinpointing potential sensitivities but are difficult to perform in such a way as to permit the full range of important edaphic and biotic factors to be varied independently. Systems have been devised, however, which allow elevated CO_2 and increased temperature treatments to be imposed upon crops under field conditions and their responses to be compared with those of similar control plots (Lawlor and Mitchell, 1991). These responses will include interactions with other environmental variables, but the values for these variables will be 'present day' rather than those of some future climate.

The second approach is to use models, both empirical and mechanistic, to extrapolate current response and thus to predict performance under some future scenario (Brignall *et al.*, 1995). This does permit integration of the effects of different variables, in so far as the original model considered them, and also allows for progressive refinement of the predictions as the scenarios themselves become more refined. The procedure does, however, involve extrapolation, with all its attendant dangers, and requires validation against good relevant data sets. Most importantly, however, is the fact that most crop growth models determine potential maximum output and assume that inputs are non-limiting.

Both mechanistic studies of response and production potential modelling also ignore the distinction between the sensitivity of the production system and the sensitivity of the industry it serves. Economic analysis of the global effects of climate change on agricultural production (Rosenzweig and Parry, 1994) suggests that developed countries are well placed to adapt, whereas less-developed countries may have difficulties in meeting demand. Altered patterns of self-sufficiency will affect agricultural trade and the effects in some sectors are likely to be larger than the primary impact of climate change. The challenge is to integrate predictions at all these different levels. This review considers the extent to which such integration is possible and whether or not it has been achieved.

CELL- AND ORGAN-LEVEL RESPONSES TO ENVIRONMENTAL CHANGE
Carbon dioxide
The hyperbolic relationship between the instantaneous rate of photosynthesis and the internal CO_2 concentration is well-known (Stitt, 1991). Doubling CO_2 concentrations from 350 to 700 vpm increases the rate of photosynthesis for C_3 plants by up to 50%, whereas the rate for C_4 plants rises by only 10%. However, over longer periods, rates of photosynthesis often decline (Sage et al., 1989). The nature of this decline appears to depend upon both genotype and environment but can involve changes in stomatal conductance (Morison, 1993), alterations in the activation state of ribulose bisphosphate carboxylase (Lawlor and Keys, 1993) and down-regulation of the genes coding for various components of the photosynthetic apparatus (Stitt, 1991). It has been suggested that the latter process is sensitive to the assimilate status of the source leaf (Sheen, 1990; Pollock and Farrar, 1996) and, thus, that it reflects the overall balance within the plant between carbon supply and demand. It would appear, therefore, that photosynthetic capacity will increase under most, if not all, climate change scenarios, but that the extent of this increase will be variable and influenced by a range of other physiological factors acting at many different levels of organisation within the plant.

Temperature
For temperate crops, particularly those which are sown in the winter or which are perennial, temperature represents a major determinant variable (Pollock, 1990; Pollock et al., 1993). Small changes in temperature around the lower threshold for growth have very large effects upon growth rate and, thus, upon demand for fixed carbon (Table 2). The short-term effects of low temperature upon growth rate appear to be manifested via changes in the extensibility of the cell walls in cells undergoing turgor-driven expansion (Pollock et al., 1990). Longer-term changes may also alter rates of cell division and patterns of organ development (Francis and Barlow, 1988). Changes in temperature around the lower threshold for growth also affect the development and loss of induced tolerance to freezing (frost tolerance) (Gay and Eagles, 1991). At temperatures closer to the optimum, increased temperatures tend to enhance both rates of growth and the rate of development (Ellis et al., 1990).

The interaction between assimilate supply and the processes of growth is a complex one. Although enhancement of the rate of growth in white clover leads to the mobilisation of starch and increased activities of degradative enzymes (L. B. Turner, J. Gallagher and J. Volenec, unpublished observations), there is evidence that large changes in assimilate abundance in the extension zone of temperate gramineae are not always associated with changes in growth rate

(Pollock, 1984). Our current hypothesis would be that there is a basal requirement for substrate to achieve the maximum potential rate of leaf extension, which is influenced both by environmental conditions and by the genetic makeup of the plant. Once this requirement is met, additional material is stored without markedly influencing growth, although it does affect strongly the patterns of gene expression in the tissue (Winters *et al.*, 1994; Winters *et al.*, 1995).

Table 2. Responses of primary processes to temperature in seedlings of *Lolium temulentum* (From Pollock *et al.*, 1993)

Parameter	Rate at			Q_{10}	
	20°	5°	2°	2-20°	2-5°
Relative leaf extension rate (d^{-1})	0.70	0.11	0.02	7.2	293.7
Relative growth rate (d^{-1})	0.064	0.025	0.008	3.2	44.6
Relative root growth rate (d^{-1})	0.069	0.030	0.015	2.3	10.1
Photosynthetic capacity (μmol O$_2$ hr^{-1} mg^{-1} chlorophyll)	220	40	24	3.4	5.3

WHOLE PLANT RESPONSES
Interactions with soil and water
Based upon cell- and tissue-level observations, the major predicted responses of forage species to climate change would be a CO_2 -induced increase in the maximum potential rate of net photosynthesis and a temperature-induced increase in the rate of growth and development. However, at the whole-plant level, there are a range of other factors which will determine how much of this potential is finally realised as increased productivity. One of the best-described interactions of this kind is the one between increased ambient CO_2 concentrations and a persistent decline in stomatal aperture (Mansfield *et al.*, 1990; Eamus, 1991; Morison, 1993). In at least some species, this reduces the magnitude of the rise in photosynthesis whilst increasing overall water-use efficiency (Lawlor and Keys, 1993). The extent to which stomatal effects rather than physical characteristics such as wind-speed and canopy architecture determine transpirational water loss at the sward level is debatable (Gay, 1994), but it seems likely that the interaction between temperature, water availability and CO_2 concentrations that determine net photosynthesis in the field will be complex.

The availability of inorganic nutrients affects the ability of plants to 'invest' additional fixed carbon in the production of new biomass (Lawlor and Mitchell, 1991) and also influences the allometric constant (Farrar, 1992). Thus soil processes may be important in determining the fate of additional fixed carbon, and consequently the extent of assimilate-driven down-regulation of photosynthesis (Pollock and Farrar, 1995). Quantitative studies on the effects of climate change on soils are rare, but changes in water status, oxygen availability and organic matter could all have significant effects upon microbial and chemical transformations (Bullock, 1996). There is also evidence to suggest that, in maize at least, some of the extra carbon fixed under elevated CO_2 concentrations would be available for secretion from the roots to improve soil-root adhesion, and that such secretion processes may be regulated at the level of gene expression by the combination of water stress and root assimilate abundance (Koch, 1995).

Pathogens, pests and weeds.

Climatic conditions are important determinants of survival, growth and spread of pathogens. Treharne (1989) emphasised the potential stimulation of infestation of a number of diseases by increased temperature, and altered patterns of precipitation or summer evapotranspiration could also increase damage in some areas. However, drier summers would tend to reduce the spread of certain diseases (Parry, 1990). The challenge for predictive modelling is that the interrelationships between climate, host and pathogen are unlikely to be identical for each combination, making it difficult to produce generic predictions. Specific studies on the most important diseases will be required, but in parallel, the search for novel genetic sources of resistance must remain a major target. This is particularly true for grassland agriculture, where the cost of prophylactic treatments is rarely justified. Similar variations in response to climatic variables have been reported for a wide range of insect and other invertebrate pests, generating equal challenges for the modeller. Simulation models have been used to predict potential redistribution of some insect pests as a result of climate change (Porter *et al.*, 1991). In addition, the potential for rapid airborne spread of some insect pests and the viruses they carry means that increased incidence of extreme climatic events may also be important. Once again, the importance of breeding for resistance is obvious.

The effects of climate change upon temperate weed growth and distribution are difficult to assess. For perennial weeds of grassland, increased CO_2 concentrations will affect partitioning into perennating organs, thus altering persistency. For weeds like thistle (*Cirsium arvense*) which accumulate fructans, the relative insensitivity of this type of metabolism to cold, when compared to starch accumulation, may also increase aggression (Housley and Pollock, 1994). Information is lacking on the population biology and ecology of grassland weeds, and appropriate management practices represent the only feasible control strategy, so further research in this area is desirable.

BRIDGING THE GAP BETWEEN PLANTS AND AGRICULTURAL SYSTEMS
Estimating primary production
As suggested above, the integrated effects of climate change on the productivity

of agricultural systems may be difficult to estimate on the basis of single-variable mechanistic studies. Growth of crop stands (including forage species) under altered environments has been used to determine sensitivity, even though not all the major factors are controlled. The most common approach is to elevate CO_2 concentrations and/or temperature at a range of scales. Controlled environment or glasshouse experiments are the most common. In general they support the predictions of increased primary productivity associated with elevated CO_2 concentrations derived from higher-resolution studies. However, environmental conditions differ strongly from those in the field (Lawlor and Mitchell, 1991). In particular, low irradiance, constant temperatures and non-limiting water or nutrient supplies are likely to strongly affect the balance between photosynthetic carbon fixation and the utilisation of fixed carbon in growth.

Open-topped chamber experiments and studies employing free-air CO_2 enrichment (FACE) are fewer in number but do allow the long-term responses of plants under fluctuating conditions to be determined. Open-topped chambers are relatively simple to install, but the microclimate does differ from surrounding open areas. FACE rigs are complex and expensive, generate large areas of crop for analysis and are well suited for analysis of the combined effects of different factors including weeds, pests and diseases. In general, the results from such systems confirm the positive effects of elevated CO_2 concentrations on primary productivity but emphasise the sensitivity of this rise to other factors, such as temperature and water stress (Lawlor and Mitchell, 1991). Studies on continuously defoliated clover and grass/clover swards using open top chambers (Parsons *et al.*, 1994) have suggested that there is a sustained improvement in primary production with no deleterious effects on the proportion of clover in the mixed swards. There have been few published studies on forage species in FACE systems, although experiments are in progress in Switzerland, but it seems likely that the responses will be broadly similar.

Interactions with animals.
Specific consideration of the responses of grassland systems should also include the animal component. The range of mean temperature changes currently envisaged for the UK are unlikely to have severe negative effects, although an increased incidence of heat waves might reduce milk production (Thatcher, 1974). Altered patterns of precipitation could reduce stock access to pastures during the winter, and requirements for shelter might change. The capacity of the livestock production industry to adapt is, however, high, and the secondary effects on the industry associated with altered land use are likely to be more pronounced (see below).

Modelling primary production and changes in land use.
An alternative approach to direct measurement is to use crop growth models to

predict productivity under different environmental conditions. The UK wheat model ARCWHEAT has been run under a range of temperatures and CO_2 concentrations and has predicted a slight decline in yield under climate change scenarios associated with a shortening of the developmental sequence (Miglieta and Porter, 1992; Semenov *et al.*, 1993). Most such models are driven by temperature, available moisture and intercepted radiation and thus, where suitable data exist, can be combined with spatial analysis to generate maps of predicted distribution and/or productivity (Brignall *et al.*, 1995). Following validation against actual yield values, the models can be run using altered inputs characteristic of different climate change scenarios. Table 3 summarises the predictions obtained for a range of systems, including the grass crop, under two representative scenarios (Davies *et al.*, 1994).

Table 3. Summary of predictions from geographical analysis of yield models for a range of UK crops run under two climate change scenarios (From Davis *et al.*, 1993).

Crop	Scenarios Temperature +2°; Rainfall +10% or -10%
Potato	Yields predicted to increase in North due to warming, precipitation changes have little effect.
Forage maize	Norther limits for cultivation increased due to warming. Reduced precipitation markedly reduces predicted yield in South East.
Silage grass	Warming increases predicted yields, but less in East than in West. Low rainfall scenario predictions restrict economic production to Wales and South West England.
Spring barley	Warming increases predicted Northern limit for cultivation. Rainfall changes produce little effect.
Pears	Predicted cultivation limits very sensitive to temperature with large shift in Northern and Western limits. Gains very sensitive to decreased rainfall.

It is unlikely, however, that the major responses of UK agricultural systems to climate change will be as a consequence of direct effects. Changes in world food production and trends in prices have been modelled (Rosenzweig and Parry, 1994) and these trends incorporated into climate land-use allocation models for the UK. These predict a contraction in the area of land used for commodity production and an increase in less intensive livestock operations (Brignall *et al.*, 1995). Although such predictions are very sensitive to a number of assumptions concerning future trends in demand and in crop improvement, they do illustrate the complex nature of the interactions which will determine the response of the agricultural industry, with the response of primary productivity being only one element.

CONCLUSIONS

The development of climate models and their integration with crop and animal science has produced a large volume of data on primary responses to climate change. Even these studies have emphasised the complexity of the links between effects at the cellular and molecular level and those on whole plants or communities of plants. The effects of climate change on weeds, pests and diseases are likely to be particularly critical in determining the overall system sensitivity, and these are obvious targets for further study. What is much less well understood is the elasticity of the industry which depends upon these production systems and the degree to which it will respond to secondary changes caused by a whole range of biological and socio-economic factors. UK agriculture has shown itself well able to adapt to altered circumstances, but the development of robust predictive models at this level of organisation will be an essential prerequisite for continued success.

ACKNOWLEDGEMENTS

Elements of the authors' work described in this review were funded via MAFF contracts and commissions, and via BBSRC Priority Programmes.

REFERENCES

BRIGNALL P., DAVIES A., HOSSELL J., PARRY M. and POLLOCK C. J. (1995) Implications for agriculture and land use. In: Parry, M. and Duncan, R. (eds) *The Economic Implications of Climate Change*, 46-63. London: Earthscan.

BULLOCK P. (1996) Soils. In: *The Potential Effects of Climate Change in the United Kingdom. Second Report of the UK Climate Change Impacts Review Group for the Department of the Environment*, London: HMSO (in press).

CULLEN J. J. and NEALE P. J. (1994) Ultraviolet radiation, ozone depletion and global biogeochemical cycles. *Photosynthesis Research*, **39**, 303-320

DAVIES A., SHAO J., BARDGETT R. D., BRIGNALL P., PARRY M. L. and POLLOCK C. J. (1994) *Specification of climatic sensitivity for UK farming systems*. Report to MAFF, 252 pp., Aberystwyth: Institute of Grassland and Environmental Research.

EAMUS D. (1991) The interaction of rising CO_2 and temperatures with water use efficiency. *Plant, Cell and Environment*, **14**, 843-852.

ELLIS R. H., HEADLEY P., ROBERTS E. H. and SUMMERFIELD R. J. (1990) Quantitative relations between temperature and crop development and growth. In: Jackson, M. (ed.) *Climate Change and Plant Genetic Resources*, 85-115, London: Belhaven.

FARRAR J. F. (1992) The whole plant: carbon partitioning during development. In: Pollock, C. J., Farrar, J. F. and Gordon A. J. (eds) *Carbon Partitioning Within and Between Organisms*, pp. 163-179, Oxford: Bios Press.

FRANCIS D. and BARLOW, P. W. (1988). Temperature and the cell cycle. In: Long, S.P. and Woodward, F.J. (eds) *Plants and Temperature*, 181-201, Cambridge: Company of Biologists.

GAY A. P. (1994) Breeding for leaf water conductance , its heritability and its effect on water use in *Lolium perenne. Aspects of Applied Biology*, **38**, 41-45.

GAY A. P. and EAGLES C. F. (1991). Quantitative analysis of cold hardening and dehardening in *Lolium. Annals of Botany*, **67**, 339-345.

HMSO (1994) *Agriculture in the UK*. London: HMSO.

HOUSLEY T. L. and POLLOCK C. J. (1993) The metabolism of fructans in higher plants. In: Suzuki, M. and Chatterton, N.J. (eds) Science and technology of Fructans, 192-225, Boca Raton: CRC Press.

HULME (1996) Scenarios of future climate and sea level. In: *The Potential Effects of Climate Change in the United Kingdom*. Second Report of the UK Climate Change Impacts Review Group for the Department of the Environment, London: HMSO (in press).

KOCH K. E. (1995) Starvation stress and genes for sucrose metabolism. *First International Symposium on Sucrose Metabolism*, Abstract 28, Mar del Plata: Fundacion para Investigaciones Biologicas Aplicadas.

LAWLOR D. W. and MITCHELL, R. A. C. (1991) The effects of increasing CO_2 on crop photosynthesis and productivity: a review of field studies. *Plant, Cell and Environment*, **14**, 807-818.

LAWLOR D. W. and KEYS A. J. (1993) Understanding photosynthetic adaptation to changing climate. In: Fowden, L., Mansfield, T.A. and Stoddart, J.L. (eds) *Plant Adaptation to Environmental Stress*, 85-106, London: Chapman and Hall.

MANSFIELD T. E and PEARSON M. (1993) Physiological basis of stress imposed by ozone pollution. In: Fowden, L., Mansfield, T.A. and Stoddart, J.L. (eds) *Plant Adaptation to Environmental Stress*, 155-170, London: Chapman and Hall.

MANSFIELD T. E., HEATHERINGTON A. M. and ATKINSON C. J. (1990) Some current aspects of stomatal physiology. *Annual Review of Plant Physiology and Plant Molecular Biology*, **41**, 55-75.

MIGLIETA F. and PORTER J. R. (1992) The effects of CO_2 induced climatic change on development of wheat: Analysis and modelling. *Journal of Experimental Botany*, **43**, 1147-1158.

MORISON J. I. L. (1993) Responses of plants to CO_2 under water limited conditions. In: Roxema, L., Lambers, H., van de Geijn, S.C. and Cambridge M.L. (eds) *CO_2 and Biosphere*, 193-209, Dordrecht: Kluwer.

PARRY M. (1990) *Climate Change and World Agriculture*, 157pp. London: Earthscan.

PARRY M. (1995) Background to possible changes in the British climate. In: Parry, M. and Duncan, R. (eds) *The Economic Implications of Climate Change*, 1-7. London: Earthscan.

PARSONS A. J., ATKINSON L. and RISH J. (1994) The effect of elevated CO_2 on the growth and composition of grass/clover mixtures and clover monocultures under simulated continuous grazing in open top chambers in the field. *EU Programme report*, 28pp., North Wyke: Institute of Grassland and Environmental Research.

POLLOCK C. J. (1984) Sucrose accumulation and the initiation of fructan biosynthesis in *Lolium temulentum* L. *New Phytologist*, **96**, 527-534.

POLLOCK C. J. (1990) The responses of plants to temperature change. *Journal of Agricultural Science*, **115**, 1-5.

POLLOCK C. J. and FARRAR J. F. (1996) Source: sink interactions: The role of sucrose.

In: Baker, N. (ed.) *Environmental Stress and Photosynthesis*, The Netherlands: Kluwer (in press).

POLLOCK C. J., TOMOS A. D., THOMAS A., SMITH C. J., LLOYD E. J. and STODDART J. L. (1990) Extension growth in a barley mutant with reduced sensitivity to low temperature. *New Phytologist*, **115**, 617-623.

POLLOCK C. J., EAGLES C. F., HOWARTH, C. J., SCHUNMANN, P. H. D. and STODDART J.L. (1993) Temperature stress. In: Fowden, L., Mansfield, T.A. and Stoddart, J.L. (eds) *Plant Adaptation to Environmental Stress*, 109-132, London: Chapman and Hall.

PORTER J. H., PARRY M. L. and CARTER T. R. (1991) The potential effects of climatic change on agricultural insect pests. *Agricultural and Forest Meteorology*, **57**, 221-240.

ROSENZWEIG C. and PARRY M. L. (1994) Potential impact of climate change on world food supply. *Nature*, **367**, 133-138.

SAGE R.F., SHARKEY T.D. and SEEMAN J.R. (1989) Acclimation of photosynthesis to elevated CO_2 in five C_3 species. *Plant Physiology*, **59**, 590-596.

SEMENOV M. A., PORTER J. H. and DELECOLLE R. (1993) Climate change and the growth and development of wheat in the UK and France. *European Journal of Agronomy*, **2**, 293-304.

SHEEN J. (1990) Metabolic repression of transcription in higher plants. *Plant Cell*, **2**, 1027-1038.

STITT M. (1991) Rising CO_2 levels and their potential significance for carbon flow in photosynthetic cells. *Plant, Cell and Environment*, **14**, 741-762.

THATCHER W. W. (1974) Effects of season, climate and temperature on reproduction and lactation. *Journal of Dairy Science*, **57**, 360-368.

TREHARNE K. J. (1989) The implications of the 'greenhouse effect' for fertilizers and agrochemicals. In: Bennet, R.M. (ed.) *The Greenhouse Effect and UK Agriculture*, 67-79, Reading: Centre For Agricultural Strategy.

WINTERS A. L., WILLIAMS J. H. H., THOMAS D. S. and POLLOCK C. J. (1994) Changes in gene expression in response to sucrose accumulation in leaf tissue of *Lolium temulentum* L. *New Phytologist*, **128**, 591-600.

WINTERS A. L., GALLAGHER, J., POLLOCK, C. J. and FARRAR, J. F. (1995) Isolation of a gene expressed during sucrose accumulation in leaves of *Lolium temulentum* L. *Journal of Experimental Botany*, **46** (in press).

Environmental and Economic Impacts of Animal Waste Management

M. B. McGECHAN

SAC, Bush Estate, Penicuik EH26 0PH

Over-winter housing of dairy cows and beef cattle results in large quantities of animal manure and slurry to be disposed of by land spreading, and this in turn can lead to water and air pollution problems. These wastes are also valuable as plant nutrients and, if managed efficiently, can substantially reduce chemical fertilizer requirements. However, poor utilization in current farming practice, resulting from inappropriate land spreading technologies and unsuitable timing of spreading operations, represents both a threat to the environment and an economic loss of a valuable resource. Modelling can be a valuable research tool to address these issues. This paper describes the scope for modelling different aspects of such problems and progress made so far.

Animal manures and slurries contain substantial quantities of the plant nutrients N, P and K, both in forms which are readily available and in forms which release nutrients a year or more after spreading. The N component, in particular, can readily become lost to the environment before reaching plants. Dyson (1992) lists typical values of the quantities, composition and availability of nutrients for manures and slurries from different types of livestock. However, these parameters tend to vary over a wide range, which creates difficulties for planned recycling. Research is in progress at various centres to provide more cost-effective means of analysing slurry to the required accuracy. As an alternative to expensive analysis procedures or unreliable guessed values of waste composition, ruminant nutrition models can be used to estimate composition from animal diets.

Environmental problems caused by animal wastes include those caused by whole slurry reaching watercourses by surface runoff or macropore flow through the soil, leaching of dissolved nutrients (particularly nitrate and phosphorus) to field drains and deep groundwater, ammonia volatilization (which leads to acid rain), emissions of nitrogen oxides (greenhouse gases), and unpleasant smells. Most of the pollution and recycling processes associated with animal wastes are very dependent on the soil moisture content at the time of, or after, spreading. To study these processes, there is a requirement for a soil moisture simulation model, with representation of precipitation, evapotranspiration, soil moisture status, and water movements over and through the soil. This needs to be coupled to a soil heat model, since some processes are dependent on snow cover and freezing of soil moisture, as well as on soil temperature. There is also a requirement for a model to simulate the conversion processes which nutrients undergo in the soil, including those which cause gaseous emissions, and the dynamics of solute movement. The loss of the N nutrient component by ammonia volatilization at the soil surface, as well as during storage and processing before field spreading, can be modelled. There may be scope for using catchment water flow models to trace the movement of pollutants beyond field boundaries.

Progress has been made at modelling some of the above processes using the Swedish model `SOIL', which is a coupled simulation of soil water and heat transport, together with its associated nitrogen cycling model 'SOILN', representing soil nutrient conversion processes. The processes are very dependent on soil characteristic parameters and treatment histories, and a programme of measurement of these parameters is in progress for a range of soils. Simulations for two contrasting soil types have been carried out using 'SOIL' to calculate numbers of 'workdays' suitable for spreading slurry during the winter, with a workday assumed to have a soil moisture content below a threshold value (at or slightly above field capacity) and no frost or snow cover (McGechan and Cooper, 1994). The combined SOIL/SOILN models have been used with one soil type in two states, a compacted grassland soil and a zero traffic uncompacted soil, to show that losses of N nutrients are predominantly by denitrification in the compacted soil and predominantly by leaching in the non-compacted soil. This suggests that if greenhouse gases are a serious environmental issue, farmers should move away from spreading slurry with heavy tankers which cause serious soil compaction. Work is also in progress with these models to improve understanding of the processes of runoff of whole slurry, and of the only partial filtering of material passing through the soil by macropore flow.

As well as modelling of individual processes, there is a need to take a broader view of the overall pattern of polluting emissions arising from field spreading of wastes, to quantify the environmental threat from each type of pollutant, and prioritise measures to alleviate such problems. This will require a 'whole system model' consisting of linked mechanistic sub-models representing individual processes. A simple whole-system model has also been developed to calculate the cost/benefits of alternative animal waste technologies, with costs of machines offset by potential savings in bought-in chemical fertilizer, as indicated by values in Dyson (1992). This is illustrated in a comparison of a system with a large store in which all slurry can be spread in the spring against one with a small store requiring frequent winter spreading, and a comparison of injection against spreading with a vacuum tanker (McGechan, 1994). In both cases, the saving in chemical fertilizer resulting from reduced N losses only partially offsets the extra investment in equipment. The long-term aim of the whole-system modelling work is to develop decision support systems for equipment, methods, timing and spreading rates for slurry spreading operations.

155

REFERENCES

DYSON P.W. (1992) Fertiliser allowances for manures and slurries. *SAC Technical Note, Fertiliser Series* No 14.

McGECHAN M. B. (1994) A model of the economic and environmental impacts of alternative animal waste management systems. *Proceedings of International Conference AGENG 94*, Milan, 29-31 August, 1088-1095.

McGECHAN M. B. and COOPER G. (1994) Workdays for winter field operations. *The Agricultural Engineer*, **49** 6-13.

Farm Waste Management Planning

R. J. UNWIN AND A. J. BREWER
ADAS London, Nobel House, 17 Smith Square, London SW1P 3JR

INTRODUCTION

Water pollution incidents following land application of manure, slurry and dirty water, caused either by surface runoff or *via* contaminated drain flow, continue to be a problem. In 1991, the Ministry of Agriculture, Fisheries and Food (MAFF) published a *Code of Good Agricultural Practice for the Protection of Water* which is available free of charge to all farmers. This provides practical guidance on all aspects of minimising water pollution risks and contains advice on categorising land in terms of pollution risk and sets a voluntary guideline of 250 kg/ha of total nitrogen per annum in applied animal manures or other organic materials. These guidelines have been adopted fairly widely for drawing up farm waste management plans. Subsequently, ADAS has produced a 'Step by Step Guide for Farmers' to enable them to produce their own plans at minimal cost. The key element of this work has been the production of a detailed farm map, assessing the pollution risk from each field or part field, using a system of colour coding to identify four different risk categories:

* Non spreading areas (red) where wastes should never be spread, including within 10 metres of ditches and watercourses and 50 metres of boreholes.
* Very high risk areas (orange) where wastes should not be spread at certain times of the year.
* High risk areas (yellow) where wastes should be spread at limited rates during certain periods.
* Lower risk areas (green) where wastes can normally be spread throughout the year.

PILOT CATCHMENT STUDY 1992/93

In October 1991, MAFF Environmental Protection Division and the Welsh Office Agriculture Department (WOAD) funded a pilot study by ADAS in four river catchments to develop a farm waste management plan, which could be completed and used by farmers. The study also assessed whether farmers could produce their own plan with sufficient accuracy for it to be useful in reducing pollution risk, whether there were any problems of farm waste disposal in those catchments, and if farmers were prepared to change their management of wastes if necessary. The catchments agreed with the National Rivers Authority (NRA) were the River Clyst (Devon), the River Frome (Somerset), the Afon Ceri (North-west Wales) and the Upper Weaver (Cheshire), all containing predominantly dairy farms.

The 'Step by Step Guide' was prepared by ADAS and contained a worked example. The main farming organisations were approached to gain their co-operation and ADAS appointed four Project Officers to co-ordinate activity in each catchment. Farmers were invited to a local launch meeting in June 1992 and from then until March 1993 all were encouraged to complete the plan documentation. ADAS checked the plans and the farmers' risk classification and provided appropriate guidance. All participating farmers were revisited between January and March 1994 to assess whether they had modified their waste management practice as a result of the plan.

A total of 257 farm waste management plans were prepared (76% of 335 eligible farms with housed livestock). About 82% of farmers classified field risks correctly and many of the rest provided plans with a sound basis for reducing pollution risks. Of the 238 farms for which data were available, 221 had adequate land area for spreading. Of the participating farmers, 201 were revisited and their response to a questionnaire indicated that the majority (83%) claimed to follow the plan, at least as a general guide. Responses to an open question regarding their attitude to plans indicated that 80% made neutral or positive comments, with a minority (14%) making negative comments.

CATCHMENT STUDIES 1993/94, 1994/95

The 'Step by Step Guide' was simplified in each succeeding year based on the practical experience gained. Six English catchments were targeted for waste management planning in 1993/94 and a total of 382 plans were prepared by farmers, representing 44% of eligible farms. Seven English catchments, including one with predominantly pig/arable units, were targeted in 1994/95 and a total of 451 plans were prepared by farmers, representing 49% of eligible farms. Between 70 and 80% of participating farmers produced plans with no major errors, which would be a satisfactory aid to reducing pollution. The majority had adequate land area and, where assessed, adequate storage facilities. A further seven English catchments have been agreed for 1995/96, building on the success of previous work.

Interactions of Grassland Managements, Soil Fauna and Microbial Populations and Activities

R. COOK[1], R. D. BARDGETT[1], C. S. DENTON[1], L. DONNISON[1],
P. J. HOBBS[2], D. K. LEEMANS[1] AND G. W. YEATES[3]
[1] IGER, Aberystwyth, Dyfed SY23 3EB
[2] IGER, North Wyke, Okehampton, Devon EX20 2SB
[3] Landcare Research, Palmerston North, New Zealand

INTRODUCTION AND OBJECTIVES

Soil biological processes underpin nutrient cycling in soils and play important roles in maintaining soil structure and ecosystem productivity. Populations and activities of the soil biota are affected by interactions which make it difficult to discern major influences from simple observations. To identify any general changes in soil fauna in response to organic management, grasslands were sampled on three contrasting soil textures (silt, loam and sand) where similar, adjacent fields had been managed either with conventional fertiliser inputs or to the organic standards of the Soil Association. Populations of soil mesofauna and microfauna were extracted and counted and soil microbial activity was estimated. Mean values are of 10 replicates, except where shown. This paper concentrates on summarising changes which appeared to be associated consistently with organic management and were not influenced by site or soil interactions.

OBSERVATIONS

There were no consistent changes associated with management in microbial activities measured as microbial C, respiration and dehydrogenase activity. The estimate (by the technique of phospholipid fatty acid analysis (PLFA) (Bardgett *et al.*, in press) of the abundance of active fungi showed an average increase of 30% in soils under organic compared with conventional management (respectively 85 and 65 $\mu mol/m^2$, SED 9.7, n=5). Numbers of mites (17000 and 11000/m^2, SED 1900), tardigrades (5000 and 3000/m^2, SED 800) and nematodes (4500 x 10^3 and 3500 x $10^3/m^2$, SED 224 x 10^3) were greater in organic than conventional fields. In contrast, at all three sites, both the number (60 and 150/m^2, SED 35, n=5) and weight (22 and 80 g/m^2, SED 19) of lumbricid earthworms extracted were lower in organic than in conventional fields.

The total nematode fauna was examined in more detail by allocating morphologically distinguished taxa to known feeding groups (Yeates *et al.*, 1993). Only those nematodes feeding on fungi showed consistent non-interacting responses to management, being more numerous in organic than conventional soils (570,000 and 259,000/m^2, respectively SED 49000). In organic fields, this group was 13% of the total nematode fauna compared with 8% in conventional fields. In spite of this consistent response, further analyses showed that the abundance of individual taxa of fungal feeders did differ from site to site.

CONCLUSIONS

Population studies of soil biota have the potential both to measure biodiversity of grassland systems and to provide indices of functional stability or sustainability. In the present study of organic and conventionally managed grassland, indices of biodiversity based upon the composition of the nematode fauna distinguished sites (soil textures) but not managements. Similar differences in fungal feeding nematode populations have been observed in mountain grassland where in peat soils they were 18% of the total nematode fauna compared with 5% in mineral soils (R. Cook, personal communication). In the grassland soils in the present study, soil organic carbon was greater in organic (6.1%) than in conventional fields (4.9%). The observed difference in earthworm numbers is contrary to preconceptions, although similar differences have been observed in Austrian meadow soils (Foissner, 1992).

Laboratory experiments are in progress to characterise some of the responses and interactions and to understand the mechanisms. This combined approach of field and laboratory study is being used to assess the contributions of groups such as fungal feeding nematodes to nutrient cycling in grassland soils.

ACKNOWLEDGEMENTS

This work was supported financially by the BBSRC, MAFF and by an IGER Fellowship. The authors thank the farmers involved for permission to sample their fields, and Peter Bowling (IGER, Aberystwyth) for his assistance.

REFERENCES

BARDGETT R. D., HOBBS P. J. and FROSTEGARD A. (in press) Changes in soil:fungal bacterial ratios following reductions in the intensity of management of an upland grassland soil. *Biology and Fertility of Soils.*

FOISSNER W. (1992) Comparative studies of the soil life in ecofarmed and conventionally farmed fields and grasslands of Austria. *Agriculture, Ecosystems and Environment,* **40**, 207-218.

YEATES G. W., BONGERS T., DE GOEDE, R. G. M., FRECKMAN D. W. and GEORGIEVA S. S. (1993) Feeding habits in nematode families and genera - an outline for soil ecologists. *Journal of Nematology,* **25**, 315-331.

The Effect of Four Management Strategies on the Flora and Fauna of Grass Field Margins Bordering Hawthorn Hedges

A. C. BELL[1], T. HENRY[2] AND J. H. McADAM[1]

[1]Department of Agriculture, Newforge Lane, Belfast, BT9 5PX
[2] Greenmount College of Agriculture and Horticulture, Antrim, BT41 4PU

INTRODUCTION

There has been a considerable amount of research on ways of improving the wildlife value of arable field margins (Way and Greig-Smith, 1987; Boatman, 1994), but there is a paucity of published work on methods to improve the conservation value of grass field margins. The area of managed grassland accounts for 31% of UK land area as a whole and 59% in Northern Ireland. In view of the importance of hedges as valuable wildlife refuges in intensive, predominantly pastoral, regions of Britain and the damage which intensive grassland management can have on hedges and field boundaries, an experiment was initiated in 1990 to investigate the effects of four controllable grassland management practices on the flora and fauna at the edges of grass fields. Results from 1993 are presented here.

MATERIALS AND METHODS

Three well maintained, mature, predominantly hawthorn hedges, separating paired grass fields, formed the blocks for this study, set up in 1990. Within a block, 4 treatments, each 30 m long, were randomly arranged across the hedge extending 10 m into the fields. The treatments were:

(1)   *Fertilise/graze.* Plots were fertilised and rotationally grazed with sheep.
(2)   *Plough/game cover.* A 2 m strip adjacent to the hedge was ploughed and sown with a game cover crop. The remaining 8 m was fertilised and two cuts of silage taken.
(3)   *Plough/unmanaged.* This was similar to the previous treatment except that the 2 m strip was left to colonise naturally.
(4)   *Unmanaged control.* These plots received no fertiliser or management treatments.

Flora were assessed in alternate years using 1 m x 1 m permanent quadrats in the hedge, hedge base, and at 0.5, 2, 6 and 9 m into the field. Carabids and arachnids were trapped using pitfall traps placed 1 - 2 m from the hedge base (margin sample), and at 8 - 10 m into the field (field sample). Catches were taken during the months of March, May, July and September of each year.

RESULTS AND DISCUSSION

In general, plant species richness was higher in the hedge-to-0.5 m zone than in the field for all treatments. TWINSPAN (Hill, 1979b) and DECORANA (Hill,

1979a) analyses of the data revealed a clear separation between the hedge samples and the remainder. Hedge samples were further subdivided into those which bordered grazed plots and those which did not, highlighting the direct damage caused by sheep grazing. All the fertilise/graze margin samples were grouped with the open field samples.

Analysis of carabid data resulted in a similar classification. Samples were categorised as either margin or field, with the fertilise/graze margin catches grouped once again with open field samples. The close cropping of the vegetation rendered the grazed margins similar to the open field habitat, and it was observed that soil temperature ranges were significantly greater in the former compared to those with an intact sward architecture. Modified Simpson's index (Usher, 1986) for carabid diversity was significantly lower in fertilise/graze margin and field later in the growing season. A distinct TWINSPAN grouping for spiders emerged for the ploughed margins, indicating the differing habitat requirements for various invertebrate taxa.

Elevated P and K levels in the fertilise/graze margin, and K in the field could be attributed to the addition of inorganic fertiliser and the return of sheep excreta. This led to a general, though not significant, reduction in plant species richness in fertilise/graze plots at the majority of the sampling stations.

The unmanaged plots were characterised by a thick vegetative mat in late season. This could lead to reduction in plant species richness and diversity over time. It is suggested that if field margins are fenced off, periodic grazing or removal of vegetation should take place after flowers have had time to set seed.

The results indicate that it is possible to generate a range of distinct habitats within a short time span, and that this is necessary to support a diverse range of flora and fauna. Intensive sheep grazing has deleterious effects in terms of direct damage to hedges, and the production of a lower wildlife value field margin.

REFERENCES

BOATMAN N. (1994) (ed.) *Field Margins: Integrating agriculture and conservation.* British Crop Protection Council Monograph, No. **58**, Farnham, Surrey.

HILL, M. O. (1979a) DECORANA - *A FORTRAN program for detrended correspondence analysis and reciprocal averaging.* Cornell University, Ithica, New York.

HILL, M. O. (1979b) *TWINSPAN - A FORTRAN program for arranging multivariate data in an ordered two-way table by classification of individuals and attributes.* Cornell University, Ithica, New York.

USHER, M. B. (1986) *Wildlife conservation evaluation.* Chapman and Hall:London.

WAY J. M. and GREIG-SMITH P. W. (1987) (eds) *Field Margins.* British Crop Protection Council Monograph No. **35**, Thornton Heath.

The Impact of Meadow Management on Nesting Birds in The Pennines

D. ASKEW

ADAS Leeds, Lawnswood, Otley Road, Leeds LS16 5PY

INTRODUCTION

Meadows in the Pennines have been traditionally managed for hay but nowadays hay or silage may be taken. The use of these fields by birds has depended on the compatibility their breeding cycle and the cycle of meadow management. Meadows provide shelter in tall vegetation free from the threat of trampling by stock through the spring and summer nesting period. Changes in meadow management, particularly the timing of cutting operations, can have a severe effect on breeding success. This is considered with respect to two species associated with Pennine meadows.

THE CORNCRAKE

The corncrake (*Crex crex*) was widespread throughout Pennine valleys in the first half of this century but has now disappeared as a regular breeding bird with the last records being from the 1970s. This decline is within the context of a decline throughout Great Britain with a 30% reduction between 1978 and 1988 (Stowe *et al.*, 1993). Its decline in the Pennines coincided with the intensification of grassland use and, particularly, earlier grass cutting and an associated switch from hay to silage production.

A preference for hay fields over silage fields has been recorded in Ireland (Mayes and Stowe, 1989). Green and Williams (1994) noted the impact of mowing dates with rapid declines in corncrake numbers occurring where the mean mowing date was earlier than late July. Reviewing the decline of the corncrake in Great Britain, Stowe *et al.* (1993) conclude that changes in grassland management are a critical factor.

THE YELLOW WAGTAIL

The yellow wagtail (*Motacilla flava*) is still a characteristic bird of Pennine meadows, although distribution is patchy and it is generally more common to the south and east of the area. Nationally, numbers have fallen since the 1980s (Marchant *et al.*, 1990). There is also some evidence of a decline within the Pennines. For example, Smith (1950) noted between 50 and 100 pairs in the Sedbergh area in 1939 whilst in 1993 ADAS recorded only a single male in enclosed grasslands in the dales around Sedbergh, to the north and east.

The Pennine Dales ESA seeks to encourage traditional meadow management for environmental benefits throughout the area designated in the mid and north Pennines. Specifically, cutting date restrictions are in part designed to protect ground nesting birds. Yellow wagtails have been monitored in Teesdale and Weardale between 1991 and 1993. In 1991, 86% of all nest sites identified were in meadows. Between 1991 and 1993 fledging was noted at 59% of sites by the end of June with the peak of fledging occurring within the last week of June (39% of nests). By the first week in July 76% of nests had fledged with fledging occurring at 90% of nests by the second week in July.

Table 1. Meadow management and field selection by yellow wagtails (Number of fields in Teesdale and Weardale, 1991 - 1993).

	Cut Before July 7	Cut After July 7	Hay	Silage
Fields with nests	1	9	9	1
Fields without nests	25	25	29	21

Sub-sample of fields from main survey.

The results illustrate the importance of the ESA restrictions on cutting dates with mowing delayed on participating holdings to 8 July or 15 July depending on the level of agreement. In 1993, on ESA agreement holdings in Teesdale and Weardale, no nests were destroyed by mowing before fledging whilst in meadows not under ESA agreement 56% of nests were destroyed before fledgling occurred. Management data were available from the ESA monitoring programme for a sub sample of meadows with and without yellow wagtail nests. A significant (P>0.05) preference was observable for meadows managed for hay and cut after the first week in July (Table 1). Overall, the monitoring results confirm the dependence of yellow wagtails on traditionally managed hay meadows.

CONCLUSIONS
Both corncrake and yellow wagtails show a preference for nesting in meadows with a significant preference for fields managed for hay and cut in mid or late July. Intensification of grassland management, particularly a switch to silage making with earlier cutting, within the Pennines has been associated with population declines. The corncrake, with its late breeding cycle, has disappeared as a regular breeding bird and mowing would have to be delayed to at least the end of July or even August to provide a suitable habitat. The yellow wagtail is also at risk from earlier cutting but ESA cutting dates of 8 July and 15 July have been shown to be effective in providing significant protection.

ACKNOWLEDGEMENT

Yellow wagtail data were collected as part of a MAFF funded programme of environmental monitoring.

REFERENCES

GREEN R. and WILLIAMS G. (1994) The ecology of the Corncrake (*Crex crex*) and action for its conservation in Britain and Ireland. In: E. Bignal and D. J. Curtis (eds.) *Third European Forum on Birds and Pastoralism.*

SMITH S. (1950) *The Yellow Wagtail.* Collins:London.

STOWE T. J., NEWTON A. V, GREEN R. E. and MAYES E. (1993). The decline of the Corncrake (*Crex crex*) in Britain and Ireland in relation to habitat. *Journal of Applied Ecology*, **30**, 53-62.

MARCHANT J. H., HUDSON R., CARTER S. P. and WHITTINGTON P. (1990) *Population Trends in British Breeding Birds.* British Trust for Ornithology:Tring.

MAYES E. and STOWE T. J., (1989) The status and distribution of the Corncrake in Ireland in 1988. *Irish Birds*, **4**, 1-12.

Environmental Effects on Chemistry and Nutritive Value of *Lotus corniculatus* (Birdsfoot-trefoil)

EUNICE CARTER, P. MORRIS AND M. K. THEODOROU

IGER, Aberystwyth, Dyfed, SY24 5BZ

INTRODUCTION

The effect of changes in environmental levels of temperature, carbon dioxide and water on concentrations of plant compounds which are nutritionally detrimental to ruminants is presently being investigated. These compounds include carbon-based condensed tannins which are nutritionally beneficial to ruminants at low concentrations but detrimental in higher concentrations (McLeod, 1974; Barry, 1989) and which are found in many forage species (Bate-Smith, 1973; Jones *et al.*, 1976). Previous experiments have shown a negative relationship (r^2=0.66) between *Lotus corniculatus* leaf condensed tannin and *in-vitro* dry matter degradation (IVDMD). No relationship was found between stem tannin and degradation. The effect of growth temperature has also been investigated on *Lotus* growth, tannin content (Carter and Morris, 1994) and nutritive value. Growth rate was greatest at 25°C and declined above and below this temperature. As growth rate fell, tannin concentration increased with peak levels in plants grown at 15°C. Again a negative relationship was observed between tannin concentration and IVDMD. No studies have been published on the effects of changes associated with global warming on secondary metabolism, although theoretical considerations on the effects of rising CO_2 on secondary plant metabolism in relation to C-partitioning and plant C/N balance were outlined by Lambers (1993). Preliminary results from an environmental study for condensed tannin concentrations, nutritive value and chemical composition are presented.

MATERIALS AND METHODS

Three *Lotus* genotype clones (s33, s41, s50, Leo cultivar) were grown and monitored in eight controlled environments and harvested at full flowering. These were combinations of the above three environmental variables each at two levels; 18/8°C or 25/15°C, ambient CO_2 or 700ppm CO_2 and, ad-libitum or 60% of water requirements. Aspects of plant growth, morphology and physiology were measured but will not be discussed here. Leaves, stems and roots were assayed for nutritive value by *in-vitro* microbial fermentation (Theodorou *et al.*, 1994) to measure rate of degradation during the first 8 hours of fermentation and by *in-vitro* pepsin-cellulase degradation (Jones and Hayward, 1975, modified) for end point determination. The botanical fractions were also assayed for condensed tannins (Terrill *et al.*, 1992), sugars and starch.

RESULTS AND DISCUSSION

Data is presented for the s41 genotype only, which contained relatively high tannin concentrations compared to the other two genotypes and averaged 44, 17

and 28mg/g dry mass for leaves stems and roots respectively (Figure 1). Tannin
levels were increased significantly in leaf and stem (p<0.001) by doubling CO_2.
Raising temperature towards its optimum for growth reduced tannin
concentration in all three fractions (p<0.002) whilst mild drought stressing
reduced concentrations in leaves (p<0.006) and roots (p<0.001).

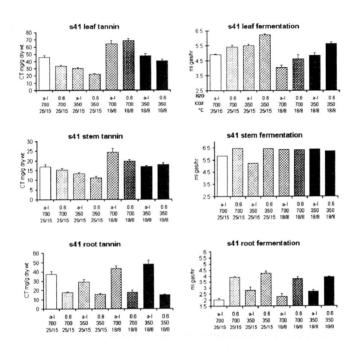

Figure 1.   The effect of environmental combinations of two levels of
temperature (25/15⁰C or 18/8⁰C for 18h light/6h dark), CO (350
orn 700ppmv) and water (ad-libitum application (a-l) or 0.6 of
plant's requirements) on condensed tannin (CT) concentration and
rate of microbial fermentation during early degradation in leaves,
stem and roots of *Lotus corniculatus*, s41 genotype.

Preliminary findings on the effect of environment on total non-structural
carbohydrate (TNC) levels is not clear cut and needs further investigation. This
may be an anomaly of *Lotus corniculatus*, which has been shown by Nelson and
Smith (1968) to express only slight seasonal and cyclic fluctuations of TNC
compared to other forage legumes. TNC contents in s41 genotype were similar
to those reported by the above investigators, averaging 72mg/g in roots and
108mg/g in leaf and stem. Doubling CO_2 increased TNC levels in s41 leaf and
stem whilst it increased levels in roots only in combination with drought stress.
Increasing growth temperature reduced both sugar and starch levels in all three

botanical fractions. High CO_2 has been reported to increase leaf starch levels (Farrar and Williams, 1991) and, in s41 leaf, starch content was more than doubled under high CO_2. Leaf starch content was reduced by mild drought stressing, in agreement with Chaves (1991) but was increased in stems and roots.

Both *in-vitro* techniques for assessing nutritive value showed the same trend between environments and botanical fractions. Fermentation rates are presented in Figure 1. A clear negative association is seen between condensed tannin content and fermentation rate in s41 leaf and root. The pattern of tannin concentration was similar in stems as in leaves but concentrations were much lower and again a poor relationship with fermentation was observed. It is more likely that stem fermentation is regulated by structural components such as lignin and hemicellulose. This may explain the two lower fermentation rates observed from plants with the greatest growth rates.

REFERENCES

BARRY T.N. (1989). Condensed tannins: Their role in ruminant protein and carbohydrate digestion and possible effects upon the rumen ecosystem. In: Nolan J.V., Leng R.A. and Demeyer R.A. (eds), *The role of protozoa and fungi in ruminant digestion'*, Penambul books.

BATE-SMITH E.C. (1973). Tannins of herbaceous leguminosae, *Phytochemistry*, 12, 1809-12.

CARTER E. and MORRIS P. (1994). The effect of temperature on polyphenol biosynthesis in *Lotus corniculatus. Journal of Experimental Botany*, 45, p49.

CHAVES M. M. (1991). Effects of water deficit on carbon assimilation. Journal of Experimental Botany, 42, 1-16.

FARRAR J. F. and WILLIAMS M. L. (1991). The effects of increased atmospheric carbon dioxide and temperature on carbon partitioning, sink-source relations and respiration. *Plant, Cell and Environment*, 14, 819-830.

JONES D.L.H. and HAYWARD M.V. (1975). The effect opf pepsin pre-treatment of herbages on the prediction of dry matter digestibility from solubility in fungal cellulase solution. *Journal of the Science of Food and Agriculture*, 26, 711-718.

JONES W.T., BROADHURST R.B. and LYTTLETON J.W. (1976). The condensed tannins of pasture legume species. *Phytochemistry*, 15, 1407-1409.

LAMBERS H. (1993). Rising CO_2, secondary plant metabolism, plant herbivore interactions and litter decomposition. *Vegetatio*, 104/105, 263-271.

NELSON C.J. and SMITH D. (1968). Growth of birdsfoot trefoil and alfalfa. 3. Changes in carbohydrate and growth analysis under field conditions. *Crop Science*, 8, 25-28.

McLEOD M.N. (1974). Plant tannins - their role in forage quality, *Nutrition Abstracts and Reviews*, 44, 803-81

TERRILL T.H., ROWAN A.M., DOUGLAS G.B. and BARRY T.W. (1992). Determination of extractable and bound condensed tannin concentrations in forage plants, protein concentration meals and cereal grains. *Journal of the Science of Food and Agriculture*, 58, 321-329.

THEODOROU M.K., WILLIAMS B. A., DHANOA M.S., M^{C}ALLAN A.B. and FRANCE J. (1994). *Animal Feed Science and Technology*, 48, 185-197.

Effects of Cattle Slurry on Grazing Performance of Dairy Cows

S. DANBY, B. F. PAIN, P. D. PENNING AND J. A. LAWS

IGER, North Wyke, Devon, EX20 2SB

INTRODUCTION

Government legislation for minimum storage period of slurry and restrictions on rate and timing of slurry applications (MAFF, 1991) may result in cattle grazing areas on which slurry has been recently spread. Short-term sward box and long-term grazing experiments were developed to examine the effects of cattle slurry on animal behaviour, herbage intake, condition score, liveweight, milk yield and quality.

MATERIALS AND METHODS

Short-term indoor experiment

Grass turves (0.25 m²), cut from a perennial ryegrass (*Lolium perenne*) dominant permanent pasture, were placed on a 20 cm deep soil base in a sward box. Two adjacent swards were placed on the ground at the apex of a v-shaped test pen and the number of bites taken by individual dairy cows on either the left (L) or right (R) sward, as well as the temporal pattern of bite selection, was recorded.

Long-term field experiments.

Five rates of slurry ranging from 0 to 47.3 m³/ha were applied to the surface of a perennial ryegrass dominant sward. Nitrogen fertiliser was applied to each plot to achieve a total of 60 kg N/ha from inorganic and organic sources. One month following application, 4 dairy cows were allocated to each treatment and strip grazed for 4 weeks. Herbage mass was assessed using a rising plate meter and the cows were offered a dry matter allowance of 34 kg DM/d/head. Milk yield and sward surface height (SSH) were monitored daily. Behaviour, condition, milk quality and live weights were recorded weekly. Intake was measured using the n-alkane technique (Dove and Mayes, 1991) for 12 days. The procedure was repeated for two further 4-week periods.

RESULTS AND DISCUSSION

Short-term indoor experiment

Results from 5 animals indicate that there was no evidence of a L/R preference (P=0.01). Laws *et al.* (1995) found the same to be true when the technique was used with beef steers. The absence of any L/R preference validates the technique for use in preference work involving slurried and clean swards.

Long-term field experiments.

Table 1.   Preliminary results from the first 4 week period.

Slurry Application rate (m³/ha)	0	11.8	23.7	35.5	47.3
SSH reduction (cm)	17.9	18.9	17.5	17.6	15.3
Mean milk Yield (litres)	26.0	26.5	29.7	26.8	27.8
Proportion of time spent grazing	0.33	0.36	0.28	0.29	0.33
Mean condition score	2.75	2.5	2.75	2.75	2.75
Mean liveweight (kg)	543.1	540.9	578.4	587.1	576.6

SSH reduction (pre-grazing SSH minus post-grazing SSH) was less at the highest application rate. Overall the proportion of time spent grazing was similar for all treatments. Digestibility analysis of herbage and intake measurements may reveal if animals were investing more time in grazing for a lower potential output. There were no signs of productivity decreasing as a result of a high slurry rate. Condition score was maintained, or improved upon, from a herd mean of 2.5 at the start of the experiment. For all measures of cattle productivity and grazing behaviour, regression analyses with the rate of slurry application were found not to differ significantly from zero (P=0.05).

CONCLUSIONS
From the first 4 weeks of the experiment, there is no evidence to suggest that there is a significant response to rate of slurry application in terms of grazing behaviour and cattle productivity.

ACKNOWLEDGEMENTS
This work was funded by the British Grassland Society.

REFERENCES
DOVE H. and MAYES R.W. (1991) The use of plant wax alkanes as marker substances in studies of the nutrition of herbivores: A review. *Australian Journal of Agricultural Research* **42**, 913-952.
LAWS J.A., ROOK, A.J., and PAIN, B.F. (1995) Diet selection by cattle offered a choice between clean or slurry contaminated swards: effects of application method and time since application. Animal Science, 60, 568.
MAFF (1991) *Code of Good Agricultural Practise for the Protection of Water.* MAFF: London.

The Effect of Extensification of Upland Pasture on White Clover

M. FOTHERGILL, D. A. DAVIES AND C. T. MORGAN

IGER, Plas Gogerddan, Aberystwyth, Dyfed SY23 3EB

INTRODUCTION

Within the European Union's Common Agricultural Policy there is a growing emphasis on reducing output from the livestock sector. One response to the ceilings imposed by quotas (sheep and beef) has been an increased interest in more extensive systems of production in which inputs are reduced in an effort to maintain economic viability. Productivity within these extensive systems relies, to a great extent, on the clover content of the swards. This paper presents information on white clover abundance from a study of the effects of withdrawing inputs to an upland permanent pasture on sward dynamics and animal output.

MATERIALS AND METHODS

An experiment was established in 1990 on 25-year old perennial ryegrass/bent dominant pasture at Bronydd Mawr Research Station. The site was at a height of 370-390 m above sea level on brown earth soil of the Milford series overlying Devonian red sandstone. Six experimental treatments were established in a complete block design replicated three times. The effects of the removal of applications of a)N, b)N, P and K and c) N, P, K and Ca were compared with a treatment receiving all four nutrients under continuous sheep grazing (sward height maintained at 4 ± 0.5 cm by regular adjustment of animal numbers). Two further treatments, of smaller plot size, were initiated at the same time to study the effect of withholding both nutrient application and grazing. One treatment (T5) was defoliated in July (simulating a hay cut), whilst the other (T6) was left completely undisturbed. Clover stolon abundance was monitored in the spring and autumn of each year by taking twenty cores of 5 cm diameter, at random, from each of the grazed plots. In the ungrazed treatments, six cores of 10 cm diameter (due to lower tiller densities coupled with larger individual plant size) were taken at random. White clover was removed from the cores allowing stolon abundance to be assessed.

RESULTS AND DISCUSSION

The initial assessment of stolon abundance took place in Spring 1991 when clover was evenly distributed throughout the area at a mean abundance of 20 m stolon/m^2 (Table 1). Although no significant differences could be detected in Autumn 1991, the clover stolon abundance did change, quite markedly, over the first growing season of the experiment. Application of 150 kg N/ha reduced stolon abundance by 54% whereas all other grazing treatments recorded increases (mean increase of 113%). Withdrawal of the grazing animal coupled with a July mechanical defoliation also recorded an increase (95% increase), whereas

171

complete lack of defoliation almost eliminated white clover from the sward (95% decrease). From Spring 1992 to Autumn 1994 significant differences were detected between the treatments and by Autumn 1994 clover abundance strongly reflected the applied managements and inputs. Under grazing, combined applications of Ca, P, K and N depressed the abundance of clover stolon as did complete lack of inputs (31 and 33 m stolon/m² respectively). Applications of Ca and Ca, P and K increased clover abundance to 45 and 117 m stolon/m² respectively. Withdrawal of grazing coupled with a simulated hay cut maintained a modest amount of clover (13 m stolon/m²) whilst, the absence of inputs and defoliation, had eliminated clover from the sward. Over Winter 1994-95, all grazing treatments lost clover with increasing percentage losses associated with increasing inputs. Thus the CaPKN and CaPK treatments lost large percentages of clover (81% and 67% respectively) whilst the 'Nil' input sward was relatively unaffected (15 % reduction). Clover increased by 100% in T5 and was still absent from T6.

Table 1. White clover stolon abundance (m/m²) 1991-95.

	1991		1992		1993		1994		1995
	Spr	Aut	Spr	Aut	Spr	Aut	Spr	Aut	Spr
1 CaPKN	24	11	11	32	38	16	26	31	6
2 CaPK	35	60	33	96	115	108	95	117	39
3 Ca	15	32	27	54	72	61	53	45	27
4 Nil	11	28	31	58	49	36	29	33	28
	16	31	3	28	23	8	10	13	26
6 Nil+Nil	18	1	4	1	0	0	0	0	0
Mean	19.8	27.2	18.2	44.8	49.5	38.2	35.5	39.8	21.0
LSD			15.01	29.3	37.91	25.86	45.44	31.81	24.39
	NS	NS	P<0.01	<0.001	<0.001	<0.001	<0.01	<0.001	<0.05

Ca - Lime 5 t/ha in 1990.
N - 150 kg N/ha; P - 25 kg P/ha ; K - 50 kg K/ha/annum.

The results indicate that semi-natural populations of clover can be encouraged to high stolon abundance, and thus productivity, by varying inputs. However, high inputs were also associated with large fluctuations in clover content and it was clearly demonstrated that the most consistent clover abundance (though not the highest) was found in the 'Nil' input swards. These data underline the importance of long-term grazing experiments. Clover declines have been reported 3-4 years after initiation of experimentation and it is only in extended studies that their real effect on pasture productivity and animal production can be assessed.

Mapping of Variation in Soil Nutrient Status within Grass Fields

M. A. FROMENT[1], S. P. PEEL[1], A. G. CHALMERS[1] AND C. J. DAWSON[2]

[1]ADAS Bridgets Research Centre, Winchester, Hampshire SO21 1AP

[2]Ox Carr Lane, Strensall, York YO3 5TD

INTRODUCTION

Soil nutrient status is known to vary significantly between fields but its variability within fields is rarely considered when making fertiliser decisions. As part of the MIDaS project, investigating the impact of dairy systems on environmental pollution, soil nutrient status was measured within a sample of permanent grass fields, providing an opportunity to quantify within-field variation in soil nitrogen and phosphorous content.

MATERIALS AND METHODS

Data is presented for soil total N and extractable P, measured in five contiguous fields in a single block of grassland (27 ha) at a depth of 0-30 cm, using a regular 50 m square grid pattern, in December 1993. A 0-30 cm sampling depth was used to ensure that the majority of soil N was included. Grassland is normally sampled to only 7.5 cm. Soil type within fields was predominantly shallow calcareous silty clay loam overlying chalk (Andover series) and swards had been managed as grazed grass with occasional cutting. The soil sample at each 'grid point' comprised four subsamples. Data for soil total N from grid points were statistically manipulated to provide a nutrient contour map, by kriging, using 'Surfer' software (Anon, 1994).

RESULTS AND DISCUSSION

There were large differences in soil total N and P within fields (Table 1). A contour map demonstrating the variation in total N is shown in Figure 1. Soil N and P status was highest in Indiana, the oldest sward. There was greater variation in soil P than total N within fields. Soil P levels in some localised areas were high. Some of the within-field differences may be explained by cow behaviour, as the highest levels of N and P were on the leeward side of a small wood. Indiana and Virginia North are closer to the main dairy complex and, historically, are likely to have been more intensively grazed than more distant fields.

Table 1.   Total soil N (%) and extractable P (mg/l), 0-30 cm sampling depth.

Field name	Indiana		Virginia North		Virginia South		Tennessee North		Tennessee South	
Nutrient	N	P	N	P	N	P	N	P	N	P
Mean	0.37	23.3	0.35	17.9	0.30	8.3	0.33	17.5	0.29	13.0
Minimum	0.15	6.0	0.21	5.0	0.14	4.0	0.20	8.0	0.24	7.0
Maximum	0.54	104.0	0.49	104.0	0.37	21.0	0.40	30.0	0.33	34.0
s.d.	0.09	22.6	0.07	23.0	0.05	3.7	0.05	6.9	0.03	7.0
Year sown	1967		1979		1979		1973		1973	
Area (ha)	6.9		4.7		5.4		4.2		6.0	
No. grid pts.	28		21		23		15		24	

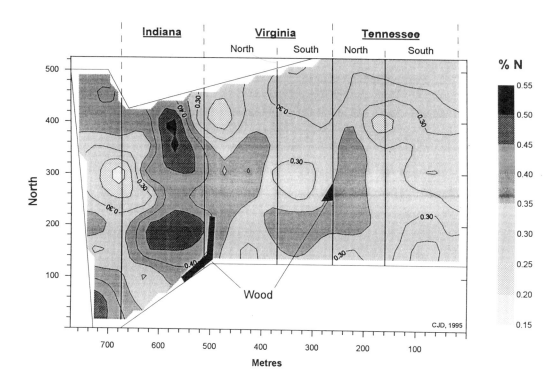

Figure 1.   Field map showing variation in soil total N (%) derived by kriging grid point data. N% scale shown on right scale

CONCLUSIONS

The results from this study clearly demonstrate that large within-field variation in soil N and P can occur in grassland fields. This is likely to be due to variation in soil type or depth, non-uniform distribution of dung and urine and/or differential application of fertilisers and manures. Grid soil sampling techniques may be useful in identifying this variation, and varying fertiliser application within fields offers the prospect of reduced environmental pollution and more efficient use of nutrients. Developments of mapping systems in arable crops are progressing rapidly and fertiliser application maps for P and K, based on soil nutrient maps derived from grid soil sampling, are being used commercially. The methodologies applied to obtain reliable nutrient maps in grassland are, however, unproved and the economic and environmental implications have not yet been determined. However, based on the results obtained here, they could be large.

ACKNOWLEDGMENTS

The MIDaS project is funded through LINK by: ADAS, BOCM Pauls, Borregaard Ligno Tech, Hydro Agri, Linbury Trust, Livestock Systems, the MGA, MAFF, Trident Feeds and Wessex Water.

REFERENCES

ANON. (1994) Surfer. *Contouring and 3D surface mapping, user's guide.* Golden Software Inc., Colorado, USA.

Grass Silage Effluent Production in England 1984-1994

P. M. HAIGH
ADAS, Pwllpeiran, Cwmystwyth,
Aberystwyth SY23 4AB

The amount of silage produced in England (MAFF, 1984-94) has increased by 136% from 20.2 million tonnes in 1984 to 27.4 million tonnes in 1994. Similarly, the proportion made as big bales has increased from 7% of that made in 1984 to 18% of that made in 1994. The average DM content of first and second cut bunker-made silages was about 247 and 262 g/kg respectively, and that of big bale silages 361 g/kg. However, there were large between-year variations in DM content, depending upon the prevailing weather conditions at ensilage. In wet years, i.e. 1987, mean DM contents were 236, 235 and 343 g/kg, whilst in the dry year of 1989 they were 261, 297 and 371 g/kg respectively, for first- and second-cut bunker-made and big-bale silages.

The amount of silage effluent produced each year, calculated from the equation of Bastiman (1976) using the proportion of effluent produced at various ranges of DM, i.e. <150, 150-170 to >270 g/kg, was highly variable. In the wet summer of 1987 it was about 1730 million litres and in the dry summer of 1989 only 670 million litres. In wet years, i.e. 1987, silage additives containing acid were used on 25% of the silage made, but, because they increase effluent production and were mainly used on lower DM silages (mean DM 202 g/kg), silages made with acid additives were responsible for about 33% of the effluent produced. Conversely, in 1989 only 6% of silages were treated but, because they were mainly used on low DM silages (mean DM 220 g/kg), they accounted for 11% of the effluent produced. From 1984-1994 the proportion of silages made as first- or second-cut bunker and big bale silage was 56.5, 28.3 and 15.2% respectively; whilst they were responsible for 68.7, 27.1 and 4.2% of the effluent produced.

Effluent was mainly produced in the wetter, western areas, with the South-West Region responsible for 31% of the silage made and 35% of the effluent produced, whilst the Eastern Region was responsible for 6% of the silage made but only 4% of the effluent produced.

ACKNOWLEDGEMENTS
This work was funded by the Environmental Protection Division (UK), MAFF.

REFERENCES
BASTIMAN B. (1976) Factors affecting silage effluent production. *Experimental Husbandry*, **31**, 40-60.
MAFF (1984-94) Survey of Agriculture, December returns for England. York: MAFF Statistics.

Effect of Changes in Assimilate Abundance on Growth and Utilization of Substrates in Cereal Leaves.

J. HARRISON AND C. J. POLLOCK
Institute of Grassland and Environmental Research,
Aberystwyth, Dyfed, SY23 3EB.

INTRODUCTION

The predicted climatic changes associated with increases in greenhouse gas emissions, namely increases in atmospheric CO_2 concentration and mean global temperature, will affect plant metabolism directly via changes in both photosynthesis and assimilate abundance. For autumn-sown cereals the changes that occur over winter, where small changes in temperature will produce large changes in growth rates, will be crucial for their subsequent survival and productivity.

The basal extension zone in cereal leaves is thought to be the site of temperature perception and transduction and it is known that large fluxes of assimilates into this zone are required to sustain growth. Fluxes of assimilates within the extending zone have been determined by the use of the continuity equation, which relates growth and assimilate supply, to determine net deposition of substrates along the extending tissue. This, along with data on respiratory costs, can be used to relate changes in assimilate supply to growth and assimilate utilization and information from these studies will then help us to predict overwintering cereal survival and productivity under climate change scenarios.

MATERIALS AND METHODS

Data on fluxes of assimilates have been collected from both normal and mutant (*slender*) barley (*Hordeum vulgare* Cb 3014) under a variety of environmental perturbations, including enhanced CO_2, low irradiance/short photoperiod and reduced temperature. The use of the *slender* mutation of barley, with a lower temperature threshold for growth, allows the separation of the effects of temperature on growth from those on assimilate supply. Plants have been grown in controlled environment cabinets, in hydroponics and supplied regularly with Long Ashton nutrient solution. Standard conditions were such that plants were grown in a 16 h photoperiod, 380 μmol/m/s photon flux density, 20°C and ambient CO_2 levels (350 ppm). Low irradiance/short photoperiod conditions consisted of 280 μmol/m/s photon flux density and 8 h photoperiod. Low temperature treatments were imposed by growing plants with roots and meristems cooled to 5°C, and enhanced CO_2 by increasing levels from ambient to 750 ppm.

RESULTS

Leaf growth has been shown to be sensitive to temperature, photoperiod and CO_2. The duration of second-leaf growth was 16 days under standard conditions which was extended to 32 days under the cold treatment, and shortened by 1 day under both enhanced CO_2 and low irradiance/short photoperiod. Both total leaf length and leaf elongation zone length of the second leaf was characteristically greater in *slender* than in normal barley for all treatments. Low temperature treatment reduced both final leaf length and leaf elongation zone length, although, as expected, *slender* was less sensitive than normal. Lowering the irradiance and shortening the photoperiod had no significant effect on final leaf length or elongation zone length, whereas enhanced CO_2 shortened leaf length.

Total carbohydrate content of the elongation zone, was similar between both normal and *slender*, relatively constant along the elongation zone and was increased in both normal and *slender* barley on cooling, primarily due to an increase in the fructan content. Low irradiance/short photoperiod reduced carbohydrate content of the elongation zone, whilst initial results indicate increased carbohydrate content under enhanced CO_2 conditions. Distribution of the predominant carbohydrates (namely glucose, fructose, sucrose and fructans) were found to vary considerably along the elongation zone. Glucose concentration increased from the base of the elongation zone towards the mature tissue, fructose remained constant at a low concentration, whilst sucrose concentration decreased from the base to the mature tissue. Results so far indicate that, although total carbohydrate content varies according to treatment, there is little variation in pattern of individual carbohydrates. Respiratory costs were slightly higher in *slender* compared to normal and in both types there was a decrease in respiration from the basal meristem through the elongation zone to the mature tissue. Cold treatment enhanced respiration, whist initial results from other treatments reveal little change compared to those of the standard conditions.

CONCLUSIONS

Net deposition of substrates along the elongation zone appears at present to be unaffected by the changes in substrate concentration along the elongation zone, indicating that the elongation zone appears to be well able to adapt to changes in environmental conditions. Studies are now in progress to determine how combining low temperature, low irradiance/short photoperiod and enhanced CO_2, a probable scenario for autumn-sown cereals under predicted climatic changes, is likely to alter the fluxes of assimilates along the elongation zone.

Restoration of Botanical Diversity of Grassland in ESAs by Different Methods of Seed and Plant Introduction

A. HOPKINS, P. J. BOWLING, R. H. JOHNSON, R. PYWELL[1] AND S. PEEL[2]

IGER, North Wyke, Okehampton, Devon, EX20 2SB

[1]ITE, Monks Wood, Abbots Ripton, Huntingdon, PE17 2LS

[2]ADAS Bridgets, Winchester, SO21 1AP

INTRODUCTION

The Environmentally Sensitive Areas (ESA) scheme operates through agreements and incentives to encourage practices that benefit nature and the landscape. Restoring botanical diversity can be very slow, particularly on fertile sites and where desired species are no longer present in the soil seed-bank or immediate vicinity, and extensification of the management alone may be insufficient to achieve the ESA objectives within an acceptable time. Techniques to re-introduce appropriate species of the native flora into existing grassland and former arable land are therefore being investigated. The aim is to derive practical, cost-effective management guidelines for converting agriculturally improved grassland and surplus arable land to species-rich grassland. Appropriate communities of the British National Vegetation Classification define the target end-point.

METHODS

Trials plots were established in 1994 on 12 sites in ESAs in England and Wales, six on existing permanent grassland and six on former arable sites. Common features include introduction of propagules and management to control competitive species and provide high seed return (hay cutting in July, winter grazing with sheep, and no fertilizers). Treatments on the permanent grassland sites include introduction of a species-rich grass/forb seed mixture (c. 40 species) by strip-seeding or by broadcast-sowing following disturbance by either light harrowing, partial rotavation or turf removal. On a fifth treatment wild flower plug plants (12 species per site) were planted in spaced patches. The undisturbed sward represents a control.

Treatments on the ex-arable sites include natural regeneration (the control), and sowing with either a species-rich grass/forb mixture or an 'ESA mixture' of the type in use for arable reversion in the respective ESA (typically five grass species, *Lolium* and *Trifolium* spp. were not included). For each mixture contrasting cultivation methods (deep ploughing and shallow cultivation) were imposed before establishment. Assessments include changes in botanical composition and soil nutrient status, and herbage production at the hay-cut stage.

RESULTS

On the grassland sites early seedling emergence was most apparent on the de-turfed and strip-seeded treatments. Winter survival of the transplanted plug

Table 1. Permanent grassland sites: numbers of grasses and other monocot. species (bold) and forbs (italic) recorded in control plots and sown treatments in post-establishment phase.

	Control		Strip-seeded		Harrowed		Rotovated		Turf removed	
Bl'down Hills	**10**	*8*	**11**	*16*	**12**	*5*	**9**	*16*	**12**	*22*
Somerset L'v's	**12**	*10*	**12**	*12*	**10**	*9*	**11**	*14*	**16**	*17*
Radnor Forest	**15**	*16*	**17**	*23*	**17**	*25*	**17**	*27*	**15**	*32*
Pennine Dales	**10**	*10*	**11**	*17*	**12**	*10*	**14**	*21*	**14**	*23*
South Downs	**8**	*7*	**9**	*19*	**10**	*12*	**9**	*15*	**12**	*28*
S. Wessex Downs	**6**	*8*	**9**	*14*	**7**	*7*	**11**	*10*	**12**	*25*

Table 2. Former arable sites: grasses (bold) and forbs (italic) recorded in plots of different treatments in post-establishment phase.

	Natural reversion		Deep ploughed				Shallow cultivated			
			(a)		(b)		(a)		(b)	
Norfolk Broads	**8**	*9*	**17**	*28*	**16**	*18*	**19**	*24*	**17**	*12*
South Downs	**10**	*11*	**14**	*28*	**9**	*13*	**16**	*26*	**11**	*5*
S. Wessex D'ns	**3**	*14*	**12**	*23*	**11**	*21*	**13**	*29*	**14**	*18*
Suffolk Valleys	**15**	*16*	**19**	*22*	**17**	*11*	**20**	*23*	**15**	*11*
Up'r Thames 1	**13**	*14*	**19**	*22*	**18**	*12*	**22**	*19*	**17**	*11*
Up'r Thames 2	**8**	*6*	**14**	*32*	**10**	*14*	**15**	*22*	**12**	*12*

(a) Sown to species-rich grass/forb mixture.
(b) Sown to typical ESA mixture (mainly wild grasses).

plants was assessed in early spring 1995, and the introduced species were recorded in over 80% of planted patches. The highest survival rate was for *Achillea millefolium*, *Plantago lanceolata* and *Primula veris*. Differences in species numbers between treatments were assessed in June 1995 (Table 1). More severe disturbance resulted in establishment of a greater number of species, and turf-removal had the greatest effect on increasing the establishment of sown forbs. On the ex-arable sites (Table 2) all sown treatments, including the 'ESA mixture', resulted in increased numbers of forbs relative to the control plots. However, plots sown with the species-rich mixture had between 10 and 25 more species than on 'ESA mixture' plots, depending on the site. Cultivation method had no consistent effect on species establishment in the early phase. On both the ex-arable and permanent grassland sites a high proportion of sown forbs had not established within the first year.

Technology For The Future - Nitrogen Value of Slurry and Its Effect on First Cut Silage

H. C. HUGHES
Blackmoss Farm, Blackmoss Road, Dunham Massey,
Altrincham, Cheshire, WA14 5RG

LAYOUT AND METHOD

The Cheshire Grassland Society R & D Group decided to continue building on the work undertaken during 1993 and to look in more detail at the use of farm slurry on first-cut silage. A range of trials were undertaken as follows:-

Farmer trial sites

Three farms were used to make single field/single cut comparisons between slurry applied with 90 kg/ha and 125 kg/ha of artificial fertiliser N.

Replicated trial sites

Two controlled sites of 36 plots/site were used for more detailed comparisons. Site 1 was on the farm of R. Ratcliffe, Hill Farm, Sound; whilst Site 2 was at Reaseheath College, Nantwich. The layout and operation of the trials were professionally undertaken, on behalf of the R & D group, by Derek Mitchell of North West Agronomy. Three slurry treatments were applied at each site; no slurry, slurry in December and slurry in both December and January. In addition, artificial fertiliser was applied at 0, 50, 100 and 125 kg/ha across each of the three slurry treatments. The two sites were soil tested before trialling and the slurry was analysed before application. The first cut of silage was taken at Hill Farm on 18th May and at Reaseheath on 31st May.

TRIAL RESULTS
Farmer Trials

Table 1.   Grass dry-matter yield from three farms applying slurry with two rates of fertiliser N application (t DM/ha).

	Cutting date	90 kg N/ha +slurry	125 kg N/ha + slurry	Soil type
Farmer 1	24th May	4.85	5.12	Heavy
Farmer 2	12th May	3.94	5.00	Light
Farmer 3	16th May	5.44	6.00	Medium

Table 1 shows the dry-matter yield as t DM/ha from one cut only. These farms varied in both cutting date and soil type. Both D value and CP% declined as cutting became later. The decline in D value was from 74 to 71%.

Replicated Trial Plots
The slurry analysis is shown in Table 2.

Table 2.   The N, P and K levels found in the slurry by time of application (kg/4500 l).

	December	January
Nitrogen	42.4	33.4
Phosphate	19.5	16.1
Potash	48.1	37.4

Available N per 6800 litres of slurry was found to be 9.4 kg in December and 11.25 kg in January-applied slurry.

Table 3.   Grass production from the three slurry treatments at Reaseheath applied with four fertiliser levels (t DM/ha).

		N Level (kg/ha)		
Slurry treatment	0	50	100	125
No Slurry	4.89	5.89	6.14	7.94
16825 l/ha in December	5.15	7.19	7.59	8.33
16825 l/ha in Dec and Jan	5.36	7.25	10.13	7.10

Grass Quality First-cut silage contained 10.7 MJ/kg DM with D-values ranging from 64.3 to 67.3. Crude protein increased with increasing N application from 0 to 100 kg/ha; first-cut silage increasing from 10.9% to 17.8% and second cut from 10.9% to 13.1%.

CONCLUSION
Farmer trials
The nitrogen benefit from slurry applications seen in 1993 was repeated in 1994. The importance of knowing the slurry quality, by analysis, and the quantity applied was highlighted. Approximately 40 kg per ha of nitrogen, worth £10-63/ha, could be saved by the careful use of farm slurry.

Replicated trial plots
One hundred kg/ha of nitrogen, together with the December and January slurry applications, gave the highest yield. A treatment using 125 kg of nitrogen appeared to produce a negative response, compared to 100 kg/ha. January application of slurry was important in 1994 as it started the grass plant growing early after the wet winter. There was little difference in grass quality between the various treatments and applications of slurry had no affect on the population of adverse bacteria nor grass silage quality. There was a considerable amount of phosphate and potash available; sufficient to grow a good crop. However, sufficient slurry storage capacity is required in order to exploit the late winter spreading window of opportunity.

An Evaluation of Farm Woodlands as Nitrate Buffers in Intensively Managed Grassland

N. J. MACEY[1], D. SCHOLEFIELD[2] AND B. W. WEBB[1]

[1]Department of Geography, University of Exeter, Rennes Drive,
Exeter, EX4 4RJ

[2]IGER, North Wyke, Okehampton, Devon, EX20 2SB

INTRODUCTION

One cause of increasing economic and environmental concern is the inefficiency with which nitrogen is used in intensively managed systems of livestock production. Of particular concern in the UK is the leaching of nitrate into watercourses, and the need to limit peak concentrations to 50 mg/l as specified by the EC Nitrate Directive. Research conducted in the USA and Germany has indicated that riparian woodlands can be effective in reducing nitrate concentrations in rivers receiving drainage from agricultural land. Such woodlands may easily be by-passed, however, because much of the leached nitrate could enter the river via drainage channels, ditches and streams. The research presented in this paper examines whether a more effective nitrate buffer would be provided by farm woodlands located downslope from each intensively managed field.

MATERIALS AND METHODS

Experiments were conducted on three scales.

(i)   On dairy farms in south-west England, where, during the drainage periods of 1993-94 and 1994-95, soil nitrate concentrations were measured along transects leading from downslope field boundaries into established broad-leaf woodland.

(ii)   With replicated hydrologically isolated plots planted with willow, poplar and a grass sward, in which applied pulses of nitrate were tracked by sampling runoff and soil solution at various plot locations downslope of a source area.

(iii)   At an intermediate scale at which pulses of applied nitrate were tracked as in (ii) through a hydrologically characterized plot containing mature willows.

In (ii) steady-state runoff conditions were established at various times of the year in order to investigate the buffering potential of trees relative to grass; in autumn at the onset of drainage; in spring coincident with the first application of fertilizer N; and in midsummer when the soil may be temporarily returned to field capacity by a storm. Denitrification was measured in (ii) during the summer. Also, ^{15}N-labelled nitrate was used in an attempt to determine the fractions of the applied N in different components of biomass. The results of the N tracking and hydrological monitoring made at the plot scale were used to interpret the results obtained from the farm sites.

RESULTS
On the hydrologically isolated plots planted with willow, poplar, and ryegrass, 75 kg N/ha nitrate pulses applied in late autumn and spring have been buffered within 15 m, although no significant differences between the treatments were measured. This may have been due to the small biomass of both tree crops. A 100 kg N/ha nitrate pulse was applied on similar occasions to those of (ii) above at the intermediate scale. The mature willow crop used had been uncoppiced for 12 years. The late-autumn experiment exhibited significant preferential flow through the plot, resulting in poor buffering capacity at this time of year. Denitrification measured on (ii) during the summer of 1994 showed mean rates of 0.0065 - 0.6233 kg N/ha/d. However, there were no significant differences between treatments, possibly due again to the immature status of the trees. The differences observed were probably the result of soil heterogeneity across the replicates. ^{15}N- labelled nitrate was applied to willow and ryegrass microplots in June 1995. The results of this biomass uptake study were unavailable at the time of going to press.

At the field scale, woodlands have exhibited gradients of declining NO_3-N concentrations with distance downslope of intensively managed pastures. The steepness of the gradients varied with season and site characteristics. Peak NO_3-N concentrations have occasionally exceeded EC nitrate limits for drinking water at the onset of drainage, but have always declined to safe levels within 20 m of woodland buffering, during the period of study. Further work on this and the other scales was conducted until October 1995.

Early results indicate trees have potential to act as nitrate sinks where preferential flow does not create a rapid by-pass situation. The results of the ^{15}N tracer experiment should indicate the magnitude of this potential under optimum conditions for N uptake by the trees.

Viability of *Cryptosporidium parvum* during Ensilage

R. J. MERRY, J. L. MAWDSLEY, A. E. BROOKS AND D. R. DAVIES

IGER, Aberystwyth, Dyfed, SY23 3EB

INTRODUCTION

Cryptosporidium parvum is a protozoan parasite which has steadily gained recognition in recent years as a pathogen of both farm livestock and man. In cattle and sheep the infection, cryptosporidiosis, and its associated clinical effects such as diarrhoea, is almost exclusive to young animals. Consequently, peaks of disease outbreak occur around lambing and calving times (Mawdsley *et al.*, 1995a). Infection with *Cryptosporidium* occurs following ingestion of transmissive oocysts which are excreted in large numbers in the faeces of infected animals (Smith, 1992). It is clear that wastes from infected animals (calves, lambs) are a reservoir of infection and returning wastes to land either directly, by animal deposition, or indirectly, by spreading, is possibly a link in the cycle of infection of both animals and humans (Mawdsley *et al.*, 1995a). Thus, if herbage is contaminated with oocysts, *via* residues of livestock waste or by disturbance of infected soil during harvesting, they may enter the silo. The aim of this study was to determine whether oocysts of *Cryptosporidium parvum* retained viability during ensilage under conditions likely to be encountered in farm practice, so that the potential for their contamination of silage and dispersal to the environment could be evaluated.

METHODS

Chopped perennial ryegrass (*Lolium perenne* cv. Aberelan) was treated by spraying with oocysts of *Cryptosporidium parvum* (inoculation rate of 5.9×10^4/g FM) and ensiled (approximately 100 g amounts) in test tube silos. The potential fermentation rate was manipulated by either ensiling the grass untreated (slow fermentation), or after inoculation (10^6/g FM) with a strain of *Lactobacillus plantarum* (rapid, controlled fermentation), or after direct acidification with formic acid (3 l/t). Silos were sampled at intervals during the fermentation and the pH values and lactic acid concentrations determined as described by Merry *et al.* (1995). Oocysts were extracted from the silages and their total numbers determined as described by Mawdsley *et al.* (1995b). Oocyst viability was estimated by labelling with monoclonal antibodies coupled with a differential dye inclusion technique (Campbell *et al.*, 1992).

RESULTS

The pH of the untreated herbage had only fallen to 6.1 by Day 1, compared to 4.7 and 4.1 respectively in acid and inoculant treated herbages. In all herbages total numbers of oocysts had not declined markedly (4.5×10^4/g FM) by this

187

time. However, oocyst viability differed at 82.6, 69.0 and 57.6 % respectively for untreated, acid and inoculant treated herbages. By Day 14 pH values were all below 4.6 with the inoculant treated silage at 4.0. At this sampling time lowest oocyst numbers were detected in the acid treated silage (9.5×10^3/g FM), but in all silages oocyst viability had decreased to approximately 50 %.

DISCUSSION AND CONCLUSIONS

The results suggest that although the ensiling process may reduce numbers of *Cryptosporidium* oocysts, some can remain viable at low pH for at least two weeks during a period when effluent may escape from the silo which, if not contained, may pose an environmental hazard. Little is known about oocyst survival in silage effluent, which is stored and often disposed of by spraying onto the land. However, exposure to low pH in the silo for up to three months or more, the usual minimum storage period for silage, may cause further losses in viability before silages are eventually fed to livestock.

ACKNOWLEDGEMENT
This work was funded by the Ministry of Agriculture Fisheries and Food.

REFERENCES
CAMPBELL A.T., ROBERTSON L.J. and SMITH H.V. (1992) Viability of *Cryptosporidium parvum* oocysts: correlation of *in vitro* excystation with inclusion or exclusion of fluorogenic vital dyes. *Applied and Environmental Microbiology*, *58*, 3488 -3493.

MAWDSLEY J.L., BARDGETT R.D., MERRY R.J., PAIN B.F. and THEODOROU M.K. (1995a) Pathogens in livestock waste, their potential for movement through soil and environmental pollution. *Applied Soil Ecology*, *2*, 1-15.

MAWDSLEY J.L., BROOKS A.E. and MERRY R.J. (1995b) Movement of the Protozoan pathogen *Cryptosporidium parvum* through three contrasting soil types. *Biology and Fertility of Soils*, (In Press).

MERRY R.J., DHANOA M.S. and THEODOROU, M.K. (1995) The use of freshly cultured lactic acid bacteria as silage inoculants. *Grass and Forage Science*, *50*, 112-123.

SMITH H.V. (1992) *Cryptosporidium* and water: A review. *Journal of the Institute of Water Management*, 1992, 443-451.

Prediction of Methane Production by Sheep from Grass Silage Diets Supplemented with a Range of Concentrates

ANGELA R. MOSS AND D.I. GIVENS

Feed Evaluation Unit, ADAS Dairy Research Centre,
Drayton, Alcester Road, Stratford upon Avon, CV37 9RQ

INTRODUCTION

Methane production by ruminant animals is an important anthropogenic source of methane to the atmosphere and is considered an important source to be estimated more accurately and to control. Large variations in methane production by ruminants have been reported. However, very few of these data were obtained using contemporary diets used in the UK, i.e. grass silage-based diets and were also mostly limited to sheep fed at maintenance (M). This has limited the understanding of the dietary factors which may be used to predict methane production. Attempts to predict methane production from either diet chemical composition or digestibility have not been successful (Moss and Givens, 1990; Johnson *et al.*, 1991). Accordingly, a range of concentrates were used to supplement grass silage at different rates (forage:concentrate, F:C ratios) and at differing planes of nutrition, in order to study the effects of diet composition on methane production.

MATERIALS AND METHODS

Grass silage was fed with different concentrates (barley, soya bean meal, fish meal, molassed sugar beet feed, distillers dark grains, distillers light grains and maize gluten feed) to mature wether sheep at varying F:C ratios at either sub-M, near to M or 1.5 x M. All diets within plane of nutrition and concentrate type were designed to be isoenergetic, and all animals received a mineral/vitamin supplement and had free access to water. Each diet combination was fed for 28 d, with rumen fluid sampling on Day 12 for volatile fatty acid (VFA) analysis. Apparent digestibility of organic matter was measured, and the methane produced was measured in open-circuit respiration chambers for four consecutive 24 h periods. The diets were fully characterised chemically.

RESULTS AND DISCUSSION

Methane production per animal varied from 18 to 60 l/d (mean = 36.7, SE = 9.71) and the organic matter digestibility of the diets ranged from 0.64 to 0.91 (mean = 0.79, SE = 0.065). Methane production (Y, l/d) was significantly related to dry matter intake (X, g/d) : $Y = 0.0353X$, (SEP = 5.84, R^2 = 63.8%), it was also significantly related to organic matter apparently digested (X, g/d) : $Y = 0.0489X$ (SEP = 5.07, R^2 = 86.3%). The latter relationship gives a significantly improved fit, although there is still substantial variation not accounted for within diets with varying F:C ratio. Methane production (Y, l/d) was also significantly related to the combination of dry matter intake (X_1, g/d) and the molar proportion of rumen butyric acid (X_2) : Y = -25.3 + 0.0349X_1 + 226X_2 (SEP = 3.53, R^2 = 86.8%). With the exception of dry matter intake the aforementioned relationships are not readily determined and are therefore of limited practical use, but may aid the understanding of methanogenesis. Methane production (Y_1, l/d) for this population of diets was also related to the combination of forage DM intake (X_1, g/d), concentrate DM intake (X_2, g/d) and the diet oil content (X_3, g/kg DM) : Y = 14.4 + 0.0343X_1 + 0.0352X_2 - 3.24X_3 (SEP = 4.91, R^2 = 74.4%). This relationship is similar to that reported (Honing *et al.*, 1994) for dairy cows (different intercepts) and is of more practical use, although the population needs to be expanded to include additional fat-rich diets.

CONCLUSION

It is concluded that methane production from sheep may be predicted, for the purposes of a methane inventory, using readily determined parameters. The study also confirms the complexity of changing diet on methanogenesis and that this is not readily explained by diet chemical composition nor rumen parameters.

ACKNOWLEDGEMENTS

We wish to acknowledge the funding for this work from MAFF.

REFERENCES

HONING Y. van der, VUUREN A.M. van and CATE R.H. ten (1994) Measurements of methane release by productive dairy cows on various rations and evaluation of factors involved. *45th Annual Meeting EAAP, Edinburgh.* 5-8 September 1994.
JOHNSON D.E., HILL T.M., CARMEAN B.R., BRANINE M.E., LODMAN D.W. and WARD G.M. (1991) New perspectives on ruminant methane emissions. *12th Symposium on Energy Metabolism of Farm Animals,* Kartause, Ittingen.
MOSS A.R. and GIVENS D.I. (1990) Effect of food type on methane produced by sheep. *Animal Production,* **50,** 552 (Abstract).

The Effect of Elevated CO_2 under Field Conditions on Starch Metabolism in White Clover Stolons

[1]L. B. TURNER, [1]J. A. GALLAGHER, [1]C. J. POLLOCK,
[2]M. FREHNER AND [3]G. HENDREY
[1]IGER, Aberystwyth, Dyfed
[2]Swiss Federal Institute of Technology,ETH-Zentrum, Zurich, Switzerland
[3]Brookhaven National Laboratory, Upton, New York, USA

INTRODUCTION

Climate change models predict substantial increases in atmospheric carbon dioxide concentration over the next fifty years. Elevated CO_2 will affect plant metabolism directly *via* photosynthesis and assimilate abundance and indirectly by greenhouse forcing. Perennial crops like white clover (*Trifolium repens* L.) often show high sensitivity to environment during overwintering. The winter survival of white clover is associated with the deposition of starch reserves in autumn, and their utilization during winter and spring. In the laboratory it is possible to produce white clover stolon material showing different patterns of starch metabolism, and to study starch accumulation and starch degradation in different environments. However, it is difficult to assess whether the effects of elevated CO_2 in controlled environments are a real reflection of the consequences of this component of climate change. Therefore, samples from field experiments have been analysed. Some samples came from open-topped chambers at IGER, North Wyke, but the main experiment is under realistic field conditions in the F̲ree A̲ir C̲arbon Dioxide E̲nrichment (*FACE*) rings at the ETH-Eschikon Experimental Station near Zurich. These rings provide good temporal and spatial control of CO_2 concentration in an environment otherwise unchanged from field conditions. There are three replicate rings: the controls have ambient CO_2 concentration (350 ppm) and the high CO_2 rings are fumigated to 600 ppm.

THE EXPERIMENTS

Cloned stolon tip cuttings of Menna were planted in April 1994. Plant establishment was good: a similar number of plants survived per plot in control and fumigated rings (Table 1). By mid-July there was nearly complete cover. In mid-October the plots were defoliated for the winter. The dry matter (leaf and petiole) removed from a 40 x 50 cm sub-plot during this defoliation was 45% greater for fumigated rings but this was not significant (Table 1). There may have been insufficient sink demand for prolonged stimulation of carbon fixation as these plots were cut only infrequently during the summer. The greatest stimulation of clover growth by high CO_2 has been observed in the dry matter removed by regular harvesting. There was little canopy to remove when the plots were cut in March 1995 after overwintering. Fumigated plots again yielded more

191

dry matter but again this was not significant (Table 1).

At both these harvests, stolon material was collected and transported to Aberystwyth for detailed analysis of starch and soluble sugar content. Older stolon sections (internodes 4-6) are the major site of storage for starch. In October these sections had a high starch content, and CO_2 fumigation had increased starch and non-reducing sugars although not significantly (Table 2). By March, as spring growth began, the major part of these starch reserves had been utilised.

Table 1.   Plant establishment and growth. Survival out of 25 through the establishment phase, and dry matter yield (g/m^2) at October and March harvests for white clover plants grown in control and high CO_2 fumigated *FACE* rings. (n=3)

	Control	Fumigated	se	
Establishment	20	22	3	NS
Autumn DM	95.3	138.1	13.1	NS
Spring DM	11.7	15.0	7.9	NS

Table 2.   Stolon carbohydrates. Reducing (R), non-reducing (NR) sugars and starch content (mg/g dw) of older (internodes 4-6) stolon sections in autumn and spring harvested from white clover grown in control and high CO_2 fumigated *FACE* rings. (n=3)

| | Autumn | | Spring | | |
	Control	Fumigated	Control	Fumigated	se
Starch	234.8	260.0	5.0	5.0	11.1
NR	99.4	109.7	125.8	151.9	10.9
R	14.7	12.8	61.9	72.4	5.9

High CO_2 and control plants now had the same stolon starch content. Soluble sugar content of stolons was higher in spring than in autumn, but there were no significant effects of fumigation (Table 2). Overall high CO_2 had few effects. In contrast, preliminary results for samples from weekly-cut clover plots in open-topped chambers during active growth in early summer suggest that elevated CO_2 may significantly reduce the deposition of starch reserves in stolons. Dry-matter production was increased by high CO_2 in this experiment. The sink demand that drives stimulation of photosynthesis under these conditions may also have shifted carbon allocation toward growth rather than storage.

The Contribution of Winter Cover Crops to the Sustainability of Agricultural Systems

CHRISTINE WATSON AND D. YOUNIE

SAC, 581 King Street, Aberdeen, AB9 1UD

INTRODUCTION

The sustainability of agricultural systems is largely determined by their ability to supply and conserve nutrients. Nitrogen is readily lost from the plant soil system by leaching. However the use of cover crops, i.e. growing a crop over the winter period between arable crops, has the potential to minimise this loss (Martinez and Guiraud, 1990). The soil N, accumulated by the cover crop during winter, may be available to the following crop as a result of mineralization of crop residues, but there is conflicting evidence over the 'fertilizer value' of these residues. Allison and Armstrong (1992) found that cover crops depressed the N uptake of the following crop, whereas others have found benefits (Thorup-Kristensen, 1993). This study was designed to examine the potential of eight cover-crops to reduce leaching and supply N to the following crop.

METHODOLOGY

The experimental site was established in 1992 at Woodside Organic Unit, near Elgin in north-east Scotland. The replicated four-block design experiment took place within the arable phase of a 6-year ley/arable crop rotation. Fallow and bare fallow (kept weed free using a flame weeder as necessary over the winter period) were established in addition to the following cover crop species on 20 August 1992: grazing rye (*Secale cereale*), 250 kg/ha; forage rape (*Brassica napus var. oleifera*), 8 kg/ha; winter peas (*Pisum sativum*), 250 kg/ha; Italian ryegrass (*Lolium multiflorum*), 35 kg/ha; winter barley (*Hordeum sativum*), 250 kg/ha; winter wheat (*Triticum aestivum*), 250 kg/ha; white mustard (*Sinapsis alba*), 15 kg/ha; fodder radish (*Raphanus sativus var. campestris*), 13 kg/ha. On 7 April 1993 all plots were ploughed, and a spring oat crop (*Avena sativa*) was sown on 8 April and harvested on 30 September 1993. Soil samples were collected from the top 45 cm of all plots in April 1993 and nitrate-N was measured in soil extracts using a colorimetric method. Cover crops were sampled on 1 April 1993, and the oat crop was sampled immediately prior to harvest and analysed for total N using a mass spectrometer.

RESULTS AND DISCUSSION

The presence of a winter cover crop reduced the nitrate-N content of soil in April by between 32 and 60% (Table 1). There was no difference in above-ground N accumulated by different species over the winter period. Naturally regenerated

Table 1. Soil nitrate-N and cover crop N content at incorporation, grain and N yield of following oat crop.

Cover crop	Soil nitrate-N (kg/ha 0-45 cm) April	Cover crop N (kg/ha) April	Grain yield of oat crop (t/ha at 85% dm)	N yield of oat crop (kg/ha grain+straw)
Bare fallow	11.93	0	4.91	43.29
Fallow	8.14	10.92	4.49	46.30
Grazing rye	6.09	11.51	4.19	50.86
Forage rape	5.74	7.24	4.59	58.36
Winter peas	7.69	10.87	4.22	44.39
It. ryegrass	4.42	7.14	3.89	32.74
Winter barley	5.37	8.12	3.95	29.02
Winter wheat	4.75	5.47	4.44	37.34
Wht. mustard	7.97	10.03	4.64	44.33
Fodder radish	7.23	9.69	4.50	58.88
Mean	6.93	9.00	4.68	44.55
SED	1.73	2.34	0.243	9.24

weeds were as effective as sown species at both reducing soil nitrate-N and taking up N over the winter. The N uptake by the cover crops was low compared with other UK studies (e.g. Allison and Armstrong, 1992) but this may reflect both the sandy, low organic matter soil type and the organic farming system, where residual N from the previous crop may be lower than in conventional systems. It is possible that most of the available nitrogen was captured by the cover crop. These cover crops were sown relatively early, on 20 August, however the establishment of cover crops in Scotland may be seriously restricted by the short growing season and late harvest of previous crops. The yield and N recovery of the oat crop were lowest following Italian ryegrass and winter barley, and N recovery was highest following forage rape and fodder radish. This probably reflects the rate of decomposition and release of nitrogen from the cover crop residues which is likely to be affected by both date and method of cover crop incorporation. In order to maximise the benefits of cover crops it is important to understand further the interactions between management and nitrogen cycling processes.

ACKNOWLEDGEMENTS
SAC receives financial support from the Scottish Office Agriculture, Environment and Fisheries Department.

REFERENCES
ALLISON M.F. and ARMSTRONG M.J. (1992) The integration of cover crops into sugar beet (*Beta vulgaris*) rotations. *Aspects of Applied Biology*, **30**, 301-308.

MARTINEZ J. and GUIRAUD G. (1990) A lysimeter study of the effects of ryegrass catch crop, during a winter wheat/maize rotation, on nitrate leaching and on the following crop. *Journal of Soil Science*, **41**, 5-16.

THORUP-KRISTENSEN K. (1993) The effect of nitrogen catch crops on the nitrogen nutrition of a succeeding crop 1. Effects through mineralization and pre-emptive competition. *Acta Agriculturae Scandinavica*, **43**, 74-81.

Nitrogen Balances in Organically and Conventionally Managed Beef Production Systems

CHRISTINE WATSON AND D. YOUNIE
SAC, 581 King Street, Aberdeen, AB9 1UD

INTRODUCTION

There is increasing concern over the loss of nitrogen to the environment from different farming systems. It is often assumed that organically managed systems, which do not rely on inputs derived from fossil fuels, will have lower nitrogen losses than conventional fertiliser based systems. However this assumption is often based on subjective judgement as very few reliable comparisons have been made between systems. The data presented here compares whole system nitrogen balances for organic and conventionally fertilized grassland systems managed for beef production.

MATERIALS AND METHODS

A conventional fertilizer based system (C), receiving 270 kgN/ha/annum and an organic system based on clover (O) have been compared on adjacent farmlets at SAC Aberdeen since 1989 (Younie et al., 1993). Each farmlet is self sufficient for grazing and silage and supports an 18-month beef enterprise (stocking rate 2.1 and 2.7 LU/ha on O and C respectively). Farm management information on purchases and sales of N has been combined with measurements of sward and animal production to calculate whole system N balances for the two farmlets. Symbiotic N fixation was estimated using a relationship based on the amount of N fixed by a grass/clover ley and the increase in herbage yield of the grass/clover mixture over an unfertilized sward; a similar approach has been published for alfalfa/grass mixtures by Barry et al. (1993). Gaseous losses of N from the two systems were estimated from the literature.

RESULTS

The calculated N balances for the two systems are given in Table 1. The total input to C was 143 kg N/ha greater than to O as a result of the difference between fertiliser N and symbiotically-fixed N. Nitrogen loss by leaching or unaccounted for was 81% higher per hectare for C than for O. The efficiency with which N was converted to saleable produce was greater in O (24%) than in C (16%), this probably reflects differences in total N inputs as shown by Garrett et al. (1992). The calculated values in kg/ha can be misleading because of the different stocking rates of the two systems. However the N balance per livestock unit shows that both inputs of N in purchased feed and output in liveweight gain (LWG) and saleable produce are similar for the two systems.

Table 1. Nitrogen balances for organically and conventionally managed beef production systems (mean of two production cycles).

kg N/ha	O	C	kg N/LU	O	C
Inputs			*Inputs*		
Atmospheric inputs	12	12	Atmospheric inputs	6	4
Non-symbiotic N fixed	5	5	Non-symbiotic N fixed	2	2
Fertilizer	0	270	Fertilizer	0	100
Symbiotic N fixed	146	0	Symbiotic N fixed	70	0
Bedding	7	9	Bedding	3	3
Purchased feed	46	61	Purchased feed	22	23
Livestock	5	7	Livestock	3	3
Total	221	364	Total	105	135
Outputs			*Outputs*		
Gaseous loss	60	84	Gaseous loss	29	31
Run-off	6	6	Run-off	3	2
Livestock	52	51	Livestock	25	19
Silage	0	7	Silage	0	3
Unaccounted for N including leaching	103	216	Unaccounted for N including leaching	49	80
Total	221	364	Total	105	135

The unaccounted-for N also reflects the difference in inputs between O and C, which is in agreement with published work (Garrett *et al.*, 1992). However, this unaccounted-for N is likely to exceed actual leaching loss since the figure calculated is the net result of many processes, including immobilisation by roots and soil micro-organisms. These data illustrate the relative inefficiency of high inputs of N fertiliser to grassland and the concomitant risks of N loss to the environment. Although LWG per hectare was 23% higher for C then for O over the same period (Younie *et al.*, 1993), output from O compared well with the average of commercial 18-month beef enterprises recorded by MLC (1992). These results must, therefore, raise questions about the wisdom of using high N inputs for beef production from grassland. The results from O and C suggest that it is the quantity of N in the system rather than the source of N (i.e. biological fixation or fertiliser) which determines its likely environmental impact.

ACKNOWLEDGEMENTS
SAC receives financial support from the Scottish Office Agriculture, Environment and Fisheries Department.

REFERENCES
BARRY, D.A.J., GOORAHOO, D. and GOSS, M.J. (1993) Estimation of nitrate concentrations in groundwater using a whole farm nitrogen budget. *Journal of Environmental Quality*, **22**, 767-775.

GARRETT, M.K., WATSON, C.J., JORDAN, C., STEEN, R.W.J. and SMITH, R.V. (1992) The nitrogen economy of grazed grassland. *Proceedings of the Fertiliser Society, No. 326.*

MLC (1992) *Beef Yearbook 1991.* Milton Keynes: Meat and Livestock Commission.

YOUNIE, D., CARR, G.W. and YACKIMINIE, D.S. (1993) A three-year comparison of profitability of organic and conventional beef production systems. *Animal Production*, **56**, 472.

Responses of Grass/Clover Swards to Two Different Methods of Slurry Application

P. S. WIGHTMAN, K. L. BOOTH,
J. F. WILSON AND D. YOUNIE
Agronomy Department, SAC, 581 King Street, Aberdeen, AB9 1UD

INTRODUCTION

The application of slurry by bandspreading has been shown to reduce N losses due to ammonia volatilisation, in comparison to the conventional splashplate method of application (Frost, 1994). This experiment compared simulated bandspreading and normal types of slurry application in pot-grown mini-swards to determine whether the method of slurry application affected growth of swards containing clover. The experiment was conducted under greenhouse conditions to allow more environmental control than is possible under field conditions.

MATERIALS AND METHODS

Perennial ryegrass cv Condesa and white clover cv S184 were grown in monoculture and in mixture in 10 1 pots of soil under greenhouse conditions (minimum temperature of 15°C). Pig and cattle slurry were applied by hand to the swards to simulate either conventional splash-plate application (normal) or application by bandspreading (root), and compared with a control (mineral fertiliser). Both slurries were applied at a rate of 40 m^3/ha to swards recently cut to a height of 4 cm; cow slurry was diluted 1:0.85 slurry:water. Nutrients

Table 1. Nutrients supplied (kg/ha)

Treatment	Total N	NH_4^+-N in slurry	P_2O_5	K_2O
Control	41		41	112
pig slurry	24	16	8	24
cow slurry	92	40	40	92

supplied are shown in Table 1. Treatments were applied in a randomised block design, using six replicates. Scorch and smother were assessed 24 h after slurry application. Herbage was harvested 5 weeks after application, to a height of 4 cm; dry-matter yields, the percentage of clover in the sward and yield components of the two species were recorded.

RESULTS

Very little scorch was evident under the conditions of this experiment, but smother was greater with cattle slurry normal application than any other treatment. Grass yields, both in monoculture and in mixture, were significantly lower with slurry treatments than the control (Table 2).

Table 2. The effect of normal and root application of pig and cattle slurry on total and component dry matter yields (g/pot) and percentage clover in the first harvest (mean of 6 replicates).

	Control	Pig slurry		Cattle slurry		s.e.m
		norm	root	norm	root	
Grass/clover						
Total dry weight	9.38	8.30	7.93	8.31	8.99	0.490
Dry weight clover	4.36	5.57	5.08	4.44	4.75	0.549
Dry weight grass	5.02	2.74	2.86	3.86	4.23	0.232
% clover in DM	48	65	64	53	52	3.691
Clover only						
Total dry weight	9.93	12.89	13.28	11.98	10.83	0.795
Grass only						
Total dry weight	7.58	3.98	3.88	5.90	5.82	0.249

Clover yields, both in monoculture and mixture with grass, tended to be greater with both slurry treatments than with the control, although in general the differences were not significant. The total dry-matter yield of grass/clover pots did not differ significantly between any of the treatments, but the slurries decreased grass and increased clover components of the sward producing higher clover contents in the slurry treatments, compared to the control. Pig slurry treatments had significantly lower grass yields and a tendency for greater clover yields (not significant) than cow slurry treatments. Thus the clover contents of pig slurry treatments were higher than cow slurry treatments.

Neither grass, clover, nor total dry-matter yields of swards receiving root slurry application (simulated bandspreading) were significantly different from swards receiving normal slurry application.

DISCUSSION

Comparison of slurry application by simulated bandspreading with conventional slurry application did not demonstrate differences in grass, clover or total yields of swards under the conditions of this experiment. Rate of N loss by ammonia volatilisation is influenced by weather conditions such as wind speed and temperature (Pain *et al.*, 1989), and thus rates of loss between the two slurry application methods may not have been greatly different under greenhouse conditions. In contrast to previous results (Wightman and Younie, 1994) pig slurry treatments had greater clover yields and clover contents than cow slurry treatments, but this was primarily a reflection of the lower N supplied by the very dilute pig slurry used in this experiment, which reduced grass yields. The lower clover content of the control probably reflected the higher grass yield in this treatment. Grass yields were higher in the control than in cow slurry treatments, despite the fact that both treatments supplied similar amounts of the major nutrients. Neither scorch nor smother appear to have been responsible for the negative effect of cow slurry on grass growth, since no smother was recorded on swards receiving root application, and scorch levels were low.

ACKNOWLEDGEMENTS
SAC receives financial support from the Scottish Office Agriculture and Fisheries Department.

REFERENCES
FROST J.P. (1994) Effect of spreading method, application rate and dilution on ammonia volatilization from cattle slurry. *Grass and Forage Science* **49**, 391-400.
PAIN B., PHILLIPS V.R., CLARKSON C.R. and KLARENBEEK, J.V. (1989) Loss of nitrogen through ammonia volatilisation during and following the application of pig or cattle slurry to grassland. *Journal of the Science of Food and Agriculture* **47**, 1-12.
WIGHTMAN P.S. and YOUNIE D. (1994) Responses of grass/clover mini-swards to slurry application. *Proceedings of the 15th General Meeting of the European Grassland Federation, Wageningen, 1994*, 611-615.

Utilization of N from Slurry Applied by Low-emission Techniques to Grassland on Sandy Soils

A. P. WOUTERS[1] AND J. H. GEURINK[2]

[1] Research Station for Cattle, Sheep and Horse Husbandry (PR),
Runderweg 6, 8219 PK Lelystad, The Netherlands
[2]Institute for Agrobiological and Soil Fertility
Research (AB-DLO), Wageningen, The Netherlands

INTRODUCTION

The Netherlands' government wishes to obtain a reduction in ammonia volatilization by 70% before 2005 (Anon., 1993). Therefore, slurry application with low emission techniques has become compulsory. Deep injection proved to be very effective in reducing the ammonia (NH_3) volatilization but sward damage made its use limited (Wadman, 1988). Therefore, other techniques like shallow injection with open or closed slits and dilution of slurry with water were developed. In three series of field experiments the utilization of N from cattle slurry applied to grassland by these techniques has been investigated to determine the fertilizing value of cattle slurry.

MATERIAL AND METHODS

The utilization of N from cattle slurry applied with low-emission techniques to grassland on sandy soils was investigated in three series of mowing experiments (completely randomized block (CRBD) or split plot design), conducted from 1990-1991. Slurry treatments in Experiments 1 (E1) and 2 (E2) included shallow injection with open and closed slits at rates of 2 x 20-30 t/ha/application in spring (before 1st and 2nd cut) and in summer (before 3rd and 5th cut), respectively. In Experiment 3 (E3) slurry treatments included surface spreading and shallow injection with open slits (both 2 x 20 t/ha; before 1st and 2nd cut), surface spreading of slurry diluted with water (2 x 80 t/ha; before 1st and 2nd cut) and by deep injection (40 t/ha before 1st cut). Slurry treatments in E1 and E2 were compared with a treatment of CAN-27 fertilizer (200 kg N/ha/year). In E3 four levels of CAN-27 fertilizer (0, 70, 140, 210 kg N/ha) were included for comparison with slurry treatments. In all experiments, DM yields and N-contents in herbage were measured. Apparent N efficiencies (ANE) and apparent N recoveries of fertilizer (ANR) and slurry N from Cuts 1-4 in E1 and E3 and all cuts per year in E2 were determined.

RESULTS AND DISCUSSION

The results presented in Table 1 show that the method of application had a clear effect on ANE and ANR of slurry. In E1 and E2, ANE and ANR from slurry applied by shallow injection with open slits in spring were equal or somewhat lower than with shallow injection with closed slits. In E3 the highest ANR from cattle slurry was obtained with deep injection, followed by shallow injection with open slits, dilution of slurry with water and surface spreading. The differences among the treatments are probably caused by differences in ammonia volatilization after application. The sequence in ANR among the different treatments agrees with results of measurements of ammonia volatilization (Bussink and Bruins, 1991).

Table 1 . The ANE (kg DM/kg N) and ANR (%) of fertilizer and cattle slurry (with total N content varying from 3-6 kg/t) when applying slurry and fertilizer N apart during two years (1990-1991).

Experiment and treatment		ANE	ANR
E.1	CAN-27 (200 kg N/ha/year)	26	71
	Shallow injection with open slits	16	42
	Shallow injection with closed slits	18	50
E.2	CAN-27 (200 kg N/ha/year)	29	78
	Shallow injection with open slits	15	42
	Shallow injection with closed slits	13	41
E.3.	CAN-27: 70 kg N/ha	33	94
	CAN-27: 140 kg N/ha	26	88
	CAN-27: 210 kg N/ha	20	88
	Surface spreading	6	19
	Deep injection	11	47
	Shallow injection with open slits	12	42
	Dilution of slurry with water (up to DM content of 3%)	12	34

ANRs with shallow injection with closed slits in spring (E1) were somewhat higher than those obtained with application in summer (E2). Comparing ANEs and ANRs of different methods, the ANE of diluted slurry in E3 was equal to results obtained with injection techniques while the ANR was considerably lower. Possibly, negative effects of injection methods like effects of distribution and placing of slurry in the soil or cutting of the sward could have had a larger effect on yield than N-uptake. ANR and working indices based on ANR are the best indicators to compare N utilization of different methods of slurry application.

REFERENCES
ANONYMOUS (1993) *Notitie mest en ammoniak beleid, derde fase [Note on manure and ammonia policy, third phase]*. Ministry of Agriculture, Nature Management and Fisheries,

The Netherlands
BUSSINK W. and BRUINS M.A.(1991) Beperking van de NH3-emissie bij verschillende toedieningstechnieken voor dunne mest op grasland. [Reduction in ammonia volatilization using slurry application techniques on grassland]. *Meststoffen 1992, Dutch/English Annual on fertilizers and fertilization, Nederlands Meststoffen Instituut, Wageningen*
WADMAN W.P.(1988) *Mestinjectie, mogelijkheden, voordelen en problemen. [Tine Injection, possibilities, advantages and problems].* DLO, 64 p Wageningen, The Netherlands

Crop Growth and Nitrogen Recovery following Ploughing of Grass/Clover Swards

D. YOUNIE AND CHRISTINE WATSON

SAC, 581 King Street, Aberdeen, AB9 1UD

INTRODUCTION

The build-up of soil nitrogen during a grass/clover ley, and its subsequent release and uptake by arable crops following ploughing, is one of the essential features of successful low-external-input agricultural systems. The extent to which the residual value of the ley depends upon its botanical composition (e.g. clover content) and previous N fertiliser inputs is not known. Ploughing of the ley is recognised as one of the main points of N leakage from ley/arable systems. It could be anticipated, therefore, that ploughing early in winter will lead to greater risk of N leaching than late ploughing. The objective of this experiment was to measure the effect of previous sward type and date of ploughing on N uptake and yield of spring barley.

MATERIALS AND METHODS

Following a systems comparison at Craibstone, Aberdeen, in which a white clover-based and a high-N fertiliser-based sward (270 kgN/ha/annum) were compared (Younie, 1992; Younie and Wightman, 1992) adjacent areas of each sward type were ploughed in either January or April 1994, prior to secondary cultivation with a harrow/leveller and sowing with spring barley cv. Derkado on 12 April. Response of the barley to fertilizer N addition was measured with N treatments as follows: 0, 30, 60, 90 and 120 kgN/ha. A basal dressing of 80 kg P_2O_5 and 80 kg/ha K_2O was applied. The crop was harvested on 14 September 1994, when grain and straw yield were measured. Crop N uptake was measured during May, June and July and in the grain and straw at harvest. The incidence of disease and extent of lodging and brackling were also recorded.

RESULTS AND DISCUSSION

Crop N uptake in plots unfertilized with N is presented in Table 1. On both sites the uptake of N in June and July by spring barley was significantly greater (by 29% overall, averaged over the two sites) following winter ploughing compared with spring ploughing. Crop N uptake was also markedly affected by the management of the previous sward. In May the barley following conventionally managed grassland, contained more N than that which followed clover-based grassland, but this trend was reversed in June and July. These results suggest a difference in the rate and quantity of mineralisation of N from organic matter in the two sward types.

Table 1. Effect of ploughing date on N uptake of spring barley following different sward types (kg N/ha).

Previous sward type	Ploughing date	Sampling Date			Mean	SED (Date)
		May	June	July		
Grass/clover	Winter	6.3	86.8	130.4	74.5	
	Spring	5.2	68.5	92.6	55.4	
	Mean	5.0	77.6	111.5		5.23
	SED	(Plough)			4.27	
High N	Winter	11.6	69.6	86.5	55.9	
	Spring	9.1	55.0	70.4	44.8	
	Mean	10.3	62.3	78.5		4.48
	SED	(Plough)			3.65	

Weather conditions were generally good, although very dry in early summer. There was no lodging in any of the crops, but where the previous sward was unfertilised grass/clover, the percentage brackling was significantly higher in early-ploughed plots and at moderate N levels. The effects of treatments on grain yield are shown in Table 2.

Table 2. Effect of previous sward type, ploughing date and fertilizer N on grain yield of spring barley (t/ha at 85% DM).

Previous sward type	Ploughing date	Fert N rate (kgN/ha)					Mean	SED (Ft. N)
		0	30	60	90	120		
Grass/clover	Winter	7.4	6.9	8.0	7.0	8.2	7.5	
	Spring	6.1	6.2	6.2	7.0	6.3	6.4	
	Mean	6.7	6.6	7.1	7.0	7.2		0.43
	SED	Plough					0.27	
High N	Winter	5.7	5.4	5.6	5.8	5.1	5.5	
	Spring	4.2	4.6	5.0	4.8	5.3	4.8	
	Mean	5.0	5.0	5.3	5.3	5.2		0.31
	SED	Plough					0.20	

Mean grain yield (6.0 t/ha) was high, even in plots which had received no fertilizer N. Yield was markedly higher (35%) from plots which followed grass/clover than plots which followed high N grassland and was also significantly higher in winter-ploughed than in spring-ploughed plots, reflecting the crop N uptake data. There was little response to N application, but, when averaged across the two sites, there was a response to N in spring-ploughed plots. Spring ploughing may have reduced the risk of N loss through leaching compared to winter ploughing, but it appears that N release and uptake by the following crop was also restricted to some extent.

The higher N uptake and grain yield following the clover-based sward cannot be explained simply. Average clover content in the two swards, over 9 years, was 28% and 8% for the clover-based and high-N swards respectively. The form of organic N built-up under grass/clover may differ from that built up under heavily fertilized grass swards and may be manifested in the mineralisation of N after ploughing up the sward. In order to exploit fully the potential of grass/clover leys in sustainable systems, these responses need to be examined in more detail.

ACKNOWLEDGEMENT
SAC receives financial assistance from the Scottish Office Agriculture, Fisheries and Environment Office.

REFERENCES
YOUNIE D. (1992) Reliability of output from clover-based and intensively fertilized grassland systems. In: Hopkins, A. (ed.) *Grass on the Move*, Occasional Symposium British Grassland Society, No. **26**, 183-185.
YOUNIE D. and WIGHTMAN P.S. (1992) Herbage production over eight years from clover-based and intensively fertilized swards under grazing and silage management. *Proceedings of the Third Research Meeting, British Grassland Society*, September 1992.

SECTION 3

FUTURE TECHNOLOGY

Improved Technology For Production Efficiency and Utilization Efficiency

R. J. WILKINS

IGER, North Wyke, Okehampton, Devon, EX20 2SB

ABSTRACT

Plant improvement will result in a progressive, gradual increase in the potential production of grasses, but more benefit may result from breeding to extend the growing season and to reduce the adverse effects of stress on growth. There will be increased opportunities for more precise control of nutrient supply to grassland both to reduce unit costs of production and to reduce risks of losses of N compounds to the environment. Fertilizer N should be used to make good deficiencies in supply from other sources. There will be progress in improving both digestibility and protein value of forages used for grazing and conservation. Future systems should be based, as far as possible, on grazed herbage with attention required to factors which increase intake and reduce losses in grazing conditions. Conservation will be based largely on silages of 25-35% dry matter using techniques for rapid field wilting with input of biological or chemical additives to control fermentation and improve feeding value. The contribution that can be made by improved sensors and models to improve the precision of grassland management is stressed as is the need for objective management of areas of grassland for particular purposes.

INTRODUCTION

The economic and social framework for grassland production and utilization into the next century has been discussed in earlier papers. This paper outlines some of the possibilities for improved technology which will impact on grassland production and utilization over the next 15 years or so. During this period there will be growing concern with a competitive world market situation but with increasing constraints to restrict losses of pollutants to water and to the atmosphere. This situation predicates systems giving low unit-cost production that are tuned to avoid pollution risk. Grassland will continue to play an important role in maintaining and enhancing landscape and biodiversity but it is not certain that substantial subsidy payments will continue to be made for such purposes.

The first part of the paper discusses opportunities for increasing efficiency of production whilst the second part focuses on herbage quality and utilization by grazing and by conservation. Possibilities arising from the use of new molecular technology will not be considered in detail as they are dealt with in the accompanying paper by Cocking (1995).

EFFICIENCY OF PRODUCTION

Production efficiency may be improved through the use and availability of improved cultivars and through improved management and technical inputs, to give appropriate plant nutrition and control of weeds, pests and diseases. Although production efficiency has traditionally been related to output per unit area of land, this index is likely to decline further in importance with increased focus on total monetary costs per unit of output and to expressions of output in relation to other limiting input factors or environmental parameters.

Improvement through better cultivars

It has often been maintained that improvements made through herbage plant breeding have been modest, with the similarity in production from permanent as opposed to recently reseeded swards used as evidence to support this view (Hopkins *et al.*, 1990). There has, however, recently been marked improvements with, for instance, the new intermediate perennial ryegrass AberElan producing 22% more dry matter than the old variety S321, first listed in 1968. The annual improvement in DM yield over this 25 year period was 0.88%, compared with annual improvements in yields of cereal grain varieties over the 33 years from 1953 to 1986 of 0.85% (Wilson, 1993). Whilst major breakthroughs in overall yield are unlikely, it is probable that production/ha of the 'best' varieties will continue to progress at about this rate from the use of conventional breeding techniques. Selection by the farmer of the best varieties currently available will give a considerable yield benefit at little extra cost.

Increased availability of materials which are resistant to, or tolerant of, particular stresses will probably be at least as important as increases in yield potential. Farmers will put a high premium on reliability of production through the growing season and also on extending production early and late in the year, particularly for grasses and legumes required for grazing rather than conservation.

Pests and diseases only occasionally cause devastating losses to grassland, but more insidious losses are common in both newly-sown and established swards, affecting both production and quality. Clements (1994) estimated the monetary loss through pests and diseases in the UK to exceed £500 million annually. Attention is given to the foliar pathogenic fungi in official testing procedures and cultivars with marked resistance are available, although no present cultivars express high levels of resistance to all fungal pathogens. More attention is required for pests, particularly leatherjackets (*Tipula* spp), slugs (*Deroceras reticulatum*) and frit fly (*Oscinella* spp), and, although variation in resistance exists, this has not been the subject of intensive breeding effort and is not specifically assessed in official testing.

Poor production during dry summer conditions can severely limit the efficiency of grazing systems. There are large differences between herbage species in water-use efficiency and in performance in dry conditions, relating generally to the depth of soil being exploited by roots (Garwood and Sinclair, 1979) and to differences in physiological characteristics (Thomas, 1994a), with tall fescue being outstanding. Much progress has been made in the production of hybrids between fescues and ryegrasses, with the characteristic of good performance in dry conditions being an important attribute from the fescues, which is being sought in the hybrids (Thomas and Humphreys, 1991). Material from this programme will progressively become available within the next 15 years.

With pressure to reduce unit costs of production of ruminant feeds, there are requirements to extend the grazing season. Efforts during the late 1950s and early 1960s to identify grasses with a longer growing season failed because of the high level of sensitivity of winter-active cultivars to winter kill in adverse conditions. However, collections of ryegrasses from the Swiss uplands provided evidence that early spring growth and winter hardiness were evolved together. This material has been used in the production of AberElan. Wilson (1993) stated that there was no indication that any limit is being reached for continued selection from existing perennial ryegrass gene pools. The promised progressive increases in the next decade in the availability of both grasses and white clovers with extended growing seasons should be one of the major developments in grassland farming, particularly for farms on free-draining soils with low poaching risk.

Shortage of plant nutrients is a major stress which has severe effects on herbage production. Over recent decades the approach in the relatively intensive production systems which predominate in Britain has been to rectify deficiencies in plant nutrient supply by fertilizer application. This contrasts with many other regions in which plant nutrient supply from the soil has been accepted, and efforts made to identify plant species which are capable of production in these conditions. With lowered product prices and moves towards extensification, it is timely to query whether consideration should not be given to exploiting species that are reasonably adapted to low fertility conditions. Hopkins *et al.* (1994) drew attention to the potential of *Lotus* spp. in conditions of low pH and low phosphorus status. In such conditions at North Wyke, *Lotus* spp. was found to establish satisfactorily, whilst white clover failed (Sheldrick and Martyn, 1992). In more intensive conditions, production will continue to be based largely on perennial ryegrass, with or without white clover. Attention has been directed recently to improving nitrogen use efficiency within ryegrass. Substantial genotype/N fertilizer-rate interactions exist (Wilkins, 1989), but there are also cultivars such as AberElan which produce more herbage dry matter over a range of fertilizer-N application rates. This gives the opportunity either for maintaining a required herbage production rate with lower fertilizer-N applications than used conventionally, or exploiting the full growth potential of such cultivars.

Improvement through better plant nutrition
Fertilizers represent a high financial cost for grassland farmers, whilst excess

nutrients in the system are at risk of loss to the aqueous or atmospheric environment. Attention has focused particularly on N, but both costs and environmental losses of P and K can also be considerable. The twin quests to reduce inputs required per unit of output and to reduce risks of environmental damage both increase the need to improve the match between the supply of nutrients to the requirements of plants, and thus to animals.

Herbage plants have a high capability to take up N from the soil during the growing season. Problems arise largely through (i) limitations in control of the supply of N to the plant and (ii) the high ratio of available N to available carbohydrate in young plant tissue giving rise to the high losses of N in the rumen.

Until recently, intensive grassland farmers have tended to make blanket high applications of N to ensure reliable high levels of production. With N recovered in animal products unlikely to exceed 80 kg/ha, it is inevitable that high losses from such a system will occur. Research by Titchen and Scholefield (1994) confirmed that N applications may be excessive in intensive grazing systems. Fields on six farms were split, with fertilizer applied in one half according to the farm's normal procedure, whilst in the other half N application was related to concentrations of soil-mineral N, determined in the soil throughout the growing season. Herbage growth did not differ between the two approaches but, on average, the 'tactical' approach resulted in reduction of fertilizer N input from 300 to 211 kg/ha.

A change in attitude to fertilizer use is required. Account should be taken, in the first place, of N supplied by mineralisation of soil organic matter, from excreta, from rainfall and from biological N fixation. Fertilizer N should only be used to rectify any deficiency of overall N supply in relation to the quantity of herbage that is required and the response potential of the sward at the time. Progress in quantifying and understanding N transformations in the soil/plant/animal system will permit better assessment of the requirement for extra N (from fertilizer) at any time. The present approach for determination of N in soil will be refined. Further developments will include assessment of herbage N status and, ultimately, improved mathematical models of the relevant processes will facilitate prediction without recourse to frequent analytical determinations.

Whilst improved quantification is likely to result in most progress in this area, there will also be opportunities for improvement in nitrogen use efficiency; through the use of improved grass cultivars, as discussed previously; through changes in slurry storage and application technology to reduce losses and increase nutrient availability, as discussed by Pain (1991); and through dietary manipulation to improve animal N efficiency. Similar approaches to better quantifying processes, transformations and pools of nutrients will be increasingly required for P and K, with the prime need being to satisfy environmental constraints rather than to improve production efficiency, apart from in 'organic' systems in which maximising internal cycling of nutrients is required to drive herbage production.

Forage legumes

The potential to exploit forage legumes in Britain was recently reviewed by Hopkins *et al.* (1994). They concluded that the UK livestock industry could realise annual savings of around £300 million from a switch to clover-based systems of production. They drew attention to the relatively low adoption of legume-based systems and suggested a need to survey farmers on reasons for non-adoption.

The likely pressures towards extensification and for lowcost production will increase further the case for the use of forage legumes, particularly white clover. The lower herbage output per ha from grass/white clover swards without fertilizer N compared to highly fertilized grass swards is already of less importance than previously. Guidelines for both establishment and maintenance of white clover in mixed swards have progressively been improved through progress in R & D, as outlined by Sheldrick *et al.* (1995).

Problems that remain include the limited growth season with clover, susceptibility to pest attack and the risks of rapid reductions in sward clover content. Progress in identifying genetic materials with ability to grow at low temperatures without susceptibility to winter damage, already noted for grass, also applies to white clover (Wilson, 1993), with promise to build in the future on progress that has recently been made. Damage through Sitona weevil and from slugs is extremely widespread and may be critical in relation to success in establishment (Murray and Clements, 1993). There is need for further work, particularly with Sitona, to identify means for reducing risk of damage either by the production of resistant cultivars or by sward management. Research on increasing resistance to Sitona through introduction of the *Bacillus thuringienesis* gene into rhizobia in root nodules already shows promise (Skøt *et al.*, 1994).

Recent work by Thornley *et al.* (1995) and by Schwinning and Parsons (1996) demonstrates that large spatial and temporal fluctuations in the proportions of grass and clover in grazed swards are a normal phenomenon, resulting from the effects of excreta return on N dynamics and the competition between the species, and that these fluctuations are consistent with long-term sustainability of the mixed sward. However, particularly if reliance on high clover content to improve animal performance is an important feature of the system, it may be appropriate to consider actions to sustain higher clover contents in swards. Hence management to maintain higher clover stolon mass and increased growing point numbers over winter, as discussed by Rhodes and Webb (1993), is important. Another approach to increase clover robustness is to produce a rhizomatous clover by hybridisation with the extremely persistent *Trifolium ambiguum* (Rhodes and Webb, 1993).

It had been perceived from the work of Ryden *et al.* (1984) that systems based on biological nitrogen fixation, rather than on fertilizer N application, would inherently give lower environmental losses of N. Recent work, however, supports the conclusion that losses are influenced much more by the total quantity of N circulating in the system rather than by the source of that N. Thus Cuttle *et al.* (1992) and Scholefield and Tyson (1992) conclude that if swards have similar carrying capacity then environmental losses of N will be broadly similar for swards based on clover and those based on fertilizer N.

Table 1. Nitrogen inputs, outputs and losses from dairy farming systems (from Jarvis *et al.*, 1996)

	Systems based on fertilizer-N		Systems based on grass-white clover*	
	Case study	Tactical fertilizer-N use and slurry injection	Low clover content*	High clover content
Stocking rate (LSU/ha)	2.17	2.17	1.74	1.74
Inputs (kg/ha)				
Fertilizer	250	155	0	0
Fixation	10	10	72	144
Other	77	77	66	66
Total	337	242	138	210
Outputs (kg/ha)				
Milk and liveweight	67	67	54	54
Losses (kg/ha)				
Leaching	56	32	16	28
Denitrification	55	32	15	27
Ammonia	49	22	31	34
Total	160	86	62	89
Unaccounted for N (kg/ha)	109	89	23	78

* Assuming efficient utilisation of recycled N sustaining output with modest rates of N fixation

However, losses per ha and per unit of animal production, particularly through leaching, increase with increasing herbage productivity and stocking rate.

Consequently losses will be higher on the most intensive fertilizer-based systems than on those based on white clover. Another situation where N losses may be particularly high is with swards dominated by white clover. Grazed white clover monocultures gave losses of 200 kg N/ha (Macduff et al., 1990), presumably resulting from the extremely high N:C ratio in the herbage produced. The calculated impact on N losses of systems based on grass-clover and on fertilizer N are given in Table 1 (Jarvis et al., 1996).

EFFICIENCY OF UTILIZATION

It is widely recognised that grassland feeds cannot satisfy the nutrient requirements of the most highly productive livestock without supplementation and that there is much variation between grassland feeds in nutritive value. Furthermore, the proportion of herbage grown that is actually consumed by livestock varies greatly in farm practice, as demonstrated by Peel et al. (1988) both in grazing and from conserved feeds. This section discusses forage quality and then considers possible improvements in technology for grazing and for conservation.

Forage quality

Over the last decades accent has justifiably been placed on the importance of digestibility and intake potential of grassland feeds. There has, more recently, been increased attention to the value of protein in grassland feeds and to the pattern of supply of substrate to the rumen and to the animal tissues (Beever and Reynolds, 1994).

Digestibility is an extremely important attribute, both in its own right as an important first stage in the conversion of feed energy to animal product, but also through the general positive correlation with voluntary intake. However, despite the availability for more than 40 years of techniques for assessing digestibility *in vitro* and the demonstration in the early 1960s that digestibility was a heritable characteristic (Cooper et al., 1962), progress in producing grasses with increased digestibility has been modest. This has arisen partly through a perception that high digestibility of ryegrass leaves gave little scope for further improvement. Recent work by Deinum (1994), however, indicates large variation in the anatomical structure of perennial ryegrass leaves, suggesting sufficient variation for selection for improved digestibility. Improvements in herbage digestibility have resulted from increases in stem digestibility and increases in the leaf:stem ratio in the crop, particularly in mid season (Wilkins and Davies, 1995). Continued progress in these directions is likely, through breeding for digestibility *per se* or for sward morphological characteristics. There are also possibilities for identifying material with enhanced digestibility resulting from blockages in stages of the lignification process, as discussed by Peacock (1993) and Monties and Calet (1993).

The nitrogenous constituents in herbage feeds are generally degraded very rapidly in the rumen, resulting in high losses of ammonia excreted as urea in urine. The situation is particularly severe with silages containing high proportions of non-protein nitrogen and with young grasses and legumes with a high ratio of N to available carbohydrate.

Nitrogen use efficiency could be increased by slowing down the rate of breakdown of N compounds in the rumen and/or by increasing the capture of N in rumen microbial biomass by providing additional energy synchronous with the release of simple N compounds in the rumen. This could be achieved either by altering the composition of herbage feeds or by the identification and use of appropriate feed supplements. There may be possibilities for reducing the rate of N release by introduction of tannins (which bind with proteins) into herbage feeds, but there is a risk of adverse effect with excess tannins (Barry and Duncan, 1984). It is also possible that differences in proteolysis may result from differences in the composition or compartmentation of proteins in the plant (Thomas, 1994b).

With grasses used for conservation there will be further opportunities to increase concentrations of water soluble carbohydrates (Humphreys, 1989) and thus improve capture of N within the rumen. It is less clear, however, that this option will be available with young grass tissues or with white clover, because of the absence of substantial sinks for readily available carbohydrate in the harvested material. Better prediction of nutrient supply patterns from grazed and conserved herbages will facilitate more precise formulation of feed supplements to optimize the use of nutrients, particularly N compounds, from herbages. An improvement in animal efficiency of 50% could lead to the quantity of N at risk of loss to the environment being nearly halved (Table 2).

Table 2. Feed N and excreta N from diets with different efficiency of N use by the animal in a situation in which animal output remains constant and dietary N is varied.

	Low N use efficiency	Improved N use efficiency
N in product as ppn. of N in feed	0.2	0.3
Feed N to animal output (g/g product)	5.0	3.3
Excreta N (g/g product)	4.0	2.3

Grazing

Nutrients supplied through grazing are less than half the cost of those supplied in silage and much lower than for concentrate feeds. This stresses the need to seek to maximise the use of grazed grass in efficient grassland systems (Wilkins, 1995). Major problems with grazing, however, arise from low levels of intake and nutrient supply and the risks of substantial losses through senescence. These factors are related because, whilst individual levels of intake generally increase with increase in quantity of available herbage (increasing animal production and feed conversion efficiency), this will also increase senescence losses (and reduce the proportion of the tissue grown which is consumed). A compromise is required in order to optimize production, and this is reflected in advice on management using sward height guidelines (Hodgson et al., 1986).

Efficiency could be improved by (i) increasing intake at a particular sward height (or quantity of available herbage), (ii) reducing senescence at a particular sward height or (iii) improving control to achieve target grazing conditions more readily. Eating rate in grazing conditions is higher with white clover than with grass (Penning et al., 1991) and this is reflected in increased total intake in conditions of high animal demand for nutrients (Penning et al., 1994). This high intake, apparently, results from the morphological and anatomical characteristics of white clover that lead to low 'handling time' (time spent in prehension and mastication per g herbage consumed) (Parsons et al., 1994). The petiole of white clover is readily severed and the leaves are rapidly broken down in the mouth. Grazing intake could be increased by more widespread use of white clover or by identifying or breeding grasses with low handling time. Antuna (1990) identified, using sward boards, large differences between grass cultivars in rate of eating/minute, but is not yet clear whether this would be reflected in differences in intake/day. Further examination is required, with the prospect of providing improved selection criteria for breeders.

Increased use of white clover as a monoculture warrants further consideration, possibly in association with other forages such as maize to improve nutrient balance. Pure white clover has disadvantages due to lower herbage production than grass/clover mixtures and through the possibility of high levels of nitrate leaching from grazed pure-clover swards, noted earlier. Recent research at Aberystwyth (L.R. Mytton, personal communication) indicates a possible novel approach to the cultivation and use of white clover. When white clover without rhizobia was grown at low levels of nitrate supply, biomass productivity was reasonably high, but the white clover produced contained less than half the normal concentration of N. In contrast, when white clover is grown with a relatively ineffective rhizobia association the plant adapts to give low biomass productivity, but with the leaves maintaining normal high N concentration. If these results are confirmed, the possibility may develop of using non-nodulated white clover, with growth rate controlled by N fertilizer (or other sources of N). The material would have the morphological and physio-chemical characteristics of white clover to give high levels of feed intake, with reduced risk of loss of N to the environment compared with normal white clover.

High senescence rates under grazing arise from the rapid turnover of leaves in grazed swards. This is a particular problem with swards grazed by cattle, for which relatively high sward target heights are recommended. Parsons (1994) illustrates the large impact that an increase in leaf longevity would have on the quantity of harvested (grazed) DM with swards maintained at particular levels of leaf area index (Figure 1). The use of grasses with the stay-green gene, giving reduced rates of senescence (Thomas and Smart, 1993), may provide one means of increasing leaf longevity.

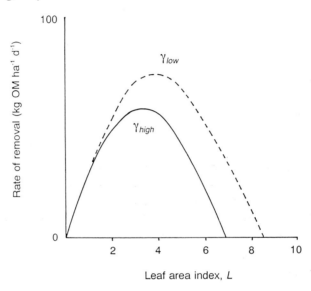

Figure 1.   The effect on the rate of removal of material that may be sustained in swards maintained at each of a range of LAIs of a change in the proportion of the standing liveweight lost per day in senescence, with low being longevity of 33.3 days/leaf and high being longevity of 26.6 days/leaf (from Parsons, 1994)

Although management systems based on sward height have been promoted for more than a decade, few farmers effect control by direct measurements on the sward. The development of sensors to scan the sward for assessment of parameters such as sward height, sward mass and green leaf mass would clearly facilitate practical implementation of sward control. A further possibility would be the direct monitoring of grazing behaviour (particularly grazing time) to guide decisions on sward management, with cheap sensors being developed for attachment to the animal (P.D. Penning and A.J. Rook, personal communication).

The use of grasses that remain vegetative during the growing season would have a major impact on grazing management. The stem normally tends to be rejected during grazing, leading to the progressive accumulation of ungrazed herbage of low quality in the sward. Furthermore, if significant stem development occurs, this may lead to low tiller numbers and sward deterioration. Stem development may be restricted by the imposition of severe grazing pressure in early season, but this may have adverse effects on animal intake and performance and may also give rise to poaching damage. Grazing management would be much more flexible if there was no propensity to head. This possibility was put forward in the 1960s but apparently rejected at the time because of the difficulty in locating adapted material (for which seed could be produced at other latitudes) which maintained sufficient vigour when entirely vegetative. The possibilities should be re-examined, particularly as alternative methods for stimulating flowering (when required for seed production) may be available and techniques for vegetative establishment and propagation of plant material are now better developed.

Forage conservation

Increased realisation of the high cost of conservation of grasses and forage legumes, reduced product prices and competition from forage maize and cereal grains, may well reduce the quantity of grasses and forage legumes that are conserved. Nevertheless, particularly in the western and northern parts of Britain, conservation will remain a key part of grassland and ruminant production systems. It will be of increasing importance to produce conserved products of predictable quality with low levels of loss but at reasonable cost and with minimum risk of environmental damage.

  The present trend towards production of silage of 25-35% DM with minimum effluent production will continue, with improved conditioning and spreading treatments being used to increase drying rates (Bosma and Gabriels, 1993). There will be further developments in biological and chemical additives to both improve preservation and to improve feeding value. With most silages being made from wilted crops, attention on improving preservation will centre more on prevention of aerobic deterioration and control of potential pathogens such as *Listeria monocytogenes*, rather than on the prevention of a clostridial or butyric fermentation. Organisms in bacterial inocula may be selected to generate acetic acid and propionic acid in order to restrict aerobic deterioration (Honig, 1991). There will also be opportunities to use bacteria with specific antagonistic effects against spoilage organisms, as demonstrated by Mayer *et al.* (1995) for *L. monocytogenes*. For improving feeding value, attention will centre on treatments to reduce protein breakdown, to improve digestibility and intake potential. Chemical approaches seeking to assist fermentation and protein breakdown by addition of sterilants will continue, but problems that have hampered previous attempts in this direction remain. These include the requirements to restrict aerobic deterioration and achieve effective rumen function. There is greater promise for treatments to restrict protein breakdown. The protein in some crops such as red clover appears to be partially protected during the silage fermentation (Jones *et al.*, 1993) and opportunities for further altering protein composition in grasses were discussed in a previous section. There is also potential to identify chemicals to restrict proteolysis, both in the silo and in the rumen (Nsereko and Rooke, 1993). Hitherto the addition of fibrolytic enzymes at ensiling has had little overall impact on the nutritive value of silages (Syrjälä-Qvist and Wilkins, 1992). However, there is potential for the development of enzymes which contribute to breaking bonds between lignin and carbohydrates and thus increase the substrate available for digestion in the rumen.

Silage making will become a more controlled process. Further progress will be made in techniques for rapid analysis of crops in the field to aid decision making on optimal cutting stage and assessing the quantity of substrate available for fermentation. This information, together with rapid assessment of the nature of the population of epiphytic microorganisms, will enable decisions to be made on the requirement for, and specific nature of, the biological or chemical additive to use. Improvements to the chemical description of silages will enable identification of appropriate feed supplements and prediction of response in physical and economic terms.

CONCLUDING REMARKS

This review outlines major possibilities for the development of grassland systems for the future. A common theme has been the identification of approaches to reduce inputs and to improve the predictability of performance. Plant improvement has major contributions to make, as has the use of sensors, rapid methods of analysis and models upon which to base decision making on factors such as the requirement for fertilizer inputs, grazing control, cutting stage for conservation, the requirements for and nature of silage additives and supplementary feeds.

There is much scope for tightening up management and reducing inputs in grass-based systems to reduce risks of environmental damage with little adverse effect on output/ha. There will, however, be increasing opportunities for exploiting forage legumes, particularly white clover, in production systems and some case for seeking to exploit the animal nutritional qualities of white clover through growth as a pure sward. There will also be opportunities for using grassland to improve landscape, biodiversity and nature conservation. However, as discussed by Wilkins and Harvey (1994), optimal land use is likely to result from the allocation of specific areas within the farm managed for nature conservation (with agricultural output a by-product) with the remainder of the farm being managed for agricultural production efficiency, although constrained to prevent pollution risk. Depending on farm circumstances the area used for grassland production may be based on fertilizer-N inputs or on forage legumes, or different parts of the area being directed to one or other of these approaches. It will be important to maintain a clear focus on the overall requirements and how each parcel of land best contributes to these requirements.

REFERENCES

ANTUNA A. (1990) *Factors affecting the intake of herbage by sheep*. Ph.D. thesis, University of Wales, Aberystwyth.

BARRY T.W. and DUNCAN S.J. (1984) The role of condensed tannins in the nutritional value of *Lotus pedunculatus* for sheep. 1. Voluntary intake. *British Journal of Nutrition*, **51**, 485-491.

BEEVER D.E. and REYNOLDS C.K. (1994) Forage quality, feeding value and animal performance. In: 'tMannetje, L. and Frame, J. (eds.) *Grassland and Society. Proceedings of the 15th General Meeting of the European Grassland Federation*, Wageningen, 48-60.

BOSMA A.H. and GABRIELS P.C.J. (1993) Optimal conditions for the drying of a grass swath. *Proceedings of the 14th General Meeting of the European Grassland Federation*, Lahti, 153-158.

CLEMENTS R.O. (1994) A review of damage caused by pests and diseases to agricultural grasses in the UK. Review commissioned by and submitted to Ministry of Agriculture, Fisheries and Food.

COCKING E. (1995) Opportunities for the new biology. In: Pollott, G.E. (ed.) *Grassland in the 21st Century. Occasional Symposium of the British Grassland Society*, No. 29, 221-227.

COOPER J.P., TILLEY J.M.A., RAYMOND W.F. and TERRY R.A. (1962) Selection for digestibility in herbage grasses. *Nature*, **195**, 1276-1277.

CUTTLE S.P., HALLARD M., DANIEL G. and SCURLOCK R.V. (1992) Nitrate leaching from sheep grazed grass/clover and fertilized grass pastures. *Journal of Agricultural Science*, **119**, 335-342.

DEINUM B. (1994) Variation in anatomy of leaves of perennial ryegrass (*Lolium perenne*). In: 'tMannetje, L. and Frame, J. (eds.) *Grassland and Society. Proceedings of the 15th General Meeting of the European Grassland Federation*, Wageningen, 148-151.

GARWOOD E.A. and SINCLAIR J. (1979) Use of water by six grass species. Dry matter yields and response to irrigation. *Journal of Agricultural Science*, **93**, 13-24.

HODGSON J., MACKIE C.K. and PARKER J.W.G. (1986) Sward surface heights for efficient grazing. *Grass Farmer*, **24**, 5-10.

HONIG H. (1991) Reducing losses during storage and unloading of silage. *Landbauforschung Völkenrode*, **123**, 116-128.

HOPKINS A., DAVIES A, and DOYLE C. (1994) Clovers and other grazed legumes in UK pasture land. *IGER Technical Review*, No. 1

HOPKINS A., GILBEY J., DIBB C., BOWLING P.J. and MURRAY P.J. (1990) Response of perennial and reseeded grassland to fertilizer nitrogen. 1. Herbage production and herbage quality. *Grass and Forage Science*, **45**, 43-56.

HUMPHREYS M.O. (1989) Water-soluble carbohydrates in perennial ryegrass breeding. III. Relationships with herbage production, digestibility and crude protein content. *Grass and Forage Science*, **44**, 423-430.

JARVIS S.C., WILKINS R.J. and PAIN B.F. (1996) Opportunities for reducing the environmental impact of dairy farming managements: a systems approach. *Grass and Forage Science* (submitted).

JONES B.A., HATFIELD R.D. and MUCK R.E. (1993) Inhibition of legume proteolysis by red clover. *Proceedings of the 10th International Conference on Silage Research*, Dublin, 106-107.

MACDUFF J.H., JARVIS S.C. and ROBERTS D.H. (1990) Nitrates: leaching from grazed grassland systems. In: Calvet, R. (ed.) *Nitrates - Agriculture - Eau*, 405-410, Paris: INRA.
MAYER J.A., MERRY R.J., EPTON H.A.S. and SIGEE D.C. (1995) Biological control of *Listeria monocytogenes* in silage. *Annales de Zootechnie*, **44** (Suppl. 1), 99.
MONTIES B. and CALET C. (1993) Variability in lignification and utilization of grasses. *Proceedings of the 14th General Meeting of European Grassland Federation*, Lahti, 111-129.
MURRAY P.J. and CLEMENTS R.O. (1993) Sitona and other pest and disease damage to clover in the UK. *White Clover in Europe - State of the Art*, REUR Technical Series, **29**, 149-150.
NSEREKO V.L. and ROOKE J.A. (1993) The effect of novel additives upon protein breakdown during ensilage. *Proceedings of the 10th International Conference on Silage Research*, Dublin, 116-117.
PAIN B.F. (1991) Improving the utilization of slurry and farm effluent. In: Mayne, C.S. (ed.). *Management Issues for the Grassland Farmer in the 1990's, Occasional Symposium of the British Grassland Society*, **25**, 121-133.
PARSONS A.J. (1994) Exploiting resource capture - grassland. In: Monteith, J.L., Scott, R.K. and Unsworth, M.H. (eds.) *Resource Capture by Crops*, 315-349, Nottingham: Nottingham University Press
PARSONS A.J., THORNLEY J.H.M., NEWMAN J. and PENNING P.D. (1994) A mechanistic model of some physical determinants of intake rate and diet selection in a two-species temperate grassland sward. *Functional Ecology*, **8**, 187-204.
PEACOCK W.J. (1993) Genetic engineering for pastures. *Proceedings of the XVII International Grassland Congress*, Palmerston North, 29-32.
PEEL S., MATKIN E.A. and HUCKLE C.A. (1988) Herbage growth and utilized output from grassland on dairy farms in south-west England: case studies on five farms, 1982 and 1983. II. Herbage utilization. *Grass and Forage Science*, **43**, 71-78.
PENNING P.D., ROOK A.J. and ORR R.J. (1991) Patterns of ingestive behaviour of sheep continuously stocked on monocultures of ryegrass or white clover. *Applied Animal Behaviour Science*, **31**, 237-250.
PENNING P.D., PARSONS A.J., ORR R.J. and HARVEY A. (1994) Intake behaviour and production responses by sheep in different physiological states grazing monocultures of grass or white clover. *Proceedings of the 45th Annual Meeting of the European Association for Animal Production*, Edinburgh, 281.
RHODES I. and WEBB K.J. (1993) Improvement of white clover. *Outlook on Agriculture*, **22**, 189-194.
RYDEN J.C., BALL P.R. and GARWOOD E.A. (1984) Nitrate leaching from grassland. *Nature*, **311**, 50-53.
SCHOLEFIELD D. and TYSON K.C. (1992) Comparing levels of nitrate leaching from grass/clover and N-fertilized grass swards grazed with beef cattle. *Proceedings of the 14th General Meeting of the European Grassland Federation*, Lahti, 1992, 530-533.
SCHWINNING S. and PARSONS A.J. (1996) Analysis of the mechanisms of coexistence of grasses and legumes in grazing systems. *Journal of Ecology* (submitted).
SHELDRICK R.D. and MARTYN T.M. (1992) *Lotus* species and varieties for acid, low-phosphate soils. *Third Research Conference, British Grassland Society*, Greenmount, 41-42.
SHELDRICK R.D., NEWMAN G. and ROBERTS D.J. (1995) *Legumes for Milk and Meat*, Canterbury: Chalcombe Publications.

SKØT L., TIMMS E. and MYTTON L.R. (1994) Effect of toxin producing rhizobium strains on larvae of *Sitona flavescens* feeding on legume roots and nodules. *Plant and Soil,* **163**, 141-150.

SYRJÄLÄ-QVIST L. and WILKINS R.J. (1992) Forage utilization. *Proceedings of the 14th General Meeting of the European Grassland Federation,* Lahti, 1992, 60-77.

THOMAS H. (1994a) Diversity between and within temperate forage grass species in drought resistance, water use and related physiological responses. *Aspects of Applied Biology,* **38**, 47-55..

THOMAS H. (1994b) Plant proteases. *Annual Report 1993, IGER,* 39-40.

THOMAS H. and HUMPHREYS, M.O. (1991) Progress and potential of interspecific hybrids of *Lolium* and *Festuca. Journal of Agricultural Science,* **117**, 1-8.

THOMAS H. and SMART C.M. (1993) Crops that stay green. *Annals of Applied Biology,* **123**, 193-219.

THORNLEY J.H.M., BERGELSON J. and PARSONS A.J. (1995) Complex dynamics in a carbon-nitrogen model of a grass-legume pasture. *Annals of Botany,* **75**, 79-94.

TITCHEN N.M. and SCHOLEFIELD D. (1994) Tactical fertilizer application on commercial dairy farms. *Annual Report 1993, IGER,* 72.

WILKINS P.W. (1989) Genotype/harvesting frequency and genotype/nitrogen level interactions for annual dry matter yield in *Lolium perenne* in relation to breeding. *Euphytica,* **41**, 207-214.

WILKINS P.W. and DAVIES R.W. (1995) Progress in combining high dry matter yield with reduced flowering intensity and improved digestibility in perennial ryegrass. *Proceedings of the 19th Eucarpia Fodder Crops Sector Conference,* Brugge (in press).

WILKINS R.J. (1995) Optimisation of grass utilization in high rainfall conditions. *Proceedings of the 4th International Conference on the Nutrition of Herbivores,* Clermont Ferrand (in press).

WILKINS R.J. and HARVEY H.J. (1994) Management options to achieve agricultural and nature conservation objectives. In: Haggar, R.J. and Peel, S. *Grassland Management and Nature Conservation, Occasional Symposium of the British Grassland Society,* **No. 28**, 86-94.

WILSON D. (1993) Breeding grasses and legumes for an extended grazing season. In: *The Places for Grass in Land Use Systems.* Winter Meeting of the British Grassland Society, December 1993, 93-104.

Opportunities from the 'New Biology'

E. C. COCKING

Plant Genetic Manipulation Group, Department of Life Science,
University of Nottingham, Nottingham, NG7 2RD

ABSTRACT

Until recently relatively little attention has been given to the development of procedures for the cell and tissue culture and genetic manipulation of forage grasses, as compared to the major efforts in cereals. New opportunities are now arising from the availability of recombinant DNA technology and cell manipulation procedures to target specific modifications for grassland improvement. The challenge is to identify the desired grassland improvements in relation to the perceived needs, both nationally and internationally, into the next century. Because of the present key role of grasslands in providing feed for ruminant stock it is necessary to analyse the likely balance that will need to be achieved between grassland for animal feed, grassland for primary food production and grassland for non-food production. The question also needs to be addressed as to whether the scenario in the 21st Century, of a different balance between croplands, forests and grasslands, precipitated by major population increases, particularly in Asia, will require specific new grassland improvements. Will the need for sustainability of grasslands, coupled with requirements for reduced pollution, direct research to reduce nitrogenous fertiliser inputs by establishing symbiotic nitrogen fixation in grasses?

THE PRESENT SCENARIO

Although grasslands and forage crops play an important role in soil conservation and good land use, the primary reason for growing them is to provide feed for ruminant livestock. As has been highlighted by Hodgson (1976) the statistics of agriculture say little about forage because most forage crops are consumed on the farm where they are grown and do not reach the market place. Viewed globally three biological systems, croplands, forests and grasslands support the world economy. In the USA, for instance, more land is devoted to grasses and legumes grown as feed for livestock than to all other crops combined; the agricultural system represented by forage crops and ruminant animals that feed on them, mostly cattle and sheep, can be said to be the backbone of the USA's agricultural economy. As we progress into the 21st Century what are the opportunities from the 'New Biology' for the required grassland improvements?

THE GLOBAL PERSPECTIVE

A recent Worldwatch Institute Report on *Progress Toward a Sustainable Society* (Brown, 1990) has pointed out that the biological activity that supplies our food and raw materials takes place on nearly one third of the earth's surface that is land. Eleven percent of this, nearly 1.5 billion hectares, is used to produce crops.

Roughly twenty-five percent is pasture, providing grass or other forage for domesticated livestock, but this grassland area has shrunk progressively during the past twenty years, as overgrazing slowly converts it to desert. Widespread grassland degradation can now be seen on every continent. This problem is highly visible throughout Africa, where livestock numbers have expanded nearly as fast as the human population. In 1950, 238 million Africans relied on 272 million livestock. By 1987, the human population had increased to 604 million and the livestock to 543 million. A study charting the mounting pressures on grasslands in nine southern African countries found that the capacity to sustain livestock is diminishing as grasslands deteriorate, soil erosion accelerates, further reducing the carrying capacity and setting in motion a self reinforcing cycle of ecological degradation and deepening human poverty (FAO, 1984).

Brown (1990) has highlighted the fact that the fodder needs of livestock in nearly all developing countries now exceeds the sustainable yields of grasslands and other forage resources. In India the demand, as we move into the 21st Century, is expected to exceed 700 million tonnes, while the supply will total 540 million tonnes. Moreover, overgrazing is not limited to the Third World; even in the USA overgrazing is commonplace. As the deterioration of grazing lands continues, some of it becomes wasteland, converted to desert by the excessive demands of growing livestock populations. As the forage available to support animals diminishes, pressure shifts to croplands to produce more grain to feed livestock, thus intensifying the competition between humans and animals for scarce food supplies.

In this connection a perceptive analysis has recently been provided by McRae (1994), suggesting that the capacity of the world to produce enough food to feed a much larger population as we progress into the 21st Century is not really in doubt, provided people are prepared to eat a smaller proportion of meat in their diet. His analysis is worthy of close study because it could be pivotal in the way we will be able to best utilise the various aspects of genetic engineering and plant biotechnology for grassland improvements. His analysis (McRae, 1994) is that "Growing grain or grass and then feeding it to animals is an inefficient use of land, for animals are inefficient at converting plant energy into human food. At present in countries like India, where meat forms a very small proportion of the diet of most people, the total plant energy consumed (actual plant food eaten, plus seed, plus animal feed) is about 3,000 calories a day. By contrast, North Americans, Australians, New Zealanders and the French consume an average of 15,000 calories a day, thanks largely to the amount of meat in their diet. The world's average is some 6,000 calories a day."

However, it is not clear that another 'Green Revolution', providing a doubling of average yields, is imminent. The success of the 'Green Revolution' depended on having suitable land, the extra fertilisers particularly nitrogenous fertiliser, the right climate and enough water. But, as McRae(1994) has pointed out, these higher yields were often achieved at costs including soil erosion, salination and environmental damage, particularly nitrate pollution from the required nitrogenous fertiliser inputs. Increasingly the sustainability of these advances is being questioned. Viewed in this perspective opportunities from the 'New Biology' linked to the procedures of genetic engineering and plant biotechnology for grassland improvement will need to embrace the need for the adequate sustainability of grasslands.

THE CHALLENGES FOR THE 21ST CENTURY

If current rates of soil erosion and deforestation continue unaltered for the next thirty-five years, it could be that the world will be trying to meet the food, fuel and timber needs of some 8 billion people, nearly 3 billion more than the current population, with 960 billion fewer tonnes of topsoil and 440 million fewer hectares of trees. Whilst it is difficult to predict what the reality will be by 2030, the analysis of Brown (1990) is that, unlike at present, land use patterns will be abiding by basic principles of biological stability: nutrient retention, carbon balance, soil protection, water conservation and preservation of species diversity. Rather than the earth's photosynthetic productivity being eaten away as at present, it will be safeguarded or even enhanced. A major factor in halting diversification will depend on eliminating overgrazing. It is forecast that the global livestock herd in 2030 is therefore likely to be much smaller than today's 3 billion. Since open grazing is likely to diminish, it has been suggested that farmers will integrate livestock into their diverse farming systems, using, for fodder, the leaves from trees or the cover crop in their rotational cropping patterns. It is also forecast that it seems inevitable that adequately nourishing a world population that could be 60% larger than today's will preclude, as previously suggested, the feeding of the one third of the global grain harvest to livestock and poultry, as is currently the case.

As far as grasslands are concerned, it is likely that farmers in some parts of the world will need to grow seed-bearing perennial grasses, creating a cropping pattern resembling the native prairies. In this respect the role of the 'New Biology' will probably mainly be a redirected use of traditional breeding improvements for the production of grasslands with edible grains, oils and other commodities. Jackson (1987) has suggested that advantage could be taken of the prairie grassland's natural diversity, drought resistance and soil-reviving capacity. This would greatly improve the opportunity for sustainability, reducing the need for chemicals (pesticides, herbicides and fertilisers), irrigation water and other intensive inputs. Grassland species that are salt-tolerant and drought-resistant will increasingly be required. Gene pools in gene banks for grassland improvement, in this respect, will be of increasing importance.

In considering the opportunities from the 'New Biology' in these respects, it is salutary to note that regardless of the details of these new technologies, including presently unforeseen advances in biotechnology, the biochemical process of photosynthesis as carried out in green plants and in the grasses of our grasslands into the 21st Century will remain the basis for meeting human needs. It has been estimated that humanity already appropriates about 40% of the earth's annual photosynthetic product on land, leaving only 60% for the millions of other species and for protecting basic ecosystem functions. The sooner societies stabilise their populations, the greater will be their opportunities for achieving equitable and stable patterns of land use that can meet their needs indefinitely (Ehrlich, 1989).

WHAT IS THE LIKELY USE OF THE 'NEW BIOLOGY'?

It is noteworthy that the world's major food crops, rice, wheat, maize, sorghum, oats, rye, barley and sugarcane are all grasses. Perhaps understandably, much more attention has been paid to the genetic manipulation of these major graminaceous food crops than to the genetic manipulation of the wide range of grassland graminaceous species. The genetics of most forage grasses is quite complicated, often associated with polyploidy, and geneticists have not devoted as much effort to understanding them as they have to the major food grasses, such as rice, wheat and maize. This unfortunate state of affairs is only slowly being rectified, and it has impacted negatively on the development of procedures for the genetic manipulation of both forage grasses and also forage legumes. The tissue culture of forage grasses using *in vitro* culture methodology has also proved difficult.

At the Institute of Grassland and Environmental Research (IGER, 1993) the use of molecular techniques such as restriction fragment length polymorphisms (RFLPs) and random amplified polymorphic DNA (RAPDs) have provided the opportunity to build a genetic map which saturates the whole genome with informative markers. This is especially useful in forage grass species since the absence of morphological genetic markers has been a serious limitation in the construction of genetic maps. Somewhat similar procedures are also being used to decipher the mechanisms for increasing the range of variation available within the germplasm both through conventional procedures, that rely on sexual recombination, or through methods exploiting non-sexual recombination. Fluorescence *in situ* chromosome hybridisation is increasingly playing a central role in these manipulations, including studies on the production of transgenic forage grasses and legumes, in which the technique is capable of identifying small introgressed segments.

Some success has been achieved in the production of transgenic forage grasses such as *Festuca* spp. and in model forage legumes such as *Lotus japonicus*. Much more basic research is required before we can contemplate using these techniques of the 'New Biology' to address meaningfully the challenging modifications of the very wide range of forage grass species required for the next century. Many of the procedures for genetic manipulation need further refinement if we are to be able not just to obtain transgenic forage grasses, but transgenic forage grasses in which the foreign gene or genes of agronomic interest are stably expressed.

Unfortunately, transgene inactivation is being increasingly recognised. Desirable new phenotypes, created by the introduction of foreign DNA into plants, are frequently unstable following propagation, leading to a loss of the newly acquired traits. This genetic instability is due not to deletion or mutation of the introduced DNA, but rather to the inactivation of the transgene (Finnegan and McElroy, 1994). Some of the problems relate to the transformation method, and to the difficulty of dealing with the introgression of several genes. Protoplast fusion between cultivated and wild species may be an alternative procedure for polygenic characters such as salinity tolerance (Finch *et al.*, 1990). Whilst methods for the transformation of dicotyledonous species (including forage legumes) have been well established using *Agrobacterium*, this has not been used, so far, in the grasses or rice. Recently a large number of fertile, morphologically normal transgenic rice plants were obtained by co-cultivation of rice tissue with *Agrobacterium tumefaciens* (Hiei *et al.*, 1994). This use of supervirulent *Agrobacterium tumefaciens* may help greatly to achieve stable transgenic forage grasses.

Into the next century, medically important proteins, such as vaccines, are likely to be produced from forage grasses, in the same way as they are currently being produced from transgenic tobacco. In a way, the possible flow through of this basic research to applications in grassland improvement illustrates Pasteur's dictum that "There does not exist a category of science to which one can give the name applied science. There are science and the applications of science, bound together as the fruit of the tree which bears it".

From these general comments it is clear that much can be achieved using conventional breeding improvements in forage grasses coupled with RFLP, RAPDs and *in situ* chromosome hybridisation to address the challenges and opportunities in grassland well into the next century. Scientists should not, however, be inhibited in trying to utilise grassland species for non-food uses utilising genetic manipulation to modify fibres, and for vaccine production. Will it also be possible to improve the digestibility and palatability of the grassland crop for ruminant livestock by novel genetic manipulations?

THE CHALLENGE TO REDUCE INPUTS OF FIXED NITROGEN FERTILISERS

Grassland species have a large requirement for fixed nitrogen and, unlike forage legumes, they are presently unable to establish a symbiotic nitrogen fixing relationship with rhizobia bacteria present in the soil. Could rhizobia be added to grasslands which would interact with the root system of the forage grasses to establish a nitrogen-fixing symbiotic system? This vista could meet the challenge of maintaining the sustainability of the world's grasslands and reducing environmental pollution. Encouragingly there is now good evidence that such a symbiotic nitrogen fixing interaction of rhizobia with wheat is possible; clear indications are now arising from our work at Nottingham that symbiotic nitrogen fixation is possible when wheat is inoculated with *Azorhizobium caulinodans* (ORS571) or *Rhizobium* ORS310.

ORS571 is known to form stem and root nodules on the tropical legume *Sesbania rostrata* that are of adventitious (lateral) root origin; the invasion pathway is by 'crack entry'. *Rhizobium* ORS310 also forms stem nodules on another tropical legume, *Aeschynomene indica*, that are of lateral root origin. Again, the invasion pathway is by 'crack entry'. Such rhizobia, isolated from stem nodules, when interacted with the roots of seedlings of maize, rice and wheat, are also able to enter these non-legume crops by 'crack entry', where the lateral roots emerge through the root epidermis. This early stage in the formation of lateral root nodules is readily detectable by light microscopic examination of sections of embedded material. It has been suggested that these particular rhizobia have invasive properties, probably associated with the secretion of bacterial cellulase and pectinase, which enable them to penetrate between the cells of the primordia of emerging lateral roots and, subsequently, into cells of the cortex. More than a century ago, Schneider (1893) undertook experiments to force an interaction between rhizobia and the roots of maize and other non-legume crops. He observed extensive infection by rhizobia in parenchymatous cells near the vicinity of emergence of maize lateral roots, but further invasion did not occur. However, he did not have available, at that time, these stem-nodulating rhizobia.

It is known that the nitrogenase of *Azorhizobium caulinodans* ORS571, unlike that of most other rhizobia, is tolerant of 3% oxygen in the gas phase when cells are grown in nitrogen-free liquid medium. *Rhizobium* ORS310 is also known to have a nitrogenase that is tolerant to 0.5% oxygen under similar conditions. Because it was anticipated that nitrogen fixation in the nodular interactions involved in the 'crack entry' of rhizobia into emerging lateral roots of non-legume crops might be inhibited by the oxygen levels present, nitrogen fixation studies were undertaken on wheat interacting with *Azorhizobium caulinodans* ORS571 and *Rhizobium* ORS310 (Cocking *et al.*, 1995).

THE OUTLOOK

Overall, when considering the likely use of the 'New Biology' for grassland improvements into the 21st Century it is also worth noting that in growing forage grasses the farmer's aim, presently, is to maximise the production of vegetative tissue, leaves and stems. In this way, the methods employed by farmers to produce and utilise forage grasses are markedly different from most other crops in which crop management is directed toward the production of fruit or seed. Into the 21st Century, crop management of grasslands will require a progressive change in these management procedures integrated with the application of the 'New Biology' approaches, if the role of grasslands in the world economy is to be satisfactorily maintained for the well being of mankind.

REFERENCES

BROWN L.R. (1990) State of the World. *Worldwatch Institute Report on Progress Toward a Sustainable Society*, pp 253, London: Unwin.

COCKING E.C., SABRY R.S., SALEH S.A., KOTHARI S.L., BATCHELOR C.A., JAIN S., WEBSTER G., JONES J., JOTHAM J. and DAVEY M.R. (1995) Symbiotic nitrogen fixation in cereals. *Abstract, International Workshop on Associative Interactions of Nitrogen-Fixing Bacteria with Plants*, Saratov, Russia, June 1995, 29-31.

EHRLICH P.R. (1989) Global Change and Carrying Capacity: Implications for Life on Earth. In: DeFries, R.S. and Malone, T.F. (eds), *Global Change and Our Common Future: Papers From a Forum*, Washington, D.C.: National Academy Press.

FAO (1984) *FAO Monthly Bulletin of Statistics*, **1(3)**, 1984; Southern African Development Coordination Conference, SADCC Agriculture: Toward 2000 (Rome: FAO, 1984).

FINCH R.P., SLAMET I.H. and COCKING E.C. (1990) Production of heterokaryons by the fusion of mesophyll protoplasts of *Porteresia coarctata* and cell suspension-derived protoplasts of *Oryza sativa*: A new approach to hybridisation in rice. *Journal of Plant Physiology*, **136**, 592-598.

FINNEGAN J and McELROY D (1994) Transgene inactivation: Plants Fight Back! *Biotechnology*, **12**, 883-887.

HIEI Y., OHTA S., KOMARI T and KUMASHIRO T. (1994) Efficient transformation of rice (*Oryza sativa* L.) mediated by *Agrobacterium* and sequence analysis of the boundaries of the T-DNA. *The Plant Journal*, **6(2)**, 271-282.

HODGSON H.J. (1976) Forage crops. *Scientific American*, February 1976, 61-75.

IGER (1993) *Institute of Grassland & Environmental Research Annual Report*.

JACKSON W (1987) In: *Altars of Unhewn Stone: Science and the Earth*, San Francisco: North Point Press.

McRAE H. (1994) In: *The World in 2020*, p 122, London: Harper Collins.

SCHNEIDER A. (1893) A new factor in economic agriculture. *University of Illinois, Agricultural Experimental Station Bulletin.* **29**, 301-319.

Cycles of Phenotypic Recurrent Selection for 2n Gamete Production in Diploid Alfalfa

O. CALDERINI AND A. MARIANI

Istituto di Ricerche sul Miglioramento Genetico delle Piante Foraggere
C.N.R., via della Madonna Alta 130, 06128 Perugia, Italy

INTRODUCTION

In alfalfa, as in all of the other polysomic polyploids, it is not possible to reach maximum heterozygosity with the traditional varieties, due to multiple allelism and the presence of linkage blocks. Fusion of 2n gametes produced by diploid hybrids is suggested to be effective in determining the maximum of favourable genetic interactions in the tetraploid progenies, but a successful pollination control system is needed in order for 2n gametes to have practical utility (McCoy, 1992).

MATERIALS AND METHODS

An alfalfa breeding program based on 2n gametes was carried out to increase the frequency of these gametes by means of phenotypic recurrent selection. Seed set [(No. of seeds produced/No. of flowers pollinated)*100] in 4x(ms)-2x and 2x-4x crosses was used as a measure of 2n pollen and 2n egg production, respectively. The best 2n gamete producers were intercrossed in each cycle to obtain two different populations, one for 2n pollen and one for 2n eggs. The first two cycles of selection (Tavoletti et al., 1991) were effective in increasing the percentage of plants producing 2n gametes and the frequency of 2n gametes per plant. Responses to selection indicated that production of 2n gametes is controlled by major and minor genes.

RESULTS AND DISCUSSION

Results of the 3rd and 4th cycles of selection are presented in Table 1. In both cycles of selection the average seed set significantly differed from the average seed set of the control population. However, in the 2n egg population the average seed sets of the 3rd and 4th cycles were not statistically different, as indeed they were in the 2n pollen population (Table 1). These results confirm those of the first two cycles of selection, which suggested that 2n egg production is controlled by one recessive major gene. In fact, the high response of the 3rd cycle is followed by no response in the 4th cycle. Production of 2n pollen, on the contrary, seems to be controlled by few major genes because selection also achieved a response in the 4th cycle. Moreover, the presence of recombinants with a high seed set (Table 1, bottom line) would seem to indicate that selection has concentrated minor genes that influence the production of both 2n pollen and 2n eggs. Research is being continued with a program of Bilateral Sexual

Polyploidization between the best 2n egg and 2n pollen producers obtained with the cycles of selection.

Table 1. Effects of selection for 2n pollen and 2n egg production in two diploid populations of alfalfa.

	2n pollen 4x(ms)-2x crosses			2n eggs 2x-4x crosses		
Population	A0	A3	A4	B0	B3	B4
No. of plants utilised	15	56	50	15	50	61
No. flowers pollinated	978	7199	6669	1125	6422	4808
No. of seeds produced	35	2488	3551	77	2654	2090
Average seed set (%)*	3.56[c]	33.54[b]	51.54[a]	7.14[b]	37.73[a]	42.40[a]
Seed set/plant (range)	0-10	1-115	8-115	0-20	1-191	0-196

A_0, B_0: control population; A_3, B_3: population of the 3rd cycle; A_4, B_4: population of the 4th cycle.
* Duncan's test was performed separately on the 2n pollen and the 2n egg populations; means not followed by the same letter differ significantly at $P \leq 0.01$.

REFERENCES

McCOY T.J. (1992) Genome manipulation and molecular genetic analysis of alfalfa (*Medicago sativa*). Proceedings of the workshop: Gametes with somatic chromosome number in the evolution and breeding of polyploid polysomic species: achievements and perspectives. Perugia, 1992, 55-59.
TAVOLETTI S., MARIANI A. and VERONESI F. (1991). Phenotypic recurrent selection for 2n pollen and 2n egg production in diploid alfalfa. *Euphytica* **57**: 97-102.

Sense Suppression as a Method for Identification and Cloning of Genes Involved in Tannin Biosynthesis

F.DAMIANI, F. PAOLOCCI, P. D. CLUSTER AND S. ARNCIONI

IRMPGF, Perugia, Italy

INTRODUCTION

Condensed tannins are produced in different tissues of many forage species and have both beneficial and detrimental effects in different situations and applications. Many forage legumes, containing high levels of tannins in their foliage, would benefit as crop plants from a reduction in their tannin content. Others, such as lucerne and clover, lack tannins in their edible parts and for this reason are not suitable for pasture and fresh consumption by ruminants.

A chimeric T-DNA containing the gene *nptII* under nos promoter (for selective kanamycin resistance) and the maize gene *Sn* under CAMV35S promoter was transferred, using an *Agrobacterium rhizogenes* binary vector, into plants of *Lotus corniculatus* cv Leo, which normally produces tannins in the foliage.

The gene *Sn* acts in maize as a strong transactivator of anthocyanin synthesis in different tissues (Tonelli *et al.*, 1991). Since anthocyanins and tannins share a large part of their biosynthetic pathway, the influence of *Sn* on tannin production was investigated. This paper reports the effect of this transformation on tannin synthesis and the practical applications derived by the utilization of these plants.

RESULTS

Several plants were regenerated from hairy roots cultured for two months in MS medium supplemented with NAA (1 mg/l), 6-BAP (1 mg/l) and kanamycin (50 mg/l). Detached leaves of outdoor grown kanamycin-resistant plants were tested for the presence of tannins using a DMACA staining (Li *et al.*, 1995) and most of these plants showed a reduced or null content of tannins while untransformed plants or control plants transformed with *nptII* only did not show any alteration of tannin synthesis. A variable number of copies of T-DNA (1-14) was observed in transformed plants through southern blot analysis and while some single-copy transformants were normal, some showed tannin suppression. Multiple-copy plants were always tannin negative.

The same plants were analysed for kanamycin resistance by testing their ability to de-differentiate in media supplemented with increasing levels of kanamycin. For this trait, a positive correlation was observed between copy number and resistance to the antibiotic. Northern analysis of mRNA showed conflicting results for *nptII* and *Sn* genes. In fact, a positive correlation between copy number and mRNA amount is observed for *nptII* while the reverse situation is observed for *Sn*. This indicates that the presence of multiple copies of a transgene does not necessarily negatively affect its expression. In the case of *Sn* an interaction between transgenes and resident genes could cause problems in gene transcription or mRNA stability. Attempts to identify the *Lotus* Sn-like genes are in progress and, although two endogenous genomic regions with oligòs derived from the most conserved domain of *Sn* have been amplified, their sequence did not show significant similarity to *Sn*.

CONCLUSIONS

Practical methods based on the intriguing phenomenon of gene silencing (Finnegan and McElroy, 1994) have been devised to intentionally reduce tannin synthesis. It is not known which and how many genes are involved in the pathway leading from leucoanthocyanidin to condensed tannins. It is suggested that a comparative analysis of mRNA in suppressed and unsuppressed plants should allow the identification and cloning of genes responsible for tannin synthesis in *Lotus*. Finally, it is hoped to activate tannin synthesis in foliage of non bloat-safe forage legumes.

REFERENCES

FINNEGAN J., and MCELROY D. (1994) Transgene inactivation: plant fight back! *Biotechnology*, **12**, 883-888
LI Y., TANNER G., and LARKIN P. (1995) The DMACA-HCL protocol and the threshold proanthocyanidin content for bloat safety in forage legumes. *Journal of the Science of Food and Agriculture*. (in press)
TONELLI C., CONSONNI G., DOLFINI S.F., DELLAPORTA S.L., VIOTTI, A. and GAVAZZI, G. (1991) Genetic and molecular analysis of Sn, a light inducible, tissue specific regulatory gene in maize. *Molecular and General Genetics*, **225**, 401-410

Targets For Marker Assisted Selection In Grass Breeding

M. O. HUMPHREYS, C. EVANS, M. S. FARRELL,
J. G. JONES, N. J. McADAM AND M. D. HAYWARD
IGER, Plas Gogerddan, Aberystwyth, Dyfed, SY23 3EB

INTRODUCTION

The ability of grassland to meet the needs of farming in the 21st Century is critically dependent upon its composition in terms of species and varieties. Forage grass breeding aims to tailor new varieties specifically to meet animal requirements. Success in this depends on good knowledge of the genetic control and relationships of relevant traits. Advanced genetic technologies provide breeders with new opportunities to produce more precisely designed varieties.

GENETIC MARKERS

Genes which are relatively easy to detect can be used to produce genomic maps. Visible single gene effects, such as seed coat colour, were used initially and later isozyme markers became available. Recent DNA technology has extended the genetic map of ryegrass from that based mainly on 18 isozyme loci to include 83 RFLP (Restriction Fragment Length Polymorphism) and 65 RAPD (Random Amplified Polymorphic DNA) markers. These are distributed over 7 linkage groups, reflecting the basic chromosome number of ryegrass and related fescue species, and can be used in the identification of genes controlling quantitative trait loci (QTLs) of agronomic importance.

QUANTITATIVE TRAIT LOCI

Although some traits of interest to grass breeders may be controlled by single genes (e.g. disease resistance), many are produced by a number of genes of small effect. Such genes are difficult to identify individually although they may be revealed by linkage to markers. For example, work on ryegrass indicated an association between water soluble carbohydrate (WSC) content and the isozyme locus PGI/2. This was confirmed by correlated changes in PGI/2 allele frequencies when ryegrass lines were selected for contrasting WSC content. New DNA markers have revealed QTLs for other traits including flowering. Part of the genome close to the I6pgd marker, near the end of Linkage Group 1 (LG1), has a significant effect on heading date and head number. A region near to the marker pLMC106 on LG6 (23.5 cM away from PGI/2) is associated with earliness of flowering, possibly through vernalisation requirements. Close to this (about 19.8 cM from PGI/2) is a region which affects plant height and ear length. In LG1, close to GOT-2, there is a QTL effect on aftermath heading and dry matter yield. The marker genes linked to these QTLs can be used for indirect selection on specific aspects of complex traits at an early stage in breeding programmes.

MARKER ASSISTED SELECTION (MAS)

The inclusion of genetic markers in a selection index has a strong advantage over traditional phenotypic selection especially if heritabilities are low. Effective MAS depends on strong linkage between QTLs and adjacent marker genes. Breakdown of linkage can be detected with flanking markers. Nine QTLs concerned with different aspects of the flowering process in ryegrass have been identified of which 3 control inflorescence emergence. Careful choice of QTLs for selection may minimise undesirable correlated responses. Thus in LG1, a QTL for heading date is closely associated with head number whereas there are separate QTLs for heading date and head number on LG2 and LG6. Future work will seek out QTLs for aspects of nutritive quality which can be improved without loss of productivity, persistency or disease resistance.

Somatic Hybrids in *Medicago*: a New Tool in Alfalfa Breeding

F. PUPILLI, P.D. CLUSTER, F. DAMIANI AND S. ARCIONI

Istituto di Ricerche sul Miglioramento Genetico delle Piante Foraggere del C.N.R., via della Madonna alta 130, 06128, Perugia, Italy

INTRODUCTION

Alfalfa (*Medicago sativa* L., 2n=4x=32) is the most important forage plant in temperate environments worldwide. Somatic hybridization of alfalfa with other species provides a mechanism to enlarge the germplasm resources of this important crop. The aim of this work was to study the genetic consequences of the somatic hybridization of alfalfa with (1) *M. coerulea* (2n=2x=16) and (2) *M. arborea* (2n=4x=32), and the possibility that these hybrids may be useful in alfalfa breeding programs.

M. sativa + M. arborea somatic hybrids (S+A) were obtained according to the same procedure reported for the production of the *M. sativa* + *M. coerulea* somatic hybrids (S+C) (Pupilli *et al.*, 1992). Both S+C and S+A were subjected to molecular analyses by a variety of techniques, including the probing of Southern blots with random RFLPs and ribosomal DNA (rDNA) 18S and 25S sequences, which flank the length-variable intergenic spacer (IGS) regions. The S+C hybrids were also analyzed for microsporogenesis.

RESULTS

From Southern analysis of the hybrids, the presence of bands specific to both parents confirmed their true hybrid origin, but the nuclear constitution of the two hybrids differed substantially. The random RFLP analysis of S+C showed that while almost all the *M. sativa* specific bands were retained in the hybrid pattern about 30% of *M. coerulea* specific bands were lost. On the contrary, S+A lost many RFLPs from both parents. In rDNA studies, the majority of *M. coerulea* and *M. sativa* rDNA genes were uniform and identical in length, but several significant species-specific length classes clearly distinguished these two species. The rDNA genes of *M. arborea*, however, were highly heterogeneous for IGS length, containing more than 15 distinct length classes which differed significantly from both other species. The S+C retained all the parental rDNA variants while S+A lost approximately half of the *M. arborea* rDNA. No somaclonal variation was detected for rDNA or RFLP markers among different plants from either somatic hybrid.

Chromosome counts showed that S+C retained the full chromosome complements of both parents while at least five chromosomes were missing in S+A. Although the majority of meioses in S+C were normal, some abnormalities in the form of lagging chromosomes and unusual orientation of spindles were

238

noted. The S+A did not flower during the first year of soil acclimatisation even though some flower buds were noted.

CONCLUSIONS
The results of the present work indicate that S+C were fertile and substantially stable and, therefore, suitable alfalfa breeding at the hexaploid level. Conversely, more disturbances were noted in S+A but this hybrid could also be useful in alfalfa breeding if and when the plants become fertile.

REFERENCES
PUPILLI F., SCARPA G.M. , DAMIANI F. and ARCIONI S. (1992) Production of interspecific somatic hybrids in the genus *Medicago*. *Theoretical and Applied Genetics*, **84**, 792-797.

Progress Towards The Ideal Pasture Grass

P. W. WILKINS

IGER, Aberystwyth, Dyfed, SY23 3EB

INTRODUCTION

The ideal pasture grass would be capable of giving high yields of high-digestibility herbage continuously throughout the grazing season. Also it would be highly persistent and competitive against weed grasses and have adequate resistance to the common diseases and pests. Considerable progress towards this ideal has been achieved by breeding perennial ryegrass (*Lolium perenne*) at IGER during the last fifteen years. The recently recommended cv. Aberelan has much improved herbage yield during the predominately vegetative phases of growth (the March-April and August-October periods) and recovers a higher proportion of fertiliser nitrogen in the herbage over the grazing season (Wilkins and Lovatt, 1989). More recently, a new variety (Ba11778) has been produced which combines a considerably lower proportion of reproductive tillers during spring and summer, which increases herbage leaf content, with even better productivity and persistency (Wilkins and Davies, 1994). Ba11778 also had a high water-soluble carbohydrate content of the herbage which has a positive effect on digestibility since it tends to increase the ratio of cell contents to cell wall (Humphreys, 1989). In 1993 an experiment was established to assess the impact of these improvements on performance under the frequent harvesting regimes typical of grazing systems.

MATERIALS AND METHODS

The experiment was arranged in four replicate blocks, with varieties and harvesting frequencies fully randomised within each block. Three varieties with similar ear emergence dates were compared: Ba11778, Talbot and Gator. Ba11778 was first sown in UK National List Trials in 1994. Talbot has been the standard control cultivar until recently and is higher in herbage leaf content than some other widely-grown cultivars, such as Merlinda and Morgana. Gator is an amenity cultivar selected for high tiller density and dark colour. Plots (3 x 1.2 m^2) were sown by hand in August 1993. They were cut to 5 cm in March 1994 when they all had good ground cover (at least 65%). In 1994, plots were cut with a Haldrup plot harvester. Four harvesting frequencies were applied: 2, 3, 4, and 5-weekly. An equal amount of compound fertiliser was applied at the beginning of each of 7 five-week periods (360 kg/ha of N in total), beginning on week 11. Dry-matter yields and *in vitro* dry-matter digestibility (DMD) using the pepsin-cellulase method (Jones and Hayward, 1975) were determined at each harvest.

RESULTS AND DISCUSSION

In 1994, the first harvest year, Ba11778 gave significantly (P<0.001) higher mean dry matter yield over all harvests than both cvs. Talbot and Gator, 12% more than Talbot and 31% more than Gator. Much larger differences in yield among the varieties occurred during the vegetative phases of growth (weeks 11-15 and 31-45), Ba11778 showing much less variation in yield through the grazing season than the other two varieties (Figure 1). It is clear however, that considerable further improvements in vegetative growth are necessary in order to achieve the same high level of productivity in the second half of the growing season as occurs in the first half.

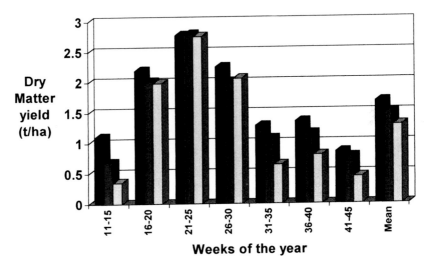

Figure 1.   Mean dry matter yield over four harvesting frequencies of three varieties of perennial ryegrass in the first harvest year,

Ba11778

Talbot

Gator

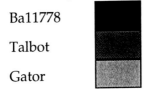

Varieties also varied significantly (P<0.001) in mean DMD over all harvests, Ba11778 being 1.2 percentage units higher than Talbot and 3.4 units higher than Gator. Again, differences among the varieties were much greater during some periods than others, the range being 0.7 units over weeks 11-15 and 5.9 units over weeks 26-30 (Figure 2). Ba11778 had a consistently high level of DMD (79% or more) throughout. Although differences among harvesting frequencies in mean DMD over all harvests were statistically significant (P<0.001) they were small (1.2 percentage units or less) and there was no significant variety/harvesting frequency interaction.

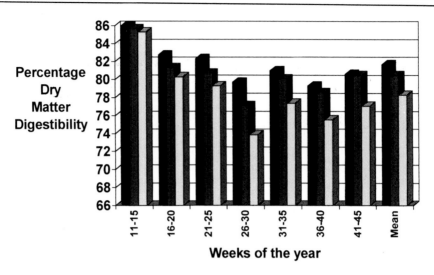

Figure 2.   Mean *in vitro* dry matter digestibility (DMD) over four harvesting frequencies of three varieties of perennial ryegrass in the first harvest year. (Shading key as Figure 1.)

ACKNOWLEDGEMENT
This work is funded by the Ministry of Agriculture, Fisheries and Food.

REFERENCES
HUMPHREYS M. O. (1989) Water-soluble carbohydrates in perennial ryegrass breeding. III. Relationships with herbage production, digestibility and crude protein content. *Grass and Forage Science* **44**, 423-430.
JONES D.I.H. and HAYWARD M. V. (1975) The effect of pepsin pretreatment of herbage on the prediction of dry matter digestibility from solubility in fungal cellulase solutions. *Journal of the Science of Food and Agriculture* **26**, 711-718.
WILKINS P.W. and DAVIES R.W. (1994) Progress in combining high dry matter yield with reduced flowering intensity and improved digestibility in perennial ryegrass. *Proceedings of the 19th Eucarpia Fodder Crops Section, Brugge*, pp. 247-252.
WILKINS P.W. and LOVATT A.J. (1989) Genetic improvement of yield of nitrogen of *Lolium perenne* pastures. *Euphytica* **43**, 259-262.

The Effect of Elevated CO_2 on Growth of Perennial Ryegrass and White Clover

J NÖSBERGER, A. LÜSCHER, T HEBEISEN, S. ZANETTI AND B FISCHER

Institute of Plant Sciences, Eidgenössische Technische Hochschule,
8092 Zurich, Switzerland

INTRODUCTION

Increase in [CO_2] increases C uptake by vegetation in the short-term, firstly because the current [CO_2] is below the level at which the carboxylation reaction of photosynthesis is saturated, and by inhibiting the wasteful oxidative process of photorespiration, which can remove some 40% of the carbon that plants assimilate. This latter effect is of particular ecological significance because it means that plants will be potentially more efficient with respect to their use of light, nitrogen, and other limiting resources, and therefore an increase in carbon gain will be expected regardless of whether other resources are limiting or not.

It has to be considered that carbon fluxes also affect the carbon:nitrogen ratio of both plants and soil. The species-specific responses of plants to CO_2 and the change in the carbon:nitrogen ratio have important implications for competition. It is therefore essential to elucidate the relevant processes that are driving these changes, conduct experiments at a scale where these processes can be meaningfully assessed and overcome the limitations which have until now been imposed by the technological limit of the open-top chamber.

Open-top and controlled environment chamber systems have provided extensive information on the possible effects of elevated [CO_2]. There is now a need to establish the validity of these effects under otherwise unmodified conditions on a field scale. The Free-Air CO_2 Enrichment (FACE) technology, developed by Brookhaven National Laboratory, is unique in allowing precise control of [CO_2] over large areas of vegetation without the use of any enclosure eliminating, all the limitations of open-top chambers.

MATERIAL AND METHODS

Since May 1993 the effect of an increase in atmospheric CO_2 to 600 vpm on growth processes in the shoot and root zone of established grassland has been investigated. The model ecosystem investigated in the Swiss-FACE experiment included monocultures of perennial ryegrass (*Lolium perenne L.*) and white clover (*Trifolium repens L.*) as well as the binary mixture of both species. The defoliation frequency (4 and 8 cuts) and the nitrogen fertilization (140 and 560 kgN/ha) was varied in a factorial design to examine the response of the plants to CO_2 when the availability of other resources was changing.

RESULTS

Swards of perennial ryegrass and white clover monocultures showed, in the first fumigation year, mean CO_2 responses of +6% for the grass and +19% for the legume, under different management treatments. This response to CO_2 was small compared to those of individual plants grown in the gaps of a perennial ryegrass sward. Harvestable biomass of non-legumes grown in gaps at elevated CO_2 increased by 30% , whereas the biomass of legumes increased by 181%. These results demonstrate that sward structure influences the extent of the CO_2 effect on growth but not the qualitative differences of the CO_2 effects on legumes and non-legumes. The management treatments had mostly a greater effect on the proportion of species than CO_2. Long-term changes in species proportion have therefore to consider the interaction between CO_2 and management effects. The greater response of the legumes was related to the performance of the symbiotic N_2 fixation. The percentage of N derived from symbiosis increased by 15%. Total yield of fixed nitrogen increased by 35%. The entire increase in above-ground nitrogen yield under elevated CO_2 could be attributed to the increased N_2 fixation; no additional nitrogen was assimilated from the soil. Symbiotic N_2 fixation enabled the sequestration of additional carbon into the ecosystem.

Studies of leaf photosynthesis conducted by Prof. S. Long (University of Essex) over the past 3 years, have shown a sustained increase in leaf photosynthesis under elevated $[CO_2]$ in both *L. perenne* and *T. repens*, at both high and low N-fertilisation and in the extensive and intensive management regimes. Increases in leaf photosynthesis ranged from 18% to 48%. Simultaneously, stomatal conductance demonstrated a sustained decrease. A loss of Rubisco was only present before a cut and was removed after the cut, suggesting that the loss was driven by source-sink balance. C-sink capacity of the grasses, grown in enhanced CO_2, appears to be very limited at the end of the regrowth period. Diurnal changes in *T. repens* leaves, however, indicate a persisting C demand at all times. Such a response agrees with the strong yield response to CO_2 of *T. repens*.

DISCUSSION

Changes have been shown in the competitive balance between grassland species over the first three years using an additive and replacement design. However, it is not known if this change in balance will become amplified in the longer term, or if the balance will be restored. Similarly, a decrease in availability of N with increased C deposition under elevated $[CO_2]$ has been found but it is not known if this effect will be amplified in the longer term or whether the decrease in N availability is a transient phenomenon as the plant-soil-microbe system comes into a new balance. Emphasis on mechanistic approaches at each level, from the primary process of photosynthesis to the level plant-plant and plant-soil interactions, should provide a sound basis for improvement of models and should permit realistic predictions about expected changes in managed grassland in the next century.

Manipulating Swards to Extend the Grazing Season

A. S. LAIDLAW AND C. S. MAYNE

Applied Plant Science Div., Dept. of Agriculture for Northern Ireland, Newforge Lane, Belfast, BT9 5PX and Agricultural Research Institute of Northern Ireland, Hillsborough, Co Down BT26 6DR

INTRODUCTION

A strategy to reduce the cost of milk production is to increase the proportion of grazed grass in the diet of dairy cows. One means of achieving this is to extend the season over which cows have access to pasture by making more herbage available for grazing in early winter. Potentially this can be carried out by encouraging herbage growth in winter and/or deferring grazing of herbage produced in autumn until winter (Mayne and Laidlaw, 1995). However the implications of adopting such a strategy on herbage production and quality in early winter have not been fully assessed. The two experiments described here were set up to investigate the effect of late autumn/early winter utilisation on grass growth and senescence (Experiment 1) and the optimum time to close off a sward in autumn for grazing in winter (Experiment 2).

MATERIALS AND METHODS

Experiment 1

A long term perennial ryegrass sward was closed off on 5 September 1992 and received 60 kg N/ha. Twenty-seven plots, each 78 m², were laid down within the sward, 9 of which were subjected to simulated grazing on 21 October, 17 November or 15 December. Herbage mass was estimated in each plot, coincident with each grazing event, by taking three 1.5 m x 0.1 m samples per plot to ground level. Tiller population density was also determined from this sample. Tissue turnover was determined on 20 marked tillers per plot, measured at two weekly intervals and remarked at monthly intervals, from which leaf growth and senescence rates were calculated.

Experiment 2

A two-year-old perennial ryegrass sward (cvs Magella and Merlinda) was divided into 12 plots to allow for four closing off dates to be replicated three times. As it was planned to graze cows on the plots throughout November, plot size was inversely related to regrowth time from closing off until use, so that the same amount of herbage was available in each plot. Closing off dates were 19 July, 8 and 30 August and 20 September and plot sizes were 0.3, 0.4, 0.6 and 0.9 ha, respectively. All plots received 180 kg N /ha in four applications from 19 July to 20 September. Herbage mass was estimated from 30 1.5m x 0.1m samples taken to ground level and leaf content was determined from subsamples.

RESULTS AND DISCUSSION

Table 1.   The effect of time of utilisation in autumn/winter on rates of leaf growth and senescence (kg/ha/day)

	Leaf growth				Leaf senescence			
Grazed on:	21/10	17/11	15/12	SEM	21/10	17/11	15/12	SEM
21/10 to 17/11	13.8	16.2		0.84	6.0	13.1		1.10**
17/11 to 15/12	8.4	7.7	14.4	1.29*	4.0	3.9	18.9	1.78**

Grazing in early winter reduced the rate of leaf production but also markedly reduced the rate of leaf senescence (Table 1). The consequences of the high senescence rate in swards last grazed in early September was to reduce the amount of herbage from mid November to mid December by 0.6t DM/ha.

Closing off too early, i.e. before the end of August, resulted in herbage quality being unacceptably low for grazing in late October and November (Table 2), confirmed by a 30 % depression in intake (Mayne and Laidlaw, 1995). Delaying closing off until late September was clearly too late. Nevertheless gradual adjustment of rotation length to achieve 7 - 8 weeks regrowths by early November should result in herbage mass of at least 3 t DM/ha, providing in excess of 2 t DM/ ha of high quality herbage available for grazing.

Table 2.   Effect of closing off date on herbage mass (t DM/ha) and leaf lamina content (%)

Closed off on:		19/7	9/8	30/8	20/9	SEM
Mass	23 Sept	4.85	3.16	2.32	1.29	0.332***
	25 Oct	4.80	3.60	3.11	1.88	0.331*
	7 Dec	3.50	2.53	2.36	1.74	0.413
Leaf	23 Sept	40.6	49.9	44.6	17.3	5.46*
	25 Oct	17.7	40.1	46.7	47.5	2.86***
	7 Dec	22.6	26.4	45.3	49.1	3.53***

REFERENCE
MAYNE C.S. and LAIDLAW A.S. (1995) Extending the grazing season - a research review. Extending the Grazing Season: Discussion Meeting, British Grassland Society, Reaseheath College, 6pp.

New Systems for Wilting Grass

A. H. BOSMA

Institute of Agricultural and Environmental Engineering (IMAG-DLO)
PO-Box 43, Wageningen, The Netherlands

INTRODUCTION

There is a progressive movement towards the greater use of silage, and the average quality of silage made is steadily increasing. As society will no longer tolerate effluent pollution (Zimmer, 1991) it is likely that, in the future, more silage will be produced with a dry matter content >30%. At such levels of DM, seepage will no longer occur and a good forage crop, a short field period, a suitable harvesting system and proper management will create the conditions for an adequate fermentation process (Bosma, 1991).

Faster wilting of a grass swath is possible by improving the drying properties of the forage and raising the energy absorption and utilization of the harvesting system. By using a mower conditioner, tedding the grass immediately after cutting, a further tedding and finally windrowing under dry weather conditions it is possible to evaporate 50% of the moisture from the crop in a short time. This complicated system is conventional in mainland Europe and gives good results.

IMAG-DLO has developed, in cooperation with manufactures of agricultural machinery, a new system for forage making. In this new system the grass is cut, treated and spread in a thin and even layer, over almost the whole area of the field, in one operation. By treating the grass in this way the drying properties are improved, and by spreading the grass conditions are optimal for the evaporation of moisture, without using a tedder. The main criteria for the new system was to start with good quality grass and to make high quality, high dry matter, silage with a short field period (maximum 1 day). Of course other factors such as machine use, labour demands and organisation of the total harvest system are also important.

During this project a large number of field experiments have been carried out. In these tests the new system was compared with the conventional system of silage making outlined above. Most attention was given to the drying rate of the grass and the feed quality of the silage. In addition attention focused on the effects on costs, fuel consumption etc.; fitting the new technique into the complete silage making process and the acceptability of the new system.

FIELD EXPERIMENTS

The field experiments were performed on a practical scale using duplicate plots. The basic aim was to produce silage without effluent losses, which means a DM content of 28 to 30%. The grass from the different treatments was ensiled in separate silos. The intention was to cut in the morning and to ensile in the afternoon. During the day the drying rate was determined, consideration was

247

given to the ensilability of the crop and eventually losses were assessed. The weather during the field tests varied, generally it was not optimal for field drying.

Naturally the drying rate of the grass depended on the weather conditions. Under better weather conditions, more radiation and higher free water evaporation, the drying rate improved. Generally the average drying rate of the grass prepared under the new system was at least the same as the drying rate of the conventional system. Compared to mowing with a mower conditioner without tedding a higher drying rate was found with the new system. Without tedding the drying rate of the top layers of grass was higher than the bottom layers. By omitting tedding field losses were reduced.

ENSILING EXPERIMENTS
The grass from the different field treatments was ensiled separately. Crops were collected with a self-loading trailer, a round baler or a precision forage harvester. The grass was ensiled in clamp silos and differences in both feed value and quality were studied. Comparing results from the new system with those using the conventional system there was no significant difference in feeding value or silage quality. Tests comparing the new system with one without using tedding showed that silage produced from the new system had a considerably lower acetic acid content, caused by a better lactic acid fermentation through better ensilability of the grass, and the silage also had a better aerobic stability.

CAPACITY AND POWER CONSUMPTION
The new equipment, used in the field experiments, was fitted to 2.4 m to 2.8 m mowers and the machines were all operated at speeds of 8 to 10 km/h. In general the more intensive the treatment the higher the power consumption but a more intensive treatment does not always result in a higher drying rate. The extra power consumption was 3-5 KW/m working width.

ADVANTAGES AND DISADVANTAGES OF THE NEW SYSTEM
Using the new system, without tedding, gave equivalent drying rates to that of the conventional system. If tedding is not a conventional practice then the new system gives a higher dry matter than a conventional mower conditioner over a similar period and effluent losses can be prevented. The ensilability of the grass is improved. Acetic acid content will be reduced, probably improving the palatability of the feed. Compared to a system using a tedder, the drying rate of the new system will be similar. Under practical conditions, however, it is often very difficult to ted within one hour of mowing. By eliminating tedding harvesting work is reduced, there is less traffic over the field, lower fuel consumption and reduced labour demand. The investment for the new system is higher than for a conventional mower conditioner and also requires slightly increased power. This is offset by elimination of the tedder and the costs of the

tedding operations.

If tedding is eliminated there is a difference in DM content between the top and the underlying layers of the grass which could adversely affect fermentation. Because the layers of grass are very thin and, due to the mixing that takes place with the harvesting system, the effects are minimal.

REFERENCES

ZIMMER E. (1991) Strategy of silage systems. In: Pahlow G and H.Honig (eds). *Proceedings of a conference on Forage conservation towards 2000, Landbauforschung Volkenrode,* sonderheft **123**, 256-262

BOSMA A.H. (1991) Efficient field treatment for silage and hay. In: Pahlow G and H.Honig (eds) *Proceedings of a conference on Forage conservation towards 2000, Landbauforschung Volkenrode,* sonderheft **123**, 71-85.

Extent of Variation in Cell Wall Degradation of Forages for Ruminants

E. R. DEAVILLE AND D. I. GIVENS

Feed Evaluation Unit, ADAS Dairy Research Centre,
Drayton, Alcester Road, Stratford-upon-Avon, CV37 9RQ

INTRODUCTION

Grass-based forages are the most important feeds for ruminant animals in the UK, providing approximately 75% of their energy and protein requirements (Beever and Reynolds, 1994). Also, while the UK occupies only 15% of the total agricultural land area within the EU, it contributes 27% of the total grass-based forage output (Lee, 1992). Of particular importance to highly productive ruminant animals in the winter is the 50 million tonnes of grass silage produced each year worth some £1.3 billion. Forage cell wall content, accounting for 400 to 600 g/kg DM (Van Soest, 1982), and its rumen degradability (CWD) are major factors influencing the animal's energy supply (as volatile fatty acids) from forages. Therefore, in order to maximize the nutritional potential of forages for ruminants, the ability to accurately and rapidly measure CWD is crucial. This is becoming increasingly important as feed evaluation methods move to assessing nutrient supply from a wide range of substrates. The aim of this paper is to describe a method to measure CWD *in vitro* and report on the variation in the rate and extent of CWD in different forages with particular emphasis on grass silage.

MATERIALS AND METHODS

A total of 113 grass silage (GS) (94 clamp and 19 big bale), 10 fresh grass (G) and 10 maize silage (MS) samples were studied. Each sample was freeze-dried and then milled (1 mm screen) prior to incubation in buffered rumen fluid *in vitro*. Incubations were carried out in duplicate in 100 ml polypropylene tubes sealed with a one-way gas-release valve. Approximately 0.5 g of each forage was accurately weighed into each tube and then inoculated with 50 ml buffered rumen fluid (1:4; strained rumen fluid:artificial saliva) and then incubated at 39°C for different lengths of time (3, 8, 16, 24, 45, 72 and 96 h). Following incubation the fermentation was stopped by acidifying to pH<2 with concentrated HCl and then the whole contents of the tube refluxed with neutral detergent solution (Goering and Van Soest, 1970) in order to measure cell wall content (determined as neutral detergent fibre, NDF). Curves describing the disappearance of cell walls (NDF) for all forages were fitted to the mean data using the exponential model of Ørskov and McDonald (1979) and the value of the lag phase and adjusted 'a' and 'b' were calculated from the revised model of McDonald (1981).

RESULTS AND DISCUSSION
The in vitro CWD characteristics for GS, G and MS are given in Table 1.

Table 1.   In vitro cell wall (determined as neutral detergent fibre) degradability characteristics for grass silage, fresh grass and maize silage (all as % unless otherwise stated).

Forage Type	Parameter	Mean	SD	Range
Grass silage[1]	a	0.0	0.10	0.0 - 1.1
	b	72.7	7.88	48.7 - 88.1
	c (/h)	0.073	0.0157	0.045 - 0.161
	Lag (h)	2.8	1.44	0.0 -7.8
	ED[2]	27.5	4.39	16.8 - 36.8
Fresh grass[3]	a	0.7	1.25	0.0 - 3.9
	b	71.9	8.12	59.0 - 82.6
	c (/h)	0.094	0.0242	0.071 - 0.146
	Lag (h)	0.4	0.64	0.0 - 1.7
	ED[2]	38.0	7.61	27.3 - 50.7
Maize silage	a	0.0	0.0	0.0 - 0.0
	b	68.1	2.74	64.0 - 72.0
	c (/h)	0.052	0.009	0.041 - 0.065
	Lag (h)	4.6	2.28	1.4 - 7.4
	ED[2]	18.9	4.24	14.3 - 28.6

[1] n = 113. [2] Effective NDF degradability at an outflow rate of 0.08 /h. [3] n = 10.

The results indicate that the mean potentially degradable fraction (a + b) was similar (P>0.10) for the three forage types although the rate of degradation of the 'b' fraction ('c') differed significantly (P<0.001) between the three forages and was highest for G (0.094/h) and lowest for MS (0.052/h). The lag time before rapid degradation began was highest for MS and lowest for G (mean, 4.6 and 0.4 h respectively). Susmel et al. (1990), using the polyester bag technique to determine NDF degradability, reported a lag time of 5.9 h for a single sample of MS. The effective CWD, calculated at an outflow rate of 0.08/h, was in the order G>GS>MS and largely reflects the differences in rate of degradation and the lag time. For all the parameters measured there was also considerable variation within each forage type, particularly for the GS and G. For GS, the rate of degradation ('c') and lag time varied over a wide range from 0.045 to 0.161/h and 0.0 to 7.8 h respectively. There was a positive relationship between 'c' and CWD after 16 h as a percent of CWD after 72 h (r = + 0.61). Effective degradability of GS cell walls, calculated at an outflow rate of 0.08/h, varied from 16.8 to 36.8%

and may indicate differences in intake potential between different GS samples.

CONCLUSIONS

The results indicate the potential for determining the dynamics of CWD *in vitro* in forages and may be more appropriate for estimating CWD than those based on the polyester bag technique since the fitted curve passes through the origin. Substantial differences in the rate and extent of CWD both within and between forage types are highlighted indicating possible differences in intake potential. Further work is required to investigate the potential application of near infrared reflectance spectroscopy (NIRS), as an accurate and rapid method, for predicting CWD characteristics of forages.

ACKNOWLEDGEMENTS

Financial support for this work from the Ministry of Agriculture, Fisheries and Food (MAFF) is gratefully acknowledged.

REFERENCES

BEEVER D. E. and REYNOLDS C. K. (1994) Forage quality, feeding value and animal performance. *Proceedings of the European Grassland Federation, Wageningen, 1994,* 48-60.

GOERING H. K. and VAN SOEST P. J. (1970) *Agricultural Handbook, USDA,* No. **379**, Washington DC.

LEE J. (1992) Feed Resource - Livestock Relationships. *Farm & Food,* **2 (1)**, 31-32.

McDONALD I. (1981) A revised model for the estimation of protein degradability in the rumen. *Journal of Agricultural Science,* Cambridge, **96**, 251-252.

ØRSKOV E. R. and McDONALD I. (1979) The estimation of protein degradability in the rumen from incubation measurements weighed according to rate of passage. *Journal of Agricultural Science,* Cambridge, **92**, 499-503.

SUSMEL P., STEFANON B., MILLS C. R. and SPANGHERO M. (1990) Rumen degradability of organic matter, nitrogen and fibre fractions in forages. *Animal Production,* **51**, 515-526.

VAN SOEST P. J. (1982) *The Nutritional Ecology of the Ruminant,* 374. Cornvallis, Oregon: O&B Books.

A Comparison of the Suitability of Different Models for Describing the Gas Production Kinetics of Whole Crop Wheat

A.T. ADESOGAN[1,2], E. OWEN[1] AND D. I. GIVENS[2]

[1]Department of Agriculture, The University of Reading,
Earley Gate, PO Box 236, Reading, RG6 6AT
[2]Feed Evaluation Unit, ADAS Dairy Research Centre,
Drayton, Stratford-upon-Avon, CV37 9RQ

INTRODUCTION

Menke *et al.* (1979), Beuvink *et al.* (1992) and Theodorou *et al.* (1994) developed techniques for measuring the time course of gas production of feeds fermented *in vitro* with rumen fluid. These techniques require description of the fermentation profile with an appropriate mathematical model. Although several authors have used these techniques to study the rumen fermentation of feeds, little information is available on the suitability of the model chosen for describing the fermentation profile of whole-crop wheat (WCW). In this study, the models of Ørskov *et al.* (1979), France *et al.* (1993) and Beuvink and Kogut, (1994) were fitted to the *in vitro* gas production profiles of ten whole-crop wheat forages (c.v. *Slepjner*) to determine the model most suited to describing the data.

MATERIALS AND METHODS

WCW forages harvested at 376, 516 and 632 g/kg dry matter were conserved in 200 l barrels with or without Maxgrass additive. Urea was applied at target rates of 20 and 40 g/kg DM to forages at the last two harvest stages. Freeze-dried, milled (1 mm screen) samples were incubated, in triplicate, in buffered rumen fluid and gas production was measured using the pressure transducer technique of Theodorou *et al.* (1994) after 0, 4, 8, 12, 16, 20, 24, 28, 32, 40, 48, 60, 72 and 96 h. Gas volumes were plotted against corresponding gas pressures and a linear regression equation used to correct gas volumes for differences in head-space volumes of culture bottles. The models of Ørskov *et al.* (1979), France *et al.* (1993) and Beuvink and Kogut, (1993, modified Gompertz) were fitted to the regression-corrected gas volumes after correction for gas production from the culture medium.

RESULTS AND DISCUSSION

A comparison of the fitted profiles of each of the ten forages revealed that the Ørskov *et al.* (1979) model fitted the exponential part of the curve poorly, the France *et al.* (1993) model underestimated the asymptotic phase, while the modified Gompertz model consistently gave the most accurate description of the

253

data. Figure 1 shows the residual mean squares (RMS) of the different models for each of the ten forages. The RMS values from the modified Gompertz model (0.005) were significantly lower (P<0.001) than for models of Ørskov and McDonald (1979) (0.030) and France *et al.* (1993) (0.021). The modified Gompertz model was developed to account for gas production arising from rapidly and slowly fermentable feed fractions, hence its superiority over the other models.

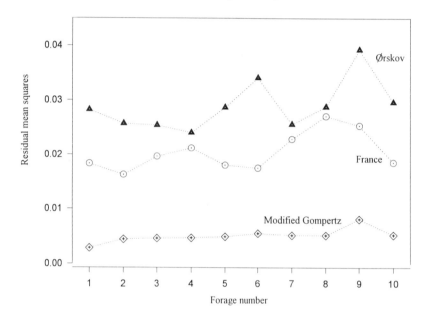

Figure 1   Residual mean squares of Ørskov *et al.* (1979), France *et al.* (1993) and modified Gompertz models fitted to gas production profiles of ten whole crop wheat forages.

CONCLUSION

The modified Gompertz model appears best for describing the gas production kinetics of WCW and is possibly preferable for similar feeds comprising cell wall and starch-rich fractions. However, this model may not be appropriate for all feed types and more attention should be paid to the model chosen to describe the fermentation profiles of different feedstuffs.

ACKNOWLEDGEMENTS

This programme is funded under a Ministry of Agriculture, Fisheries and Food (MAFF) LINK programme by Agricultural Genetics Co Ltd, BOCM Pauls, Hi Spec Engineering Ltd, ICI Nutrition, J Bibby Agriculture Ltd, Maize Growers Association, Milk Marketing Board of England and Wales, MAFF, Rumenco, Trouw Nutrition UK Ltd and Zeneca Seeds UK Ltd. The contributions of Jan Kogut and Mewa Dhanoa to this study are gratefully acknowledged.

REFERENCES

BEUVINK J.M. W., SPOELSTRA S.F. and HOGENDORP R.J. (1992) An automated method for measuring time-course of gas production of feedstuffs incubated with buffered rumen fluid. *Netherlands Journal of Agricultural Science*, **40**, 401-407.

BEUVINK J.M. W. and KOGUT J. (1993) Modelling gas production kinetics of grass silages incubated with buffered rumen fluid. *Journal of Animal Science*, **71**, 1041-1046.

FRANCE J., DHANOA M. S., THEODOROU M. K., LISTER S.J., DAVIES D.R. and ISAC D. (1993) A model to interpret gas accumulation profiles associated with *in vitro* degradation of ruminant feeds. *Journal of Theoretical Biology*, **163**, 99-111.

MENKE K.H., RAAB L., SALEWSKI A., STEINGASS H., FRITZ D. and SCHNEIDER W. (1979) The estimation of the digestibility and metabolizable energy content of ruminant feedingstuffs from the gas production when they are incubated with rumen liquor *in vitro*. *Journal of Agricultural Science, Cambridge*, **93**, 217-222.

ØRSKOV E.R. and McDONALD I. (1979) The estimation of protein degradability in the rumen from incubation measurements weighted according to rate of passage. *Journal of Agricultural Science*, **92**, 499-503.

THEODOROU M. K., BARBARA A.W., DHANOA M. S., McALLAN A.B. and FRANCE J. (1994) A simple gas production method using a pressure transducer to determine the fermentation kinetics of ruminant feeds. *Animal Feed Science and Technology*, **48**, 185-197.

A Comparison Between *In Vitro* Digestibility, *In Situ* Degradability and a Gas Production Technique for Predicting the *In Vivo* Digestibility of Whole Crop Wheat

A.T. ADESOGAN[1,2], E. OWEN[1] AND D. I. GIVENS[2]

[1]Department of Agriculture, The University of Reading,
Earley Gate, PO Box 236, Reading, RG6 6AT
[2]Feed Evaluation Unit, ADAS Dairy Research Centre, Drayton,
Stratford-upon-Avon, CV37 9RQ

INTRODUCTION

Public aversion to animal experimentation demands the replacement of expensive and lengthy *in vivo* forage evaluation techniques with non-invasive, laboratory-based techniques. This study compared the suitability of less animal-dependent techniques *in vitro* digestibility (IVD) (Tilley and Terry, 1963), *in situ* degradability (ISD) (Ørskov and McDonald, 1979) and gas production (GP) (Theodorou *et al.*, 1994)) for predicting the *in vivo* digestibility of whole crop wheat (WCW).

MATERIALS AND METHODS

Ten winter wheat forages (cv. *Slepjner)* harvested at 376, 516 and 632 g/kg dry matter were conserved in 200 l barrels with or without Maxgrass application at rates of 5, 4 and 3 l/t respectively. Urea was also applied at target rates of 20 and 40 g/kg DM at the last two harvest stages. All forages were fed to four Suffolk cross wethers at maintenance (MAFF, 1984) and apparent DM digestibility (DMD) measured. Wethers fed non urea-treated forages were offered 20 g/kg DM dietary urea supplements to ensure the adequacy of nitrogen for digestion. IVD and GP were determined on freeze-dried, milled (1 mm) samples while ISD was determined on fresh, homogenised samples in ruminally fistulated wethers fed a grass silage and barley diet (60:40 DM basis). GP and ISD were measured after incubation times of 0, 3, 8, 12, 16, 24, 45, 72 and 96 h. Cumulative regression-corrected gas volumes and degradability kinetics were fitted to the models of Beuvink and Kogut (1993, modified Gompertz) and Ørskov and McDonald (1979) respectively. The DM and nitrogen solubility of the forages was determined by soaking fresh homogenised samples in distilled water (22° C) for one hour and analysing the residue obtained after vacuum filtration through a Whatman Number 9 filter paper.

RESULTS AND DISCUSSION

The *in vitro* DMD, gas pool size and potential degradability of the untreated, 350 g DM/kg forage were notably lower than indicated by the *in vivo* trial. This was

Table 1. Relationship between the *in vivo* apparent digestibility (g/kg) of dry matter (y variate) of nine whole crop wheat forages and their *in vitro* dry matter digestibility values (g/kg), kinetic parameters of gas production (ml/g DM) and *in situ* degradation (g/kg DM).

Technique (x variate)	Equation and factors used	R^2	P
In situ degradability	0.552 + 0.232000 c	0.60	0.015
	0.456 + 0.000464 b	0.49	0.035
	0.772 - 0.000362 a	0.37	0.084
	0.404 + 0.000230 A	0.09	0.409
	0.668 - 0.000083 U	0.06	0.526
	0.416 + 0.000393 p	0.00	0.576
Gas production	0.546 + 0.044200 Cr	0.75	0.000
	0.420 + 3.740000 Ds	0.64	0.010
	0.717 - 0.003970 Ti	0.62	0.011
	0.470 + 0.492000 Dr	0.58	0.017
	0.604 + 2.880000 Cs	0.53	0.026
	0.449 + 0.000729 A∞	0.22	0.205
	0.541 + 0.000115 Egas	0.00	0.858
In vitro digestibility	0.106 + 0.831 DMDi	0.83	0.000

a = immediately soluble fraction; b = potentially degradable but not immediately soluble fraction; c = rate of degradation of b (/h) A = a+b = potential degradability; U = 1000 - (a + b) = undegradable fraction; A∞ = upper asymptote representing gas pool size; Cr and Cs are specific initial and final rates (/h) of gas production respectively; Dr and Ds are fractional constants governing the decay (/h); Ti = point of inflection (h); DMDi = dry matter digestibility *in vitro*; p = effective degradability and Egas = effective gas production calculated using parameters from the Ørskov and McDonald (1979) model.

thought to be due to insufficient nitrogen for optimal fermentation *in vitro* indicated by the low nitrogen solubility of this forage (118 g/kg DM compared with the average value of 490 g/kg DM, s.e. 68). Consequently, results presented in Table 1 are based on the remaining nine forages. The immediately soluble fraction derived from the degradability trial was consistently higher than the fraction derived from water solubility measurements. This was due to an appreciable loss of fine particles (203 g/kg DM, s.e. 19), through the pores of the polyester bags, which comprised 507 g/kg DM (s.e. 0.44) starch. *In vivo* DMD was poorly related to effective degradability, effective gas production and potential degradability (Table 1) but was better related to gas pool size. The rates of GP and ISD correlated well with *in vivo* DMD. The inflection point and decay constants of the gas technique also related well with *in vivo* DMD, but more work is needed to enable their interpretation in biological terms. The superiority of the IVD technique over the GP and ISD techniques was reflected in a high correlation between DMD *in vitro* and *in vivo* (R^2 = 0.83).

CONCLUSIONS

The rates of GP or ISD appear better than either potential degradability or gas pool size for predicting the *in vivo* DMD of WCW. The high loss of fine particles observed using ISD limits its validity for describing fermentation kinetics of WCW. The GP technique may be a valid alternative. The IVD technique appears superior to both ISD and GP techniques for estimating digestibility.

ACKNOWLEDGEMENTS

This programme is funded under a Ministry of Agriculture, Fisheries and Food (MAFF) LINK programme by Agricultural Genetics Co Ltd, BOCM Pauls, Hi Spec Engineering Ltd, ICI Nutrition, J Bibby Agriculture Ltd, Maize Growers Association, Milk Marketing Board of England Wales, MAFF, Rumenco, Trouw Nutrition UK Ltd and Zeneca Seeds UK Ltd. The contributions of Jan Kogut and Mewa Dhanoa to this study are gratefully acknowledged.

REFERENCES

BEAUVINK J.M. W. and KOGUT J. (1993) Modelling gas production kinetics of grass silages incubated with buffered rumen fluid. *Journal of Animal Science*, **71**, 1041-1046.
MAFF (1984) *Energy allowances and feeding systems for ruminants*. ADAS Reference Book No. 433. HMSO:London.
ØRSKOV E.R. and McDONALD I. (1979) The estimation of protein degradability in the rumen from incubation measurements weighted according to rate of passage. *Journal of Agricultural Science*, **92**, 499-503.
THEODOROU M. K., WILLIAMS B.A., DHANOA M. S., McALLAN A.B. and FRANCE J. (1994) A simple gas production method using a pressure transducer to determine the fermentation kinetics of ruminant feeds. *Animal Feed Science and Technology*, **48**, 185-197.
TILLEY J.M. A. and TERRY R.A. (1963) A two stage technique for the *in vitro* digestion of forage crops. *Journal of the British Grassland Society*, **18**, 104-111.

The Effect of Companion Grass on the Overwintering and Spring Growth of White Clover

R. P. COLLINS, M. FOTHERGILL AND I. RHODES

IGER, Plas Gogerddan, Aberystwyth, Dyfed SY23 3EB

INTRODUCTION

Considerable variation in the white clover (*Trifolium repens*) content of grass/clover mixtures has been observed between clover cultivars, locations and years. Some of this variation has been attributed to the inferior winter survival and growth at low temperatures of clover compared with its companion grass. AberHerald, a new winter-hardy white clover cultivar developed at IGER, Aberystwyth, is currently being used in a multi-site experiment at 12 European locations. This experiment encompasses a range of winter environments in order to investigate the basis of overwintering and spring growth in white clover. The UK site for the experiment is at IGER, Aberystwyth.

Since 1991 this research has been carried out within the framework of COST (European Cooperation in the field of Scientific and Technical Research) as Action 814. All sites have included AberHerald and a control cultivar of white clover, Grasslands Huia, sown as mixed swards with perennial ryegrass (*Lolium perenne*) cv. Preference. At the Aberystwyth site another perennial ryegrass, Ba 10761, was incorporated into the experiment. This grass has the same ploidy level and a similar flowering date to Preference. By studying the effects of companion grass on the morphology of white clover during the critical winter/spring period it may be possible to gain an insight into the nature of grass/clover compatibility. Results are presented for winter/spring 1994/95 at the Aberystwyth site.

MATERIALS AND METHODS

The experiment was established in July 1992 at Plas Gogerddan, Aberystwyth (30 m asl). The experimental design was a split plot, replicated four times, with the two grasses as main plots and the clovers as sub-plots. The experiment was managed under a five cuts-per-year regime, with an application of N equivalent to 25 kg/ha after each cut. Agronomic yields of the components of the mixtures were determined from botanical analysis of the cut samples. Morphological changes occurring in the clovers during winter/spring were assessed by making detailed measurements on the plant material contained in four 12 cm diameter cores taken from each plot on each sampling occasion. Six samples were taken during winter/spring 1994/95.

RESULTS AND DISCUSSION

Higher numbers of grass tillers/m² were recorded for Ba 10761 than Preference on all sampling dates. Sward height was measured at the end of January, and it was significantly higher in Ba 10761 plots.

Table 1.   The effects of companion grass on clover morphological characteristics, averaged over two clover varieties, in Autumn 1994.

Characteristic	Preference	Ba 10761	P and SED
Total plant weight (g/m^2)	325.6	247	P<0.062
No. leaves/m	6378	5015	*301
Leaf area index	1.28	1.10	ns
Specific leaf wt. (mg/cm^2)	3.56	3.30	*0.06
Petiole length (cm)	5.14	5.18	ns
Stolon unit weight (g/m^2)	1.19	0.96	ns

Table 2.   The effects of companion grass on clover morphological characteristics, averaged over two clover varieties, in Spring 1995.

Characteristic	Preference	Ba 10761	P and SED
Total plant weight (g/m^2)	260.1	212.3	p<0.067
No. leaves/m	3457	2376	*344
Leaf area index	1.11	0.83	*0.09
Specific leaf wt. (mg/cm^2)	3.39	3.34	ns
Petiole length (cm)	7.83	9.28	*0.39
Stolon unit weight (g/m^2)	0.83	0.8	ns

The effect of companion grass on clover morphological characteristics, averaged over two clover varieties, in Autumn 1994 and Spring 1995 is shown in Tables 1 and 2. Total clover plant DM/m^2 was consistently higher with Preference than with Ba 10761. There was little difference between the clovers in the average area of individual leaves, but clover leaf number/m^2 was significantly higher in AberHerald than in Huia on most sampling dates. This characteristic was also significantly affected by companion grass, with the Preference/AberHerald combination consistently having the highest number of clover leaves/m^2. Clover leaf area index was higher with Preference than with Ba 10761. There was also a grass effect on clover specific leaf weight (mg/cm^2), such that clovers grown with Preference had higher values than those with Ba 10761. In the early part of the winter clover cultivars differed in petiole length and there was no effect of grass treatment. However, between February and April the companion grass modified the clovers' environment to such an extent that clover with Ba 10761 had significantly longer petioles than that with Preference. This effect can be explained by the greater sward heights in Ba 10761 plots at this time, to which clover responded by extending its petioles. Clover stolon unit weight (g/m) decreased during the winter. Thicker stolons were associated with Preference.

CONCLUSIONS

The effect of suitable grass/clover cultivar selection on spring production (a parameter of particular importance in agricultural systems) was clearly demonstrated in this experiment. There was little difference in total (i.e. grass plus clover) yield between the grass/clover combinations, but the most compatible combination (Preference/AberHerald) contained 37% clover whilst the clover contribution in the least compatible mixture (Ba 10761/Huia) was only 19%.

Competition between the Perennial Ryegrass Cultivar LP100 and Three White Clover Cultivars at the Seedling Stage

FIONA JENNINGS AND GRACE O'DONOVAN
Plant Science Department,
University College Cork, Ireland.

INTRODUCTION

Recent research on grass/clover interactions has elucidated the effects of competition at the seedling stage (Fothergill and Collins, 1993; Collins and Rhodes, 1994). To assess the competitive ability of Irish white clover varieties, Avoca, a medium-leaved variety, was chosen and grown in competition with a recently developed variety of perennial ryegrass, LP100. A small-leaved variety, Kent, and a large-leaved variety, Aran, were also grown with LP100 for comparison. The effect of fertilizer on competition was also assessed.

METHODS

One thousand seeds altogether of Avoca and LP100 were sown separately and in mixtures in a total of eight seed trays. The mixtures consisted of Avoca and LP100 sown alternately, 1 cm apart. They were grown in a 50/50 mixture of peat and gravel. Avoca and LP100 were also grown separately, 2 cm apart as controls. Fertilizer in the form of ammonium nitrate was added to half the trays, both mixtures and controls, to the equivalent of 200 kgN/ha. Above- and below-ground biomass, root number and root length, leaf number and leaf length were measured in all experiments on a weekly basis after germination. A separate, similar experiment was set up with Kent and Aran for comparison.

RESULTS

Overall, clover growth was suppressed in competition with LP100, both above and below-ground. Analysis of variance showed that Avoca performed better in the controls without nitrogen, particularly in terms of root length (P<0.01). LP100 showed significantly greater root length in competition with Avoca in the absence of nitrogen (P<0.01). LP100 performed significantly better above-ground with Kent than with Aran in the presence of nitrogen (P<0.01). Also, Aran appeared to suppress root growth of LP100 under nitrogen treatment (P<0.05) compared to Kent.

CONCLUSIONS

Overall, LP100 showed aggressive competitive behaviour above-ground in the presence of nitrogen and below-ground in the absence of nitrogen leading to a reduction of clover growth. In mixtures however, LP100 was significantly less productive with Aran below-ground than with Kent under fertilizer treatment. This might suggest that leaf size in clover varieties has an effect on the biomass of the companion grass, although this was not evident at the seedling stage. Alternatively, Aran may be in some way actively suppressing the root growth of LP100.

REFERENCES

COLLINS R.P. and RHODES I. (1994) Influence of root competition on compatibility between white clover and perennial ryegrass populations during seedling establishment. *Grass and Forage Science*, **49**, 1-4.
FOTHERGILL M. and COLLINS R.P. (1993) Effects of perennial ryegrass cultivar on establishment of white clover seedlings. In: *Crop Adaptations To Cool, Wet Climates. Proceedings of COST 814 Workshop*, 295-299. Aberystwyth.

The Future Role of Tetraploid Hybrid Ryegrass in Agriculture

M. LL. JONES AND R. W. DAVIES

IGER, Plas Gogerddan, Aberystwyth, Dyfed, SY23,3EB

INTRODUCTION

Tetraploid ryegrass hybrids combine the characteristics of both Italian and perennial ryegrass species. Modern hybrids can meet the farming requirements for conservation and grazing in medium term leys of four to five years. These new hybrids, which will soon be available to UK farmers, show significant advantages in terms of good productivity throughout the growing season, combined with a high leaf content (low stem) ensuring high digestibility and water soluble carbohydrate content for good silage fermentation and ruminant digestion. They also exhibit good tolerance to environmental stress and disease resistance, which results in good persistency (Jones and Humphreys, 1993; 1994). This paper reports on the performance of a new hybrid (bAB 506) compared with four commercial varieties over 3 harvest years, and illustrates the improvements made recently in hybrid ryegrasses at IGER.

METHODS

The trial sown in August 1991 compared bAB 506 and Augusta (tetraploid hybrid ryegrass), Roberta and Macho (Italian ryegrass) and Merlinda (perennial ryegrass). Sowing rate was 50 kg/ha for Italian and hybrid ryegrasses and 33 kg/ha for perennial ryegrass. The overall cutting regime followed the NIAB combined management system, comprising 7 cuts per annum. The first spring cut was at a height of 3 cm, to simulate grazing, followed by three conservation cuts at 6 cm and then three more simulated grazing cuts in the autumn. All plots received 350 kg/ha of nitrogen, which was applied equally between March and October in a compound fertiliser. Harvesting was carried out using a Haldrup plot harvester. A sample of about 400 g was taken from each plot at each of Cuts 2 and 3 during the first year and transferred to a hot oven (80°C) for eight hours. Dried samples were milled and used for DMD and WSC analysis.

RESULTS

bAB 506 yielded equally as well as the Italian ryegrasses in Year 1 and was significantly better in Years 2 and 3 (Table 1). It also outyielded the perennial ryegrass Merlinda in the first 2 years and was not significantly lower in the 3rd year. The ground cover of bAB 506 was a significant improvement over Roberta, Macho and Augusta and its DM yield in the 3rd year was close to Merlinda.

bAB 506 exhibited good mid-season quality (Table 2) with a higher DMD than Augusta, Macho and Merlinda in Cut 2 and a DMD equal to Merlinda and significantly higher than the other varieties in Cut 3. WSC was also generally higher in bAB 506 compared to Augusta.

Table 1.   Total DM yield (t/ha) over 3 years and persistency in Year 3.

	Year 1	2nd Year	3rd Year	%ground cover
bAB 506	22.37	12.36	12.44	49
Augusta	19.57	11.10	11.31	44
Roberta	23.31	11.47	11.01	21
Macho	22.44	12.11	10.79	38
Merlinda	19.62	11.59	12.50	59
SED	0.90	0.46	0.47	4.5

Table 2.   DMD and WSC content of the five varieties in Year 1.

	Year 1	% DMD	Year 1	%WSC
	Cut 2 (28/5)	Cut 3(25/6)	Cut 2	Cut 3
bAB 506	61.9	76.8	24.3	37.9
Augusta	60.3	74.8	18.5	32.0
Roberta	63.8	73.0	26.5	39.6
Macho	61.0	73.1	24.4	34.5
Merlinda	57.2	77.1	14.1	32.1
SED	1.41	1.08	3.41	2.57

CONCLUSION

There is clearly a place for bAB 506, and similar tetraploid hybrid ryegrasses, in modern-day farming systems where swards are used for both conservation and grazing.The advantage in medium-term leys is clearly shown by the maintenance of high yields and ground cover into the third harvest year. The high nutritive value also provides the high quality required to produce improved silage and ensures good animal production from grazing. Combining these traits in new hybrid ryegrasses will assist in improving the flexibility and reliability required by grassland farmers today and in the future.

REFERENCES

JONES M. LL. and HUMPHREYS M. O. (1993) Progress in breeding interspecific hybrid ryegrasses; *Grass and Forage Science*, **48**, 18-25.
JONES M. LL. and HUMPHREYS M. O. (1994) The growth and quality of ryegrass hybrids in relation to flowering time and cutting date. *Aspects of Applied Biology*, **39**, 173-177.

Extensification and New Scales for Population Dynamics of Grassland Species

DANIELE MAGDA AND G. BALENT
INRA.- Unité de Recherches sur les Systèmes
Agraires et le Développement, B.P. 27 31326 Castanet-Tolosan, France

INTRODUCTION

Changes in management, related to extensification, leads to less human pressure on grassland. These new conditions, and the consequent disturbances induced by changes in practices, create the opportunity for different species to express a different population-dynamic strategy. The study of these dynamics should take into account spatio-temporal scales, not normally considered with conventional management practices. To control the biodiversity of grassland at the field and landscape level, it becomes important to identify these scales related to a population functioning under extensive management. This paper considers the invasive methods of some species as representative of such interactions between ecological and extensive management processes. The hypothesis used suggests the existence of synergy between levels of organisation of some plant populations and those management practices which aid their ability to colonise grassland.

OBJECTIVE

Using the example of one invasive species of Pyrenean grassland, *Chaerophyllum aureum*, the effects of extensive agriculture on the organisation and functioning of its populations were studied. As a first step, the spatial structure of the population was studied, and these structures were related to the patterns and types of spatial management in grassland.

METHODS

At the field level, a detailed survey of the presence and abundance of the species' tillers was conducted on 50 hectares of a Pyrenean valley, used for sheep and cattle grazing (a total of 330 fields). Farm monitoring provided information about fertiliser application, cutting and grazing practices and management history in recent years. From data on the biological characteristics of the species (reproduction strategy, distance of dispersion, etc.) and from a hypothesis about the primary structure of populations at the field level, the spatial organisation of the populations at a higher level were simulated by the construction of artificial exchange networks between 'field populations' (Jurgens, 1992).

RESULTS AND DISCUSSION

The spatial distribution of this species was well related to the distribution of space at the field level, suggesting that the current level of management intensity was a very important determinant of the current population. The presence and abundance of the species was related to a relatively high fertility and low intensity of utilisation (especially through cutting) (Figure 1). Spatial distribution inside the field was hardly influenced by the hay harvesting creating, or not creating, 'border populations' for which the status of 'residual populations' and a source of colonisation could be postulated.

OLD FIELDS AND ONE CUT MEADOWS

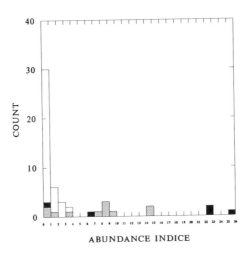

Figure 1. Distribution of 'field populations' number according to the abundance index and two factors: the management history (previous crops with high fertility level in hatching grey) and actual management (field with only one summer cutting in black).

Extensification tends to create heterogeneity between close fields, associating in space both intensified and abandoned fields. Contrary to previous management patterns, which tended to organise space in homogeneous areas and grouped fields on the basis of the same management practices, this actual mosaic seems to enhance the probability of colonisation from fields already invaded, viewed as sources to the closer and more intensified fields. From the hypothesis of enhancing exchanges between fields, due to this space heterogeneity, simulations of exchanges between 'field populations' for dispersion distances from 10 to 30 m reveals a potential pattern in 24 to 48 networks of 2 to >100 'field populations' and isolated populations on which higher probability of extinction is associated (Figure 2). Analysis of polyphenol diversity reveals six divergent profiles among one dominant suggesting differentiation at field level for this species (Gonnet, 1989).

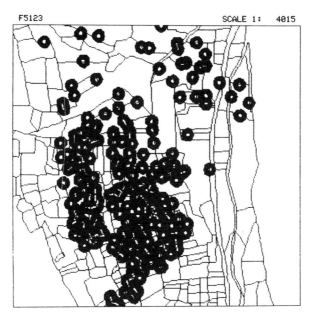

Figure 2.   Simulation of the potential network of exchanges between 'field populations' on part of the area studied and the associated isolated populations for a dipersion distance of 15m. Each circle represents the potential area of colonisation for a 'field population '.

From the validation of specific levels in the organisation of populations under different agricultural practices, the study will be continued to establish the role of management practices in the colonisation and stabilisation process of invasive species. New scales for the extensive management of grassland will perhaps be proposed to prevent invasion and degradation of resources.

REFERENCES
GONNET J.F. (1989) *Apport de la biologie micromoléculaire (flavonoïdes) à la compréhension de la structure et du fonctionnement de l'espèce allogame Centaurea montana (Composées) et de l'espèce autogame Chaerophyllum aureum au sein de deux groupements végétaux subalpins: prairie et mégaphorbiaie.* Thèse d'Etat, Université Claude Bernard, Lyon I.
JURGENS C.R. (1992) *Tools for the spatial analysis of land and for the planning of infrastructures in multiple-landuse situations.* Landbouwuniversiteit Wageningen Press.

Effects of Feeding by Larvae of *Sitona flavescens* on White Clover Seedlings.

P. J. MURRAY[1], D. J. HATCH[1] AND J-B. CLIQUET[2]

[1]IGER, North Wyke, Okehampton, Devon, EX20 2SB

[2]Laboratoire associé INRA de Physiologie et de Biochimie Végétales,
Institut de Recherche en Biologie Appliquée,
Université, 14032 Caen Cedex, France.

INTRODUCTION

Sitona flavescens is one of the most common insect pests of white clover in the UK (Clements and Murray, 1993). The adults feed on the leaves of the plant, whilst the larvae feed on the roots and nodules. The extent and the effects of adult feeding on the foliage of white clover has been shown to be severe on both seedlings and mature plants (Murray and Clements, 1992). The damage caused below ground by the root feeding larvae is more subtle but could be significant in terms of gross effects on plant growth and functioning. Earlier work (Murray and Hatch, 1994) has shown that feeding by *Sitona* larvae can facilitate nitrogen transfer from white clover and enhance the growth of companion grasses, and a preliminary screening was made of the N-containing organic compounds present in the root exudates from the clover plant.

MATERIALS AND METHODS

One seedling of white clover was grown under controlled conditions in each of 18 micro-lysimeters. At the second trifoliate leaf stage six of the seedlings were each infested with five first instar larvae of *Sitona flavescens* and the 12 remaining were uninfested. After 20 days the plants were harvested and shoot and root dry-matter contents determined. The number of active nodules on each plant were counted and the plants analysed for N%. Immediately prior to harvest 12 of the micro-lysimeters were flooded with demineralised water and then drained. The remaining six plants were removed from the growing medium and the main root excised approximately half way along its length. The plant was then stood in a vial of demineralized water for 10 minutes to allow exudation of sap into the water. The resultant liquid, which included root exudates, was then analysed for amino acids by GC-MS.

RESULTS AND DISCUSSION

Plants infested with *S. flavescens* were significantly lower in dry matter and N% content, and had significantly fewer active nodules than uninfested plants (Table 1). Analysis of the exudates showed a significantly higher amino acid concentration in the solution from the infested plants than in the solutions from the control plants and those which were cut. (70 ± 11, 30 ± 7 and 24 ± 7 nM respectively). The most abundant amino acid in all three cases was serine.

Table 1.   Effect of infestation of white clover seedlings by larvae of *Sitona flavescens*.

	Infested Seedlings	Control Seedlings	SED (5 d.f.)
Shoot DM yield (mg)	23.0	31.5	2.68
Root DM yield (mg)	18.5	30.5	4.66
Total DM yield (mg)	41.4	62.0	4.66
No. Nodules	2.3	26.5	4.64
Shoot N%	1.51	3.41	0.17
Root N%	1.73	1.97	0.17

The lower N content can be explained by a reduction in the N-fixation capacity of the plant and in direct leakage of N from wound sites. Root herbivory by insects such as *S. flavescens* play a major role in sward dynamics both in terms of direct effects on host plants and in more subtle effects such as altering the flux of nutrient in the rhizosphere.

ACKNOWLEDGEMENTS
This work was funded by BBSRC, MAFF and the British Council.

REFERENCES
CLEMENTS R.O. and MURRAY P.J. (1993) *Sitona* damage to clover in the UK. *Proceedings 6th Australasian Conference on Grassland Invertebrate Ecology.* Prestidge R.A. (ed) AgResearch, Hamilton New Zealand. 260-264.
MURRAY P.J. and CLEMENTS R.O. (1992) Studies on the feeding of *Sitona lineatus* L. (Coleoptera; Curculionidae) on white clover (*Trifolium repens* L.) seedlings. *Annals of Applied Biology*, **121**, 233-238
MURRAY P.J. and HATCH D.J. (1994) *Sitona* weevils (Coleoptera; Curculionidae) as agents for rapid transfer of nitrogen from white clover (*Trifolium repens* L.) to perennial ryegrass (*Lolium perenne* L.) *Annals of applied Biology*, **125**, 29-33.

Effects of Applying Nitrogen Fertiliser or Acidified Slurry to Grassland on Grass Ensilability and Silage Composition

[1]P. O'KIELY, [2]O. CARTON, [3]R. J. STEVENS AND [1]J. J. LENEHAN
[1]Teagasc, Grange Research Centre, Dunsany, Co. Meath, Ireland
[2]Teagasc, Johnstown Castle Research Centre, Co. Wexford, Ireland
[3]DANI, Newforge Lane, Belfast BT9 5PX, Co. Antrim, N. Ireland

INTRODUCTION
The present series of four experiments examined the effects of untreated and nitric-acid-treated slurry applied by splashplate or bandspreader, and of N fertiliser, on grass ensilability and silage composition.

MATERIALS AND METHODS
Cattle slurry, untreated or treated with 11.8 mol nitric acid added to reduce slurry pH to 5.5, was applied to new *Lolium perenne* swards by splashplate or bandspreader, while three N fertiliser treatments were included to determine the effects of N application rate. Each treatment was replicated six times with a plot size of 50 m^2. The day following harvesting, the herbage from the six replicate plots was precision chopped, mixed and ensiled in laboratory silos. Experimental details are summarized in Table 1.

Table 1. Experimental details of slurry treatments.

Exp. No.	Site	Slurry DM (g/kg)	Applic. rate m^3/ha	Slurry N (kg/ha) Untreated	Treated	Date Applic.	Harvest
1	Oakpark	78	20	39	135	5/3	20/5
2	Johnstown	89	20	64	130	15/3	20/5
3	Johnstown	85	20	38	96	22/7	21/9
4	Greenmount	90	15	36	85	5/8	28/9

RESULTS
Nitrogen fertiliser reduced DM concentration (unless the grass was wet from rain) and tended to result in grass ensilability indices consistent with a more difficult to preserve crop. The resultant silages correspondingly had higher acetic acid and ammonia-N concentrations. Treating slurry with nitric acid resulted in similar effects to N fertiliser application, the magnitude of which was between

the medium- and high-N fertiliser application rates. Untreated slurry, applied at 20 m³/ha or less, did not have a marked effect on grass or silage composition. Splashplate spreading slurry resulted in similar effects to bandspreading, whether the comparison was with untreated or treated slurry (see Tables 2 and 3).

Table 2.   Chemical composition of grasses and resultant silages.

| Slurry applied | No slurry | | | Slurry | | | | |
| Slurry application | | | | Splashplate | | Bandspread | | |
Inorganic N applied	Low[5]	Med.[6]	High[7]	None	Acid	None	Acid	SEM
EXPERIMENT 1								
Grass composition (n=4/treatment)								
Dry matter[1]	147	143	142	160	145	144	139	1.1***
WSC[2]	106	98	71	104	100	94	98	3.0***
Buffer. capacity[3]	505	492	510	475	472	484	485	10.5
C. protein[2]	211	195	224	201	196	205	207	3.6***
DMD *in vitro*[1]	798	782	780	803	791	794	792	4.6*
Silage composition (n=4/treatment)								
pH	4.23	4.63	4.78	4.20	4.75	4.33	5.33	0.03***
Lactic acid[2]	118	99	79	135	64	112	13	3.9***
Acetic acid[2]	32	46	53	27	59	34	71	2.6***
Ethanol[2]	27	39	33	22	45	28	59	1.7***
NH_3-N[4]	70	105	124	84	128	88	199	5.1***
EXPERIMENT 2								
Grass composition (n=4/treatment)								
Dry matter[1]	302	247	213	291	246	297	239	2.7***
WSC[2]	134	79	84	131	94	130	120	5.0***
Buffer. capacity[3]	295	379	427	288	326	292	331	5.4***
C. protein[2]	94	122	149	98	116	97	110	2.6***
DMD *in vitro*[1]	759	762	761	754	724	751	757	5.9**
Silage composition (n=4/treatment)								
pH	4.30	4.35	4.23	4.48	4.43	4.38	4.43	0.03***
Lactic acid[2]	33	59	104	31	48	35	49	3.3***
Acetic acid[2]	16	21	22	14	18	16	17	0.7***
Ethanol[2]	12	20	17	11	15	12	18	0.5***
NH_3-N[4]	36	73	89	49	64	44	75	2.6***

Superscripts: 1 = g/kg, 2 = g/kg DM, 3 = m.Eq./kg DM, 4 = g/kg N. For Experiments 1 through 4, respectively, superscript 5 = 0, 0, 0 and 20 kg N/ha, 6 = 75, 75, 60 and 60 kg N/ha and 7 = 125, 125, 100 and 100 kg N/ha.
Grass and silage composition data were analysed as randomised block and completely randomised block designs, respectively.

CONCLUSIONS

The application of moderate rates of undiluted slurry, either by splashplate or bandspreading, did not make grass more difficult to preserve. Increasing rates of N application, as fertiliser N or nitric acid in slurry, did make grass more difficult to preserve.

Table 3.   Chemical composition of grasses and resultant silages continued.

| Slurry applied | No slurry | | | | | Slurry | | |
| Slurry application | | | | Splashplate | | Bandspread | | |
Inorganic N applied	Low[5]	Med.[6]	High[7]	None	Acid	None	Acid	SEM
EXPERIMENT 3								
Grass composition (n=2/treatment)								
Dry matter[1]	306	254	213	287	221	299	214	4.2***
WSC[2]	73	74	72	93	81	70	78	6.9
Buffer. capacity[3]	329	354	390	324	353	329	343	7.4**
C. protein[2]	133	133	159	135	148	134	146	2.0***
DMD *in vitro*[1]	727	715	704	723	747	720	740	10.0
Silage composition (n=2/treatment)								
pH	4.30	4.30	4.20	4.30	4.00	4.30	4.05	0.02***
Lactic acid[2]	42	52	72	38	72	39	78	2.8***
Acetic acid[2]	11	15	17	13	34	12	21	1.1***
Ethanol[2]	22	25	18	29	25	28	23	1.5*
NH_3-N[4]	74	88	103	71	98	76	104	4.9**
EXPERIMENT 4								
Grass composition (n=3/treatment)								
Dry matter[1]	217	202	192	223	195	215	211	2.3***
WSC[2]	155	171	189	145	159	151	171	13.9
Buffer. capacity[3]	343	338	352	352	334	354	345	4.7
C. protein[2]	97	104	110	102	106	104	104	1.7**
DMD *in vitro*[1]	763	782	795	714	744	744	783	4.0***
Silage composition (n=4/treatment)								
pH	4.00	3.90	3.93	4.00	3.83	3.98	4.03	0.02***
Lactic acid[2]	74	84	83	60	80	71	61	1.8***
Acetic acid[2]	28	31	36	26	29	24	26	1.0***
Ethanol[2]	81	81	46	74	75	80	101	5.4***
NH_3-N[4]	51	53	60	54	49	49	52	1.4***

See Table 2 for superscripts

Grazed Grass and Grass/Clover Swards for Beef Production

E. G. O'RIORDAN

Grange Research and Development Division, Dunsany, Co. Meath, Ireland.

INTRODUCTION

Beef production in Ireland is typically characterised by low stocking rates and low nitrogen usage, which on many grassland beef farms is less than 50 kg N/ha/annum. With EU emphasis on extensive, environmentally-compatible production systems, the role for white clover to support animal production is being re-examined. Most estimates of nitrogen fixation by white clover suggest that 50-150 kg/N/ha/annum may be fixed. These fixation values are at least equivalent to the fertiliser nitrogen usage on grassland for many beef farms. Clover, as a component of ruminant diets, is generally considered to be nutritionally beneficial. However, seasonality of clover production, variation from year to year, lack of persistency and the likely animal health problems associated with bloat have limited the attractiveness of white clover. The present trial was undertaken (a) to measure beef production from grass/clover swards, (b) to compare it with output from nitrogen fertilised pasture and (c) to measure dry matter production by grass and clover throughout the grazing season.

MATERIALS AND METHODS

During August 1992, four areas of old pasture were identified, half of each was ploughed and reseeded with a *Lolium perenne* (Green Isle)/*Trifolium repens* (Susi) mixture, and approximately two thirds of the remainder had the Susi white clover stitched-in to the existing sward. Three grazing treatments were imposed on each pasture type: Treatments A, B and C on old pasture represented an animal stocking rate, in spring, of 3000, 2500 and 2000 kg liveweight/hectare; Treatments D, E and F represented the corresponding stocking rates on reseeded swards. All swards received 50 kg N/ha in early spring and while treatments B, C, E and F received no further nitrogen fertilisers, Treatment A and D received approximately 35 kg N/ha after each grazing cycle (giving a total input of 220 kg N/ha). Each treatment consisted of seven paddocks which were grazed rotationally. Fifteen steers, mean initial liveweight 570 kg, were used per treatment, and two stocking rate reductions per year each of 33% (by removing the heaviest animals) took place before the final removal of animals. Stocking rates for all treatments on old or new pasture were reduced at the same time. Animal sale dates were determined by herbage supply and all animals were slaughtered immediately after removal from the experiment. Pasture measurements consisting of pre- and post-grazing herbage yields, proportions of clover and grass leaf and stem and dead matter in the pre-grazed swards, and pre- and post-grazing sward height, were recorded on five of seven paddocks (80% of area) throughout the grazing season.

RESULTS

Mean herbage mass on offer between turnout and mid-November was 1907, 1952, 2141, 2388, 2121 and 2332 (s.e. 118) kg DM/ha for treatments A, B, C, D, E and F, respectively. Corresponding post grazing herbage mass was 575, 819, 981, 746, 652 and 1076 (s.e. 68) kg DM/ha and post-grazing residual sward height was 4.4, 5.2, 5.9, 5.7, 5.3 and 6.5 (s.e. 0.18) cm. The proportion of clover in herbage DM for the control old pasture treatment (A) ranged from 0 to 0.05 throughout the season. The clover content of all other treatments averaged 0.05 during April and increased steadily to 0.15 to 0.20 in early July. The proportion of clover in the control new pasture treatment (D) increased to 0.25 in late July before decreasing gradually to less than 0.10 in November. Other treatments increased to 0.30 (B), to 0.40 (E) and to 0.45 (C and F) in the August to October period. These treatments then decreased to less than 0.20 in November.

Table 1. Effect of treatment on steer average daily gains (ADG), final liveweight, carcass weight and conformation and fat score.

| | | | Pasture Type | | | | | |
| | | Old | | | New | | | |
Treatment	A	B	C	D	E	F	s.e.	P
ADG (kg/day)	0.97	0.95	1.01	0.83	0.91	0.93	0.063	NS
Final liveweight (kg)	728	730	743	722	741	741	7.0	NS
Carcass weight (kg)	383	387	390	386	402	405	4.3	***
Conformation score[1]	3.4	2.8	3.1	3.1	3.2	3.3	0.16	NS
Fat score[2]	4.0	4.0	4.0	3.9	4.0	4.2	0.13	NS

[1]Conformation score 5 = best, 1 = poor. [2]Fat score 1 = lean, 5 = fat

The initial liveweight was based on weights when animals were consuming silage-based diets, indoors. Consequently, there was a gut fill adjustment when animals commence grazing grass. Animal liveweight gains from turnout (mid-April) to late August (1st sale date) averaged 0.91 kg/day and were not significantly affected by treatment. Gains from early May to late August averaged 1.09 kg/day and there were significant differences (P < 0.001) between the control in old (A, 1.21 kg/day) and new (D, 0.96 kg/day) pasture. Gains for animals at pasture until early October (2nd sale date) averaged 0.79 kg/day from turnout and there were no significant differences between treatments. Gains from early May to early October averaged 0.95 kg/ha/day and old pasture resulted in better gains overall (P < 0.001). Treatments B and C were significantly better (P < 0.01) than treatments E and F, respectively. Animal daily gains from turnout to late

November averaged 0.73 kg/day with higher values achieved for treatment C (0.87 kg/day) than treatment A (0.64 kg/day). Gains for these animals from early May to late November averaged 0.82 kg/day. Old pasture resulted in the highest liveweight gains ($P < 0.01$). Treatment C had greater gains than treatment F (1.01 v. 0.78 kg/day, $P < 0.01$). Overall gains, final liveweight, carcass weight, conformation and fat scores are shown in Table 1. Differences in liveweight did not attain significance, however heavier carcass weight were produced by animals on the new pastures (B v E, $P < 0.05$; C v. F, $P < 0.01$) and the clover treatments E ($P < 0.05$) and F ($P < 0.001$) had higher carcass weights than the fertilised control (Treatment D).

A Process Control Model for Sward Height Adjustments in a Continuous Variable Stocking System

A. J. ROOK

IGER, North Wyke, Okehampton, Devon EX20 2SB

INTRODUCTION

Continuous variable stocking systems are widely used for grazing management in both experimental and commercial systems. The aim is to match animal intake to herbage production by maintaining a target sward height. This is achieved by varying stocking rate, either by adding and removing animals while holding the grazed area constant or by maintaining animal numbers while adjusting the area grazed. There is much published work on the relative merits of fixed or variable stocking rates and of adjusting animal numbers or area grazed. However, with the exception of work by Hutchings *et al.* (1992), there has been relatively little research into the degree and timing of adjustments to stocking rate .

In practice the degree of adjustment appears to be decided on an *ad-hoc* basis, relying on the experience and judgement of the individual operator. Adjustments are often nominally triggered when the sward height exceeds the 95% confidence limits about the target height but formal control charts are rarely used. As a result sward heights can often fluctuate considerably about the target. This is of great importance especially in experimental applications. For example, Penning *et al.* (1991) found that in a sheep grazing experiment in which sward height varied by only 5 mm about the target of 6 cm, variations in sward height in fact accounted for 48% of the variation in herbage intake. The aim of this study was to develop more objective and precise methods for the control of sward height.

METHODS

Continuous variable stocking can be regarded as a feedback system in which the effects of an unmeasured and uncontrolled variable (herbage production) on an output (sward height, SSH) can be compensated by adjustments to another variable (herbage consumption, i.e. stocking rate, SR). Such systems are widespread in manufacturing industry, where methods have been developed to allow objective decisions to be made about the adjustments required. These approaches were pioneered by Box and Jenkins (1976).

A simple Box-Jenkins feedback control model has been developed, using sward height data from pastures continuously stocked with lactating dairy cows and nominally maintained at 6.5 cm sward surface height. A first order model proved adequate to describe the data, that is the current sward height depended only on adjustments to stocking rate made immediately after the previous measurement and on the random noise in the system. The model consists of a transfer-function model relating deviations in sward surface height to adjustments in stocking rate and a noise model that describes the behaviour of the uncontrolled disturbances to the system. These are used to derive a control equation that gives the adjustment necessary to correct for any particular deviation from target sward height and restore the sward height to the target by the next measurement occasion, in this case 3 days later.

RESULTS
The control equation obtained for these data was:

$$SR_t = 11.037 \, SSH_t - 0.2082 \, SSH_{t-1}$$

where SSH is expressed as a deviation from the target value, SR is the change in stocking rate required and t is the current measurement occasion.

DISCUSSION
The model presented here is a first simplistic attempt to introduce the concepts of Box-Jenkins modelling into the control of sward surface height. The model contains assumptions, for example, that herbage intakes are constant over time and between animals. These assumptions can, however, be easily modified as required. The system is modelled as a simple feedback loop in which adjustments are made solely on the basis of the observed deviations from the target output. It is, however, amenable to extension to include feed-forward elements. For example, the current or forecast weather conditions or the soil N status could be incorporated. Such development should improve the accuracy of the model.

REFERENCES
BOX G.E.P. and JENKINS G.M (1976) *Time Series Analysis: Forecasting and Control.* San Francisco: Holden-Day.
HUTCHINGS N.J., BOLTON G.R. and BARTHRAM G.T. (1992) Decision rules for controlling the sward height of continuously grazed experimental pastures. *Grass and Forage Science*, **47**, 41-49.
PENNING P.D., ROOK, A.J. and ORR, R.J. (1991) Patterns of ingestive behaviour of sheep stocked on monocultures of ryegrass or white clover. *Applied Animal Behaviour Science*, **31**, 237-250.

Effect of Ammonia Applied with a Formic Acid-based Silage Additive on Feed Intake

I. SELMER-OLSEN

Department of Animal Science, Agricultural University of Norway,
PO Box 5025, N-1430 Ås, Norway

INTRODUCTION

Ammonia is used to make formic acid-based silage additives less corrosive and less irritant. It is well known that ammonia from degraded protein in silage is closely related to reduced intake (Heikkilä *et al.*, 1989). Questions have been raised whether ammonia applied with the silage additive has a negative effect on intake.

MATERIALS AND METHODS

A mixed sward of timothy, meadow fescue and red clover was cut (2nd cut) 23 August for a 30-40 hour wilt. It rained the day before and there were showers and sun during wilting. Grass was harvested with a metered chopper and ensiled in 12 small tower silos (6 m³). At harvesting mean DM content was 199 g/kg, with the following composition (g/kg DM); CP:153, WSC:108, NDF:515 and ADF:284. Formic acid-based additives with 0, 3, 6 and 9% ammonia, respectively, were all applied at a rate of 3.5 kg formic acid equivalents per tonne of grass. After five months storage, the four silages were offered *ad lib.* to 20 individually fed steers (200 kg liveweight) in a 4x4 latin-square-designed experiment with periods of 14 days. Average liveweight gain was 652 g/d.

RESULTS AND DISCUSSION

All silages were well fermented with low pH and no butyric acid (Table 1). Increasing application of ammonia with the additives increased the ammonia content in silage. True protein content was, however, not affected. Increasing application of ammonia slightly increased silage pH and lactic acid content of the silages. Feed intake was not significantly affected by treatments (p=0.88). It appears that ammonia *per se* is not responsible for reduced intake of high ammonia silage. Low silage intake is more likely to be related to amines or other fermentation products rather than ammonia. Nevertheless, ammonia is a good indicator of silage quality. When ammonium formates are used as silage additives, ammonia-N should be corrected before evaluating silage quality.

Table 1. Effect of increasing content of ammonia in formic acid-based silage additives on effluent production, silage fermentation quality and silage intake of steers.

% ammonia in the additive		0	3	6	9	SEM	p
Application rate							
Formic acid,	kg/t	3.66	3.54	3.80	3.51		
Ammonia,	kg/t	0	0.16	0.36	0.51		
Silage quality							
Effluent, kg/t grass		154	146	153	148	18.7	ns
pH		3.89^{ab}	3.87^{a}	3.92^{bc}	3.95^{c}	0.013	<0.02
DM,	g/kg	210	208	206	207	4.0	ns
CP,	g/kg DM	149	151	159	163	4.4	ns
True protein,	g/kg DM	89	87	90	91	1.7	ns
NH_3-N	g/kg TN	72^{a}	94^{b}	122^{c}	149^{d}	4.1	<0.0001
WSC,	g/kg DM	65	69	66	54	6.1	ns
Lactic acid,	g/kg DM	89^{a}	100^{b}	98^{b}	104^{b}	2.0	<0.02
Acetic acid,	g/kg DM	12	10	12	13	0.8	ns
Formic acid,	g/kg DM	9	11	11	11	1.1	ns
Ethanol,	g/kg DM	4	3	2	2	0.9	ns
Silage intake							
Kg DM/d		4.19	4.21	4.12	4.21	0.087	ns
Kg DM/100 kg lw		2.23	2.27	2.22	2.26	0.048	ns

[a,b,c,d] Means with no common letter differ significantly

REFERENCES

HEIKKILÄ T., VÄÄTÄINEN H. and LAMPILA M. (1989) Effect of silage quality on milk yield and composition in dairy cows. *Proceedings of the International Symposium on: Production, Evaluation and Feeding of Silage. Rostock*, 12th-16th June 1989, 177-183.

Field Wilting of Grass after Maceration and Spreading

CECILIA STANHELLINI, A. H. BOSMA AND H. G. BREEMHAAR

Institute of Agricultural and Environmental Engineering (IMAG-DLO)
P.O. Box 43, 6700 AA Wageningen, The Netherlands

INTRODUCTION

Pre-wilting of grass is necessary for the production of good quality silage. As field drying is the cheapest way to remove water, a lot of new techniques and systems are aimed at enhancing it (Bosma and Knight, 1992). Grass drying implies removal of water that is variously bound to the material. Reduction of moisture content to 50% of its value at mowing (a ceiling to water content short of fermentation during silage) is often taken as the standard by which drying systems are evaluated. The present work proposes a method for evaluating the drying efficiency of some treatments, as measured under various weather conditions.

MATERIALS AND METHODS

The drying rates of perennial ryegrass treated with three degrees of conditioning: none (untreated); light; and heavy (intensive), each exposed with two simulated yields (2 and 4 kg/m^2), were experimentally determined. The experiment took place in parcels of 50 m^2 each. The dry-matter content of at least five samples per treatment was determined by gravimetric methods, several times during the first day after mowing. The experiment took place during 9 selected days (of quite different weather), between May and July 1994.

In order to compare drying rates under various conditions, weather was characterized by a 'reference potential evaporation', in this particular instance calculated by the formula (Makkink, 1957) used by the Dutch Royal Meteorological Institute for their forecast, that is a function of sun radiation and air temperature only.

The relationship between water loss data (W) and cumulative reference evaporation (E_r) was best-fitted by a 'saturation function', of the form:

$$W = A \left(1 - R^{E_r} \right) \qquad\qquad \text{mm} \quad (1)$$

where A and R are best-fit parameters. A, the asymptotic value for very large potential evaporations, is obviously the water content at mowing. After checking that this would not significantly worsen the performance of the best-fit curves (r^2 above 0.9 anyhow), A was fixed beforehand at 3/4 of yield, in order to allow a discussion of the performance of the treatments, based solely on the parameter R. The resulting fit lines can be seen in Figure 1, together with measured values (none and heavy conditioning being on the left and right hand side panels, respectively).

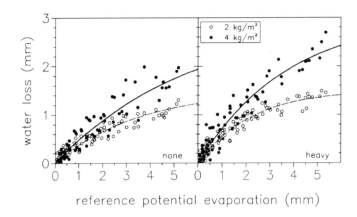

Figure 1.   Cumulative water loss (W) v cumulative reference evaporation (E_r). Points are measured values for spreadings of 2 and 4 kg/m², as indicated, and for none (left panel) and heavy conditioning (right). The lines are the fitted lines with the asymptote (parameter A of Eq(1)) fixed beforehand to 1.5 and 3 mm for the 2 and 4 kg/m² spreadings, respectively.

DISCUSSION
By differentiating Equation (1) it can be shown that *ln R* is an 'initial efficiency' of evaporation, that is roughly the fraction of present water that would be evaporated when reference evaporation, E_r, has cumulated 1 mm. Values are shown in Figure 2. Figure 3, on the other hand, quantifies the total potential evaporation required for halving initial water content. From both figures one may deduce that the effect of conditioning is largest with small yields, that is, wide spreading. De Lorenzi *et al.* (1995) reached the same conclusion through a physical model of the drying process, based on Thompson's (1981) work. In fact, maceration has the sole effect of boosting release of water from the material, whereas in a thick swath the factor limiting evaporation may often be the rate of vapour removal from within the swath.

CONCLUSION
Using potential evaporation as a compound 'weather parameter' for reference, allows for data measured under very different conditions to be compared to each other. By this means the 'efficiency' of various treatments can be evaluated *a posteriori*. It is stated that the present empirical results can be explained by the predictions of an explanatory model of the drying process.

REFERENCES

BOSMA A.H. and KNIGHT A.C. (1992) New mechanization in forage harvesting, handling and storage. In: Pellizzi G. *et al.* (eds.), *Possibilities offered by new mechanization systems to reduce agricultural production costs.* EC-DG VI , Luxembourg, 143-158.

DE LORENZI, BOSMA A.H. and STANGHELLINI C. (1995) Simulating the effect of conditioning on wilting of grass. *Acta Horticulturae,* Mathematical and Computer applications in Agriculture, **406**.

MAKKINK G.F. (1957) Testing the Penman formula by means of lysimeters. *Journal of the Institution of Water Engineers,* **11**, 277-288.

THOMPSON N. (1981) Modelling the field drying of hay. *The Journal of Agricultural Science,* Cambridge, **97**, 241-260.

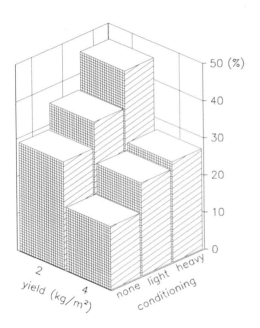

Figure 2. Initial water loss efficiency. That is the fraction of water present at mowing that would be evaporated after 1 mm potential evaporation, were the initial rate mantained.

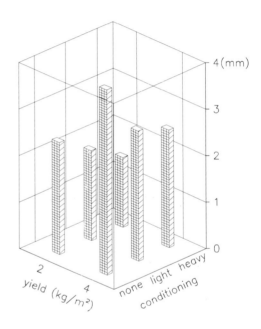

Figure 3. Potential evaporation required for a reduction of 50% in initial water content, as a function of spreading and conditioning.

The Response of Perennial Ryegrass, Cocksfoot and Tall Fescue to Sodium Fertilization

R. M. TAIT[1], K. HANSON[1] AND L. J. FISHER[2]

[1] Department of Animal Science, University of British Columbia, Vancouver, B.C., Canada, V6T 1Z4

[2] Agriculture and Agri-Food Canada, Pacific Agricultural Research Centre, Agassiz, B.C., Canada, V0M 1A0

INTRODUCTION

Several positive effects of sodium fertilization of perennial ryegrass (*Lolium perrene*) pasture in terms of forage quality and animal performance have been reported by Chiy and Phillips (1993). There are concerns about the negative effects of sodium on soils. However sodium fertilization may be beneficial in areas where soil potassium levels are high and there is adequate precipitation. It is known that different species and varieties within species have different affinities for sodium (ap Griffiths *et al.*, 1965). The effects of sodium fertilization of three species of pasture grasses were examined in an experiment conducted at the Pacific Agricultural Research Centre in the lower Fraser Valley of British Columbia, which has an annual precipitation of 1800 mm.

MATERIALS AND METHODS

A total of 96 plots (13 m^2) of perennial ryegrass (*Lolium perrene*), cocksfoot (*Dactylis glomerata*) and tall fescue (*Festuca arundinacea*) were established on a sandy-loam soil in a randomised-block design. There were two varieties of each species, with 16 plots of each variety.

Four levels of sodium (0, 30, 60 and 90 kg/ha) in the form of sodium nitrate were applied in 5 split applications over the season. All plots received 200 kg N/ha in 5 applications. The sodium levels were based on those used by Chiy and Phillips (1993).

The plots were harvested and samples taken 5 times at intervals of 4 weeks between early May and September 1994. Dry-matter yield was measured and samples were analyzed for crude protein, ADF, Ca, P, Na, K, Mg, Cu, Zn and Mn.

RESULTS

Only the results for one variety of each species are reported here, perennial ryegrass (var, Frances), cocksfoot (var. Mobite) and tall fescue (var. Courtenay). The sodium content of the grasses from the control plots was low and averaged 2.07, 0.81 and 0.28 g/kg DM for perennial ryegrass, cocksfoot and tall fescue respectively.

Sodium levels in the three species of grass increased (P<0.05) approximately linearly in response to sodium fertilization. There was no significant (P>0.05)

effect of treatment on dry matter yield, ADF, protein, Ca, K, Mg content of the
forages or rumen nylon bag dry matter disappearance (Table 1).

Table 1.   Effect of sodium fertilization on grass composition (g/kg DM) and
yield (kg /ha) (average of 4 cuts).

	Grass species					
	Ryegrass		Cocksfoot		Tall fescue	
	Sodium fertilizer level (0 or 90 kg/ha)					
	Control	High	Control	High	Control	High
Yield	1011	854	1689	1464	1729	1747
ADF	288	287	313	320	310	321
Protein	174	177	175	174	160	162
Na	2.07	3.76	0.81	1.70	0.28	0.67
K	23.0	25.1	22.6	22.9	19.5	22.2
Mg	2.55	2.25	2.23	2.30	3.10	3.05
Effective degradability (P)	690	700	556	554	na	na

These results are in contrast to those of Chiy and Phillips (1993). This may be
due to the fact that the initial levels of sodium were low and the levels achieved
with 90 kg Na /ha were below those attained by Chiy and Phillips (1993). It may
also be due to the different species and varieties involved in the two studies.

REFERENCES
ap GRIFFITHS G., JONES D.I.H. and WALTERS R.J.K. (1965) Specific and varietal
differences in sodium and potassium in grasses. *Journal of the Science, Food and Agriculture*,
16, 94-98.
CHIY C.P. and PHILLIPS C.J.C. (1993) Sodium fertilizer application to pasture. 1. Direct
and residual effects on pasture production and composition. *Grass and Forage Science*, **48**,
189-202.

An Evaluation of a High Magnesium Perennial Ryegrass Variety

R. C. BINNIE[1], D. T. JOHNSTON[2] AND D. M. B. CHESTNUTT[1]

[1]Agricultural Research Institute of Northern Ireland, Hillsborough, Co Down
[2]Department of Agriculture for Northern Ireland,
Plant Breeding Station, Loughgall, Co Armagh

INTRODUCTION

In the United Kingdom hypomagnesaemia results in the death of a large number of cattle and sheep each year, with additional losses due to reduced production. Although the relationship between the magnesium content of herbage and the incidence of hypomagnesaemia is complex, hypomagnesaemia is usually associated with the turnout of animals onto lush spring pasture when the Mg content of the herbage is at its lowest. The incidence of hypomagnesaemia can be reduced by supplying additional Mg to grazing animals and administering prophylactic treatments in extreme cases. In addition grass breeding programmes have been initiated to identify varieties with improved Mg status. The aim of this study was to investigate the effects of grazing a high Mg grass variety on blood Mg status and the incidence of hypomagnesaemia of sheep.

MATERIALS AND METHODS

Two plots of each of the perennial ryegrass (*Lolium perenne*) varieties Frances and the high Mg cultivar Ramore were established and grazed by Greyface (Border Leicester x Scottish Blackface) ewes suckling twin lambs. The sheep grazed from turnout on 26 March and 6 April to weaning in July in 1992 and 1993 respectively. Herbage samples were taken at regular intervals throughout the grazing period and Mg content determined. Blood samples were obtained from ewes by jugular venepuncture and Mg status determined. In addition a proportion of each sward was cut daily and offered to ewes housed indoors in metabolism crates. In 1992 twelve non-lactating Greyface ewes were housed in metabolism crates and used in change-over design studies to evaluate herbage digestibility, Mg intake, apparent absorption and retention and blood Mg status. In 1993 six ewes each suckling twin lambs were used in a similar change-over design study.

RESULTS

Herbage from Ramore swards had a higher Mg content than Frances (2.24 v 2.09 g/kg DM; SEM 0.028, P<0.001). Blood Mg levels over the spring periods in both years averaged 0.854 and 0.793 µ mol/l (SEM 0.0086, P<0.001) in ewes grazing Ramore and Frances respectively. One ewe died from hypomagnesaemia while grazing a sward sown to the variety Frances. The chemical composition of the

Table 1. Effect of variety on intake, OMD and chemical composition of herbage during the metabolism studies (g/kg DM unless otherwise stated)

	1992			1993		
	Ramore	Frances	SEM	Ramore	Frances	SEM
DM intake (kg/ewe/d)	0.806	0.813	0.014 NS	1.42	1.44	0.014 NS
OMD coeff.	0.836	0.848	0.0030 *	0.842	0.855	0.005 NS
DM content	166.8	175.0	2.59 *	148.1	146.4	3.69 NS
N content	25.7	26.0	0.24 NS	30.0	31.2	0.68 NS
ADF content	273.1	267.9	2.64 NS	245.6	249.2	4.22 NS
Mg content	2.00	1.77	0.073 ***	2.00	1.67	0.022 ***

Table 2. Effect of variety on the Mg balance of sheep (g/ewe/day unless otherwise stated)

	1992			1993		
	Ra	Fr	SEM	Ra	Fr	SEM
Mg intake	1.61	1.40	0.025 ***	2.83	2.41	0.031 ***
Faecal Mg output	1.30	1.18	0.031 *	2.00	1.85	0.088 NS
Urinary Mg output	0.204	0.161	0.0108 **	0.188	0.144	0.020 NS
AA of Mg (prpn)	0.194	0.151	0.0150 *	0.300	0.240	0.028 NS
Mg retained	0.110	0.054	0.023 NS	0.645	0.422	0.087 NS
Prpn. Mg retained	0.058	0.026	0.015 NS	0.234	0.180	0.031 NS
Blood Mg(μ mol/l)	0.713	0.723	0.015 NS	0.631	0.563	0.056 NS
Mg in milk (g/l)	ND	ND	ND	0.192	0.202	0.012 NS

ND = not determined; AA = Aparent availability

two herbages offered to the ewes in the metabolism crates was similar with the exception of Mg content and organic matter digestibility (OMD) (Table 1). Results of the metabolism studies indicated that Mg intake was significantly ($P<0.001$) higher in ewes offered Ramore compared with those offered Frances (1.86 v 1.60 g/d; SEM 0.026) with no significant difference in dry-matter intake between the two varieties. During the metabolism study periods the apparent availability and retention of Mg tended to be higher in Ramore compared with Frances (Table 2). Differences in Mg intake and retention between years were not reflected in blood

Mg status and this may be related to the different metabolism of non lactating and lactating ewes. The level of Mg in the ewe's blood or milk was not significantly influenced by variety.

CONCLUSION

The results indicate that swards established from varieties bred for a high Mg content had a significantly higher Mg content than a control variety and this was reflected in the Mg metabolism of sheep. Further improvements in Mg content of selected varieties are required to reduce the risk of hypomagnesaemia in grazing sheep.

Influence Of Nitrogen On Crown Rust

TH. V. VELLINGA AND G. HOLSHOF
Research Station for Cattle, Sheep and Horse Husbandry (PR)
Runderweg 6, 8219 PK Lelystad, The Netherlands

INTRODUCTION
The infection of grasses with crown rust (*Puccinia coronata*) leads to a lower DM production and to a lower herbage intake. An increased infection with crown rust was seen in 1988 and 1989. This increased infection was thought to be caused by reduced nitrogen inputs on grassland. Since a further reduction of nitrogen inputs is expected, this trial investigated the influence of different levels of fertilizer nitrogen and different ways of partitioning of the nitrogen on the crown rust infection from 1991 until 1994.

MATERIAL AND METHODS
The experimental site was on a 'rust sensitive' paddock on clay soil, with more than 80 % perennial ryegrass. There were two treatments (with four replicates): nitrogen level (200, 300 and 400 kg N/ha/year) and nitrogen partitioning

1)   slow decrease of dressings according to current recommendations (Unwin and Vellinga, 1994)
2)   equal dressings in six cuts, later cuts unfertilized
3)   equal dressings in five cuts, later cuts unfertilized
4)   equal dressings in four cuts, later cuts unfertilized
5)   fast decrease, 75% of N in cuts 1 - 3, remaining N in other three cuts, later cuts unfertilized.

The grass was cut at the grazing stage (1700 kg DM/ha). Maximum growth period per cut was six weeks. The number of cuts was a result of growing conditions and nitrogen level. When crown rust was seen, 20 tillers per plot were randomly taken and the coverage with spores of crown rust on the second and third fully expanded leaf was estimated.

RESULTS
The nitrogen level per year has no significant influence on the infection with crown rust (Figure 1). There was a very strong year effect. In 1991 and 1992 there was a high infection, caused by drought. The level of crown rust was much lower in 1993 and 1994. The differences between the treatments in 1991 and 1992 were caused by differences in growth stage.

Also the partitioning of the nitrogen had no significant influence on the infection with crown rust (Figure 2). In 1991 and 1992 there was a tendency to lower infection at the recommended application scheme and to a higher infection in the scheme with dressings in four and five cuts. Interactions between nitrogen level and nitrogen partitioning were not significant.

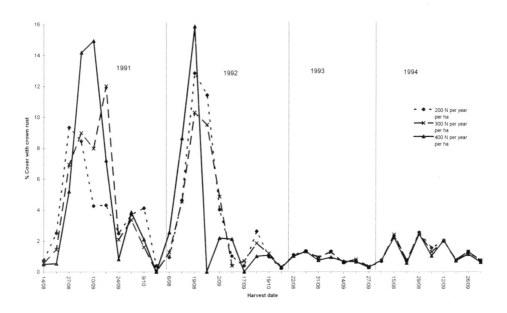

Figure 1.   The infection with crown rust (average of leaf 2 and 3) per N level in the years 1991-1994.

DISCUSSION
Although only small differences in infection were measured, large visual differences were seen when inspected from a small distance from the plots. Grass leaves were more yellowish and more dying leaf tops were seen at lower nitrogen levels. It is assumed that this appearance of the grass sward is often interpreted in practice as a higher infection with crown rust. Especially in 1991 and 1992 it was observed that growing conditions and growth stage of the grass had a large influence on crown rust infection. Infection with crown rust occurs especially when grass is under stress, like drought. Very strong increases of crown rust infection have been seen. In grass of less than 2 weeks, the infection was at a lower level than in older grass.

CONCLUSION
The infection of grass with crown rust is hardly influenced by nitrogen level and nitrogen partitioning over the cuts. Growing conditions like drought and the growth stage of the grass seem to be more important factors.

REFERENCES

UNWIN R. and VELLINGA TH.V. Fertilizer recommendations for intensively managed grassland. In: Mannetje L.'t and Frame J. (eds) *Grassland and Society. Proceedings of the 15th General Meeting of the European Grassland Federation*, Wageningen, 1994, 509 -602.

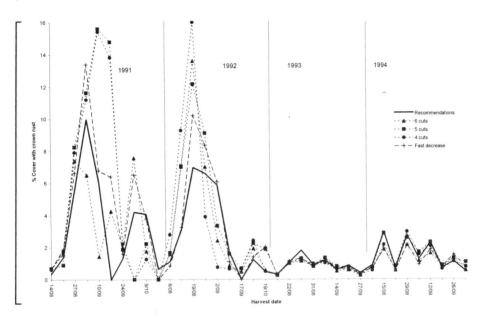

Figure 2.   The infection with crown rust (average of leaf 2 and 3) per N partitioning in the years 1991 - 1994.

The Effect of the Grazing Management of Mixed Swards on Herbage Production, Clover Composition and Animal Performance

R. F. WELLER AND A. COOPER

IGER,Trawsgoed, Aberystwyth, Dyfed, SY23 4LL

INTRODUCTION

Changes in the management of grazed swards of grass can have a marked effect on both the sward and the performance of the dairy herd. When white clover (*Trifolium repens L.*) is the main source of nitrogen in mixed grass/clover swards, grazing severity may have a critical effect on both the composition and yield of the sward and also the production and profitability of the dairy herd, particularly a herd of spring-calving cows in early lactation.

The effect of grazing height on animal performance (stocking rates, milk production, milk quality and profit margin), herbage yield and sward composition was determined over two consecutive grazing seasons. Spring-calving dairy cows grazed unfertilized mixed swards of predominantly perennial ryegrass (*Lolium perenne L.*) and white clover to residual heights of either 6 or 4.5 cm.

METHODS

Three unfertilized swards of grass (predominantly perennial ryegrass) and white clover were sub-divided into paddocks and continuously grazed by spring-calving Holstein/Friesian dairy cows to target sward heights of either 6 or 4.5 cm. Cows calving between February and April were allocated to treatments according to milk yield and calving date. The sward heights were measured twice weekly using a rising-plate meter, and the target residual heights maintained by increasing/decreasing the available grazing area in each paddock. All cows received a concentrate supplement of 4.5 kg DM/day (metabolisable energy value 12.5 MJ/kg DM, crude protein 180 g/kg) in both grazing seasons. The swards were grazed from May 8 - October 10 (Year 1) and May 4 - October 11 (Year 2). Herbage yields and sward composition were determined monthly from quadrats cut within enclosure cages at 2.5 cm above ground level. Milk yields were recorded twice daily and milk composition weekly. In both years the body condition score of the cows was measured at the start and end of the grazing season.

RESULTS

As shown in Table 1, reducing the grazing height from 6 to 4.5 cm reduced the total DM yield of herbage in Years 1 and 2 by 1.66 and 1.25 t/ha, respectively. Grazing height did not significantly affect the mean clover content of the swards in Year 1, with a 64 g/kg lower content recorded in Year 2 for swards grazed at 4.5 cm.

Table 1. The yield and white clover content of the grazed swards.

Grazing height (cm):	6	4.5
DM yield (t/ha):		
Year 1	9.69	8.03
2	8.55	7.30
Clover content of the total DM (g/kg):		
Year 1	303	292
2	278	214

The clover content of the swards (g/kg) during the grazing season ranged from: Year 1 - 141 to 494 (6 cm) and 179 to 360 (4.5 cm); Year 2 - 185 to 369 (6 cm) and 104 to 351 g/kg (4.5 cm).

Table 2. The effect of grazing height on milk production and income (mean of the 2 grazing seasons).

Grazing height (cm):	6	4.5
Milk production/cow (kg)	3,942	3,749
Milk production/ha (kg)	10,291	12,384
Milk fat (g/kg)	38.6	39.7
Milk protein (g/kg)	32.5	33.0
Margin over concentrates :		
(£/cow)	667	640
(£/ha)	1427	1773

Reducing the sward height from 6 to 4.5 cm increased the mean stocking rate from 2.61 to 3.30 cows/ha (Year 1: 2.69 and 3.37; Year 2: 2.52 and 3.23 cows/ha, respectively). The effect of the grazing strategy on the performance of the cows is shown in Table 2. The lower herbage yields in the second year reduced milk production/cow (kg) for both groups: 6 cm - 4,200 and 3,684; 4.5

cm - 3,946 and 3,551 kg, for Years 1 and 2, respectively. Differences between treatments in margins over concentrates was similar in both years.

Changes in the body condition of cows at the beginning and end of the grazing seasons were - Year 1: 6 cm - 2.44 and 2.81; 4.5 cm - 2.63 and 2.50, Year 2: 6 cm - 2.21 and 2.33; 4.5 cm - 2.23 and 2.27, respectively.

CONCLUSIONS

Although reducing the grazing height from 6 to 4.5 cm reduced both milk yield/cow and margin over concentrates, stocking rates increased by 0.7 cows/ha, milk production/ha by 2,093 kg and margin over concentrate by £346/ha. Both total herbage DM yield and the proportion of white clover in the sward were reduced when the residual grazing height was reduced from 6 to 4.5 cm, with the reduction in both yield and clover content of the sward more marked during the second grazing season.

The Potential for Alternative Use of Grass and Forage Species in the UK

P. S. WIGHTMAN, S. E. BATCHELOR AND C. K. MACKIE

Agronomy Department, SAC, 581 King Street, Aberdeen, ABA9 1UD

INTRODUCTION

Surplus food production and the resulting EU set-aside policy has stimulated interest in production of agricultural feedstocks for industrial and energy production. Current trends of reduced meat consumption reinforce the need to develop alternative markets for grass and forage crops. Possible alternative uses for grass and forage crops are:

Energy production

The development of large scale energy production from biomass will rely on specifically-grown energy crops, and herbaceous crops offer a significant potential source of biomass energy. A yield of 20 t dm ha^{-1} represents the equivalent of 8 t of oil. Biomass can be converted into energy by: direct combustion for heat and/or power generation; gasification to produce a combustible gas; pyrolysis which produces gases, liquids and char; anaerobic digestion to produce biogas; fermentation to produce ethanol, for use as a transport fuel.

Fibre production

The largest potential market for UK-produced fibre crops is in the pulp, paper and board industries, although the replacement of man-made fibre composites, plastics and metal represents a smaller, but more lucrative market (Carruthers, 1994).

Industrial feedstock production

A wide range of chemicals can be derived either directly by wet fractionation of green biomass, or indirectly via chemical conversions.

POTENTIAL CROPS

Biomass production requires high yield at low cost. Perennial grasses are extremely promising as biomass crops (Christian, 1994) due to rapid development of a full canopy and lack of annual establishment costs. Yields of some candidate species are shown in Table 1. Miscanthus (*Miscanthus sinensis*), a high yielding perennial grass well suited for pulp production both for paper and fibreboard (Carruthers, 1994), is currently being evaluated in UK trials. Switchgrass (*Panicum virgatum*) is also considered promising; both species are expected to remain productive for 10 harvests or more (Christian,

1994). A number of *Spartina* species and reed canarygrass (*Phalaris arundinacea*) produce high yields. Other grass species appear to be high yielding, but have not been evaluated in the UK, including pampas grass (*Cortaderia selloana*) and bamboos.

Table 1.   Reported dry matter yields of crops.

Crop species	DM yield (t DM/ha/yr)	
Miscanthus sinensis	11-25.3	Speller and Harvey (1992)
Spartina townsendii	7-20	Long *et al* (1989)
Reed canarygrass*Phalaris arundinacea*	9-20	Schoth (1929)
Stinging nettle *Urtica dioica*	2-11	Weiß (1993)
Whole crop wheat	14.6-17.4	Weller *et al*(1995)
Short rotation coppice	10-15	ETSU (1990)
Fodder beet	20	Speller (1993)
Lucerne *Medicago sativa*	10	Spelman (1994)
Broom *Cytisus scoparius*	18	Bywater *et al* (1994)
Gorse *Ulex europaeus*	14.4	Marriott (1990)
Lupin *Lupinus albus*	11	Williams (1984)
Goat's rue *Galega orientalis*	9-13	Yarosevich (1994)

Legumes are of particular interest due to their low N requirement. Scotch broom (*Cytisus scoparius*) and gorse (*Ulex europaeus*) are high-yielding and cold tolerant. Gorse has a high dry matter content (30-47%); broom has potential for fibre production (Carruthers, 1994). Lucerne (*Medicago sativa*) has good potential for commercial production of leaf protein concentrate and a number of high value chemicals. Stinging nettle (*Urtica dioica*) has potential for fibre production, giving fine, high quality fibre which has been used in the past for textiles (Carruthers, 1994). Other species may be useful in paper making. Whole-crop cereals, fodder beet and fodder/sugar beet hybrids have potential for fuel production. Combined production of fibre and special products may be possible from some species.

CONCLUSIONS

A number of grass and forage crops appear promising for biomass, fibre and industrial feedstock production. Many of the candidate species require evaluation under UK conditions. Genetic improvement, technological advances in conversion efficiencies, investment in infrastructure, and assignment of economic value to socio-economic and environmental benefits, would enable widespread adoption of alternative uses for grass and forage crops.

REFERENCES

BYWATER I., SCOTT K. and ARNOUX L. (1994) Competitive power generation from biomass. *Renewable Energy*, **5**, 849-851.

CARRUTHERS S.P. (1994) Fibres. In: Carruthers, S. P., Miller, F. A. and Vaughan, C. M. A. (eds) *Crops for Industry and Energy*, Centre for Agricultural Strategy Report, **15**, 92 - 108.

CHRISTIAN D. G. (1994) Quantifying the yield of perennial grasses grown as a biofuel for energy generation. *Renewable Energy*, **5**, 762-766.

ETSU (1990) Coppiced trees as energy crops. *Report B1078*. Energy Technology Support Unit, Harwell.

LONG, S.P., POTTER, L., Bingham, M.J. and Stirling, C.M. (1989) An analysis of limitations to the production of C4 perennials as ligno-cellulosic biomass crops, with reference to trials in E. England. In: Grassi, G., Gosse, G. and dos Santos, G. (eds.) *Biomass for energy and industry 1, Policy, environment, Production and Harvesting*. pp 235-241. Elsevier: London.

MARRIOTT C. (1990) Potential productivity and use of N2 fixing shrubs. *The Mauculay Land Use Research Institute Annual Report 1989-1990*, 49-50.

SCHOTH H.A. (1929) Reed canarygrass. *USDA Farmers Bulletin 1602*.

SPELLER C.S. (1993) The potential for growing biomass crops for fuel on surplus land in the UK. *Outlook on Agriculture*, **22**, 23-29.

SPRLLER, C.S. and HARVEY, J.J. (1992) The potential for biomass production from crops on set-aside land. In: Clarke, J. (ed) *Set-aside*. BCPC Monograph No. 50, Proceedings of a British Crop Protection Council Symposium, Cambridge, 209-214.

SPELMAN C.A. (1994). *Non-Food Uses of Agricultural Raw Materials*. CAB International: Wallingford.

WEDDELL J.R. and SWIFT G. (1994) *Grass and clover varieties for Scotland 1994-95*. Scottish Agricultural College, Edinburgh.

WEIβ F. (1993) Effects of varied nitrogen fertilization and cutting treatments on the development and yield components of cultivated stinging nettles. *Acta Horticulture*, **33,1** 137-144.

WELLER R.F., COOPER A. and DHANOA M. S. (1995) The selection of winter wheat varieties for whole-crop cereal conservation. *Grass and Forage Science*, **50**, 172-177.

WILLIAMS, W. (1984) Lupins in crop production. *Outlook on Agriculture* **13**, 69-76.

YAROSEVICH, M. (1994) Main research results of *Galea orientalis* Lam. in Belorussia. In: Nômmsalu, H. (ed.) *Fodder Galea Research in Estonia*. The Estonia Research Institute of Agriculture, Saku, 60-61.

Modelling the Vegetation Dynamics of Pasture Including Several Species

C. P. D. BIRCH

Macaulay Land Use Research Institute, Craigiebuckler, Aberdeen

INTRODUCTION

The composition of the sward, which is usually measured as its species composition, affects not only forage quality but also many other interlinked objectives of grassland management (West 1993). These include nature conservation, landscape quality, the conservation of soil fertility and the exclusion of undesirable species. These objectives are often most important in less productive areas, such as in the uplands and permanent grassland, so prediction of vegetation dynamics in these communities is of increasing interest.

Unfortunately, predicting the dynamics of natural systems of many species is difficult. Direct study of every interaction would require hundreds of experiments and the solution of thousands of mathematical equations. Because of this, theoretical ecological analyses have often concentrated on the stable states of ecosystems. However, pastures are unstable ecosystems maintained by management, in which the rate of change is often more important than the theoretical eventual outcome. A simplified model has been developed to allow simulation of the short-term dynamics of these systems.

THE MODEL

The model starts from the observation that the production of pasture varies with the amount of biomass of vegetation present, often measured by sward height (Milne and Fisher 1993). In any particular environment a curve relates the growth rate of each species in monoculture to its biomass. Each species' curve can be adequately represented by three parameter values. These represent the maximum biomass of the species, its maximum production and the rate at which its production declines above the optimum biomass. A fourth parameter, representing offtake from the species, allows prediction of the effect of grazing. The dynamics of a mixture of species can be predicted by combining the parameters of all the species in a system of equations, then solving by computer. It is assumed that each species is equally sensitive to all the other species present and is most sensitive to competition from itself.

RESULTS AND DISCUSSION

The model simulates, quantitatively, many of the known qualitative features of pasture ecosystems. For example, it shows that grazing favours perennial species that are most abundant early in the colonization of ungrazed sites and suppresses species that would otherwise dominate in the longer term.

Selective grazing can be incorporated but, even without it, the model shows that some species in mixtures are much less affected by grazing than others.

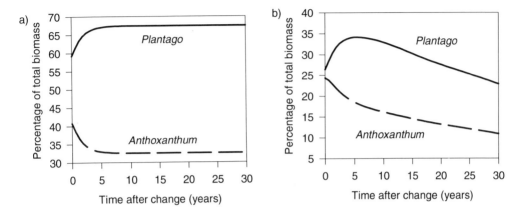

Figure 1.   Predicted dynamics of *Plantago lanceolata* and *Anthoxanthum odoratum* for 30 years after a change from light grazing to no grazing. a) In a two species sward. b) In an hypothetical ten species sward.

Another way to simplify vegetation dynamics would be to combine species into groups so that fewer interactions need be modelled. However, results from this model suggest that the dynamics of small numbers of species such as two or three are qualitatively different from the dynamics of larger numbers. For example, curves representing the growth in a moderately fertile hay-meadow of *Anthoxanthum odoratum* and *Plantago lanceolata* were fitted by least squares to observations on monocultures made by Berendse (1983). The predicted short term dynamics of the two species together matched his observations: *A. odoratum* substantially exceeded *P. lanceolata* after 100 days regrowth from low density. Their longer term dynamics were then simulated in a two species mixture and as part of a mixture with eight other randomly generated species. The hypothetical scenario simulated was the first thirty years after a change from uniform light grazing to no grazing (Figure 1). Alone, the two species reached a new equilibrium within a few years of the management change, and the short term dynamics were dominated by movement towards the new equilibrium (Figure 1a). When there were ten species, they approached equilibrium much later and the short term dynamics were weakly related to it (Figure 1b). These observations suggest that the diversity of the ecosystem should be represented in any vegetation dynamics model, even at the expense of less detail in the representation of each element.

REFERENCES

BERENDSE F. (1983) Interspecific competition and niche differentiation between *Plantago lanceolata* and *Anthoxanthum odoratum* in a natural hayfield. *Journal of Ecology,* **71**, 379-390.

MILNE J.A. and FISHER G.E.J. (1993) Sward structure with regard to production. In: R. J. Haggar and S. Peel (eds.) *Grassland Management and Nature Conservation, Occasional Symposium of the British Grassland Society,* **No.28**, 33-42.

WEST N.E. (1993) Biodiversity of rangelands. *Journal of Range Management,* **46**, 2-13.

Estimation of the Nutritive Value of Mixed Winter Grasses on the Pastures of Northwest China

JIA-QI WANG

Animal Science Institute, Chinese Academy of Agricultural
Sciences, Beijing 100094, China

INTRODUCTION

In northwest China, ruminants survive by grazing mixed pasture grasses during the winter. Little information is available on the nutritive value of these winter grasses and, as a result, it is very difficult to supplement the ruminants properly and economically during the winter. The objective of this research was to study the carbohydrate and nitrogen degradation of winter grasses in the rumen using an *in sacco* technique.

MATERIAL AND METHODS

Grass sample preparation

The mixed winter grass samples were collected from pastures at the beginning of winter and ground through a 2.5 mm sieve for composition analysis and *in sacco* measurement.

Animals and the *in sacco* technique

Six wethers, of 40 kg average live weight and with permanent rumen cannulae, were used. The diet was middle-quality hay, containing 8.3% crude protein (CP), fed *ad libitum* to the sheep. The *in sacco* method (Dhanoa, 1988) used nylon bags, measuring 8x16 cm with pores of 50 microns, which were attached to a 30 cm long PVC plastic tube rod. Each bag contained a 3 g grass sample. Each rod had 2 bags and each sheep had 6 rods in the rumen. Six incubation times were chosen: 6, 12, 24, 36, 48 and 72 h. The OM, CP, NDF, ADF, before and after ruminal degradation, were measured (AOAC, 1980).

Calculation

The degradabilities of OM, CP, NDF and ADF were calculated according to the equations (Orskov and McDonald, 1979): $p=a+b(1-e^{-ct})$ and $P=a+bc/(c+k)$, where a was the rapidly degradable fraction, b was the potentially degradable fraction, c was the degradation rate constant of the b fraction, t was the incubation time, P was the effective degradability, and k was the outflow rate of the rumen digesta. A value of k=0.0300 was used in this experiment.

RESULTS AND DISCUSSION

The mean compositions of the winter grasses were: OM 93.9, CP 3.8, NDF 67.5 and ADF 42.4% respectively (see Table 1). The *in sacco* results showed that the rapidly degradable fractions were 16 and 50% for OM and CP respectively. Half of the CP disappeared immediately after the start of incubation, and the remaining CP had a much slower degradation rate (c=0.013) than that of OM (c=0.026). This means that the energy and nitrogen in the grasses cannot be released synchronously to support optimum microbial synthesis in the rumen. For the optimum microbial synthesis and fibre digestion in the rumen, FOM and rumen degradable protein (RDP) have to match each other in both the releasing rates and amount. Fermented organic matter (FOM) degradability was 25.9 and 73.5%, crude protein degradability was 52.5 and 71.9% at 6 hours and 72 hours respectively. According to NRC (1985), the optimum proportion between FOM and RDP is 161 g RDP per kg FOM. Because of the low crude protein content in the grasses, RDP/FOM (g/kg) was much lower than the optimum level at any time in the rumen (p<0.05) (Table 1). Supplying rumen degradable nitrogen, such as urea, may increase the microbial yield and animal production in the winter.

Table 1.   Chemical compositions and kinetic degradation of the mixed winter grasses.

Items	%DM	Degradability %									
		6h	12h	24h	36h	48h	72h	a	b	c	p
OM	93.9	25.9	35.2	48.6	56.4	65.8	73.5	16	56	0.026	47.3
CP	3.8	52.5	55.3	60.5	63.3	65.5	71.9	50	23	0.013	35.9
NDF	67.5	10.3	19.5	35.7	39.6	57.9	68.0	2	67	0.017	60.8
ADF	42.4	4.5	20.0	33.4	41.9	55.4	65.5	0	66	0.025	33.4
RDP/FOM (g/kg)		82.3	63.5	50.4	45.5	40.3	39.6				

k=0.0300.

In conclusion, both the lower amount and releasing rate of RDP compared to FOM, in the winter grasses, is the main limiting nutritive factor for both microbial synthesis in the rumen and animal growth during the cold season in the northwest China pastures. The supplementation of degradable N may be one way to improve the grass utilization and the animal productivity.

REFERENCES
AOAC (1970) *Official methods of analyses.* 11th edition. Association of Official Agricultural Chemists, Washington, D.C.
DHANOA M. S. (1988) On the analysis of dacron bag for low degradability feeds. *Grass and Forage Science*, **43**, 441-444.
NRC (1985) *Ruminant Nitrogen Usage.* National Academy Press,Washington, DC 20418.
ORSKOV, E.R. and MCDONALD, I. (1979) The estimation of protein degradability in the rumen from incubation measurements weighted according to rate of passage. *Journal of Agricultural Science*, **92**, 499-503.

The Presence of Cell Wall Glycosidase Inhibitors in Extracts from Temperate Grasses

A. L. WINTERS, S. T. PARISH, R. J. NASH AND A. C. LONGLAND

IGER, Plas Gogerddan, Aberystwyth, Dyfed

INTRODUCTION

The structural polysaccharides of grass cell walls can be a major source of dietary energy for grazing livestock. Glycosidases produced by the gut microflora are required to break down the cell wall polysaccharides prior to their being utilised to yield ATP. The principal cell wall polysaccharide is cellulose, β-glucosidase being the final enzyme required to hydrolyse it to monomeric glucose. However, a number of glycosidase inhibitors have been extracted from several plant species, with obvious implications for animal nutrition. Furthermore such inhibitors may be detrimental to animal health as has been reported to be the case with swainsonine from the genus *Swainsona*, which causes neurological disorders in Australian livestock. A different group of compounds, corynetoxins, produced by bacteria in grasses in Australia, Africa and USA are also known to cause neurological damage by inhibiting protein glycosylation.

AIM

To date glycosidase inhibitors have not been reported in temperate grasses. This work investigated the presence of glycosidase inhibitors in 5 species of temperate grasses at different stages of maturity.

EXPERIMENTAL

Five species of temperate grasses, commonly fed to UK livestock (*Dactylis glomerata, Festuca arundinacea, Festuca pratensis, Lolium perenne, Phleum pratense*) were harvested during spring and summer in 1994 and 1995. Samples were homogenised in 70% ethanol prior to being subjected to ion-exchange chromatography on a strongly acidic cation exchange column, DOWEX 50W (H$^+$). The bound fraction was eluted with 2N ammonia, and taken to dryness under reduced pressure. The effect of the bound fraction on glycosidases was assessed.

RESULTS

Over a 7-week collection period in 1994, each of the extracts from *F. arundinacea* inhibited β-glucosidase activity to varying degrees, rising from 18% (First Harvest) to 71% (Harvest 4) whereupon the degree of inhibition declined over the subsequent harvests to 18%. Varying amounts (7-84%) of β-glucosidase activity were inhibited at some, but not all of the harvests by the other species. Results for 1995 on a wider range of glycosidases will also be presented.

CONCLUSIONS
Clearly inhibitors of β-glucosidase inhibitor reside within these grass species. Such variations in glucosidase inhibitor activity with growth stage has not been reported previously. The implications of this may include fluctuations in the nutritive value of grasses hitherto unexplained by traditional chemical analyses of nutrients, and possibly unresolved sporadic animal health problems. Purification and characterisation of the inhibitor(s) is in hand.

Relationships between a Theoretical Model of Partitioning by Grazed Plants and Experimental Observations

C. P. D. BIRCH AND B. THORNTON
Macaulay Land Use Research Institute, Craigiebuckler, Aberdeen

INTRODUCTION

In the past, partitioning of carbon and nutrients within plants has been modelled assuming that the processes of photosynthesis and nutrient uptake should be balanced, so as to maximize growth. This may be appropriate for crop plants, but pasture plants must also tolerate severe defoliation. Grasses have been observed to rapidly transfer carbon and nutrient reserves from leaf bases immediately after defoliation to support refoliation. Therefore, partitioning in grazed plants can be modelled by assuming that the main role of resources not allocated for growth is as a reserve protected from grazing. However, partitioning to reserves will reduce growth (and production) between defoliations, so it is likely to have an optimum level.

THE MODEL

The model was derived from the following principal assumptions: 1) plants consist of parts that contribute to growth but are exposed to defoliation, and parts that do not contribute to growth but are protected from defoliation; 2) growth is not nutrient limited, so it only depends on parts exposed to defoliation; 3) all exposed parts make an equal contribution to growth; 4) the proportion of growth partitioned to the protected parts is constant; 5) resources are only transferred from protected to exposed parts immediately after defoliation, transfer being instantaneous.

The model was used to predict the optimum partitioning to protected parts to maximize the net growth from immediately after one defoliation to immediately after the next. The model calculated the optimum partitioning from information about the amount of growth between defoliations and the relationship between the amounts of exposed tissue before and after defoliation.

THE EXPERIMENT

Four grass species were grown in sand culture and defoliated weekly to 4 cm for 12 weeks, by which time the clippings taken each week were nearly constant (Thornton et al., 1993). After the twelfth defoliation, ^{15}N labelling allowed estimation of the amount of nitrogen transferred from the roots and leaf bases to the leaf laminae. The proportional allocation of growth between the twelfth and thirteenth defoliations to the roots and leaf bases was then

305

calculated. A performance index was also calculated by dividing net growth achieved in that week by the amount transferred from the leaf bases and roots. These observations were compared with the model's predictions. Since the second assumption of the model was that growth was not nutrient limited, plant biomass could be measured in terms of nitrogen content. (The nitrogen concentration in the plants was observed to be nearly constant after 12 weeks of defoliation.)

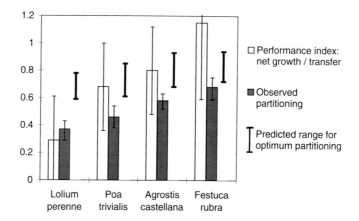

Figure 1.   Relationships between observed partitioning, predicted optimum partitioning and performance of grass species in a clipping experiment. The vertical axis is a dimensionless numeric scale indicating the proportion of growth partitioned to reserves and the performance index. Error bars are 95% confidence limits.

RESULTS AND DISCUSSION

Figure 1 shows that the model predicted significantly greater partitioning than observed for three of the four species. However, the more closely a plant matched the predicted optimum, the higher its performance index. Thus, the model's predicted optima may have been correct for the experimental conditions, but the plants' partitioning was suboptimal, perhaps because they would usually be influenced by factors absent from both the model and the experiment, such as seed production and competition. These possibilities are currently being analysed. If the model had included a plant nutrient requirement, the predicted partitioning to the roots and leaf bases would have been even higher. This suggests that, in pasture, nutrient uptake is often not the dominant factor in partitioning. This model emphasizes the importance of reserves and remobilization in helping an understanding of competition in grassland ecosystems, where evolution has been dominated by herbivory.

REFERENCES

THORNTON B., MILLARD P., DUFF E.I. and BUCKLAND S.T. (1993) The relative
contribution of remobilization and root uptake in supplying nitrogen after defoliation
for regrowth of laminae in four grass species. *New Phytologist*, **124**, 689-694.

New Approaches to Measuring Supplementary Feed Intake at Grass

J. E. VIPOND AND M. HASKELL

Genetics and Behavioural Sciences Department, SAC

Bush Estate, Penicuik, Midlothian EH26 0QE

INTRODUCTION

Large variation between group-fed individuals in the intake of supplementary trough-fed compounds feed blocks offered at pasture have been recorded; coefficients of variation of 67-107% have been reported (Kendall *et al.*, 1983). Variation may be due to behavioural and social factors at the feeding site (Lawrence, 1988) or previous exposure (Green *et al.*, 1984). Physiological differences in requirements between animals may also be involved, an area that has recently been reviewed by Forbes and Kyriazakis (1995). Progress in research in this area could be significantly simplified if accurate, cheap and easy determinations of individual intake in grazed group feeding situations could be made. The correlation between two different techniques was determined in the work reported here. An Australian method, which uses lithium chloride as a marker in the feed (Khan, 1994) followed by blood assay, was compared with physical monitoring of feed intake by changes in block weight using electronic balance equipment and automatic animal identification, in a commercial adaptation of a Hokofarm feeder. The lithium method used trace amounts given at levels below those at which either physiological effects or feed aversion occur.

MATERIALS AND METHODS

Twenty Suffolk ewes were run on a 0.15 ha pasture of perennial ryegrass of sward height of 8-10 cm at the start of the experiment. All sheep had previously been accustomed both to eating feed blocks and the Hokofarm feeder. Each ewe was fitted with a transponder and given access to Rumenco high energy feed blocks, in the Hokofarm feeder, for 2 days. On the third day, these blocks were replaced, from 0730-1930 h, by ones containing 5 mg LiCl/kg of fresh block. Ewes were blood sampled by venepuncture starting 18 hours later using non-heparanised vacutainers; sampling time was about 30 minutes. The amount of lithium tracer block consumed during the 12 hour exposure period, as measured by the Hokofarm feeder, was regressed on the concentration of LiCl found in the blood (measured by inductively coupled plasma emission spectrometry).

RESULTS

Mean feed block intake for the 12 hour test period was 491 g (s.d. 241). This compares with feed block intake over the 3 day period of 451 g/day (s.d. 229, CV 51%). Block intake over the test period was 0.71 of that day's consumption, and there was considerable daily variation in intake. Lithium concentration in plasma was 1.85 mg/l (s.d. 0.797). There was a highly significant correlation between the two measurements (r = 0.89; p<0.01).

DISCUSSION AND CONCLUSIONS

Regression analysis of feed intake on lithium blood level revealed the following equation:

$$Y = -9.8 + 270.2 \, X \quad \text{(s.e. of Y estimate was 114.0)}$$

where X = lithium concentration in blood (mg/l) and Y = feed block intake in 12 hours (g). The residual coefficient of variation was 23% of the mean. It was concluded that the lithium tracer technique gave a reasonable indication of block intake in the field situation. The correlation coefficient of 0.89 was similar to that achieved in an earlier trial (Vipond et al., 1995) where individually fed animals were offered a range of lithium intakes from 0-258 mg/day and showed a correlation between lithium intake (mg/kg liveweight) and blood plasma lithium concentration (mg/l) of 0.93. The lithium technique gave a useful and fairly accurate snapshot of intake but, since this varied from day to day, the method would require repeated estimates for accurate estimation. The cost of analysis was around ú3/sample so it was inexpensive. The Hokofarm feeder could be misleading if some animals were averse to entering the machine. It did give more information about the pattern of feed intake but was relatively expensive to buy and operate.

ACKNOWLEDGEMENT

The authors acknowledge financial and technical support from Rumenco.

REFERENCES

FORBES J.M. and KYRIAZAKIS I. (1995) Food preferences in farm animals: why don't they always choose wisely? Proceedings of the Nutrition Society, 54, 429-440.

GREEN G.C., ELWIN R.L., MOTTERSHEAD B.E., KEOGH R.G. and LYNCH J.J. (1984) Long term effects of early experience to supplementary feeding in sheep. Proceedings of the Australian Society of Animal Production, 15, 373-380.

KENDALL P.T., DUCKER M. J. and HEMMINGWAY R.G. (1983) Individual intake variation in ewes given feed blocks or trough supplements indoors or at winter grazing. Animal Production, 36, 7-20.

KHAN L.P. (1994) The use of lithium chloride for estimating supplement intake in grazing sheep. Estimates of heritability and repeatability. Australian Journal of Agricultural Research, 45, 1731-1739.

LAWRENCE A.B. and WOOD-GUSH D.G. (1988) Influence of social behaviour on utilisation of supplement feedblocks by hill sheep. Animal Production, 46, 203-209.

VIPOND J.E., HORGAN G.W. and ANDERSON D.H. (1995) Estimation of food intake in sheep by blood assay for lithium content following ingestion of lithium-labelled food. Animal Production, 60, 513.

Grassland Management Systems to reduce N Losses and Increase Efficiency: a Farmlet Approach

J. A. LAWS, B. F. PAIN AND S. C. JARVIS

IGER, North Wyke, Okehampton, Devon, EX20 2SB

INTRODUCTION

Losses of nitrogen from farming systems are of major environmental concern. Imbalance between N inputs and crop requirements leads to reduced efficiency and pollution of the wider environment. In this study, self-contained farmlets provided an experimental means to quantify transfers of N derived from fertiliser, animal excreta (grazing returns and slurry) and biological fixation, and to measure herbage production and animal performance in different grassland management systems.

MATERIALS AND METHODS

	Conventional N (CN)	Tactical N (TN)	No mineral N (GC)
Sward type	Grass monoculture.	Grass monoculture.	Grass/white clover.
Mineral N (ammonium nitrate) application	280 kg N ha^{-1} applied from March to August at set times and amounts in line with current recommendations.	Fortnightly, based on measurements of soil mineral N to maintain NO_3-N in leachate <11.3 ppm.	No mineral N fertiliser.
Slurry application	Surface application in spring and post-silage harvests.	Injected in spring and post-silage harvests.	Injected in spring and autumn (+ nitrification inhibitor).
Grazing period	May to October.	May to August.	May to October.
Silage harvest	3 times (excluding grazed areas).	4 times (once in autumn from grazed and cut areas).	3 times (excluding grazed areas).

Three grazing management systems were each represented by 1 ha farmlets and, as far as was feasible, provided sufficient herbage for grazing and winter fodder for a fixed number of beef cattle. The treatments (described above) were replicated twice on each of two contrasting soils: a freely draining, coarse, sandy loam (Site 1), and an impermeable, silty clay (Site 2). Each farmlet was grazed by 4 autumn-born Limousin-cross steers (200 kg mean liveweight at turnout) and divided into areas which were either grazed only (0.3 ha), grazed and/or cut (0.5 ha) or cut only (0.2 ha). A target sward surface height (SSH) of 8 cm was maintained by adjusting the area available for grazing with an electrified fence and surplus herbage was cut for silage. Slurry was applied to the area designated for cutting, with rates of application based on estimated amounts of N excreted by the housed cattle over winter.

RESULTS

This paper presents preliminary data for one year only (Table 1).

Table 1.   Annual N budgets, and herbage and animal production / farmlet.

	Site 1: Freely draining soil					Site 2: Soil with impeded drainage				
	CN	TN	GC	SED	P	CN	TN	GC	SED	P
N inputs (kg.ha⁻¹)										
- mineral N	281	173	0			277	142	0		
- other inputs†*	15	15	115			15	15	65		
Total N inputs	296	188	115			292	157	65		
N losses (kg.ha⁻¹)										
- animal liveweight gain†‡	15	10	17			17	8	15		
- gaseous and water soluble N§	129	65	49			66	56	26		
Total N losses	144	75	66			83	64	41		
N transfers (kg.ha⁻¹)										
- as slurry	69	96	69			75	101	75		
- as conserved herbage	114	102	90			118	113	41		
Surplus N (inputs - losses)										
-/unit area (kg/ha)	152	113	49			209	93	24		
-/unit product (kg/100kgLWG)	28	32	8			35	32	4		
Herbage and animal production										
Herbage DM conserved (t)	6.6	5.0	4.8	0.66	0.126	5.6	6.4	2.2	0.39	0.003
Liveweight gain (kg.head⁻¹.d⁻¹)	0.95	0.79	0.98	0.07	0.152	1.03	0.73	0.89	0.12	0.194
Liveweight gain (kg.ha⁻¹)	537	357	593	83.6	0.130	594	287	538	59.1	0.027
UME (GJ) output	107	75	92	7.2	0.049	96	85	58	5.0	0.010

†, estimated values. *, Comprising biological fixation and atmospheric deposition. ‡ assumed 28 g N kg⁻¹ liveweight gain. §, Comprising ammonia volatilisation, denitrification and nitrate leaching (ammonia volatilisation not measured at Site 2. Estimated value included).

Highest N inputs and losses and UME output were associated with conventional N management. Nitrogen surplus was lowest on GC reflecting lower inputs and losses on this treatment, while animal performance comparable with CN was maintained. Least silage was made on GC (being an estimated 40% of the DM required during the winter period at Site 2), reflecting the low clover content at this site (8% of sward DM mass, cf. 27% at Site 1). Conserved herbage accounted for the greatest transfer of N, being greater than the amount of N returned in slurry in each treatment except GC at Site 2. DLWG was lowest on TN, and the reduced period of grazing on this treatment, designed to minimise nitrate residues in the soil during winter, resulted in the lowest LWG/ha.

CONCLUSIONS

Preliminary results indicate that tactical N application and the exploitation of N fixation by white clover reduced N surpluses compared with conventional management systems, but overall output was reduced.

ACKNOWLEDGEMENTS This work was funded by MAFF.

Changing from Conventional to Organic Dairy Farming: Management Implications for the Grassland Farmer

R. F. WELLER AND A. COOPER

IGER, Trawsgoed, Aberystwyth, Dyfed, SY23 4LL

INTRODUCTION

Interest in organic farming and the marketing of organic milk products has increased sharply in both the UK and Europe. Many factors are responsible for this increased interest including the environmental impact of many intensive systems, over-production of food and public concerns about animal welfare and food safety.

Over a three-year period, IGER has undertaken a research programme to determine the effect of changing from conventional to organic dairy farming on the management and performance of the Ty Gwyn dairy herd at Trawsgoed, including stocking rates, forage production, animal performance and animal health. The main objective during the conversion period was to convert the farm from a system based on high inputs of nitrogen (380 kg/ha) to one based on organic practices and in compliance with the standards required by UKROFS for organic certification. The animal health of ten commercial organic dairy herds was also monitored during the study.

MANAGEMENT CHANGES

The farm was converted in the minimum period of time, with the land converted after two years followed by the conversion of the animals three months later. The major change was to convert from a system based on producing forage for both grazing and conservation from predominantly grass swards, receiving inputs of 380 kg N/ha, to one that is based on clover as the primary source of nitrogen. This change has led to the establishment of an effective crop rotation that provides sufficient forage (grazed, conserved) for the dairy herd while maintaining soil fertility and fully utilizing farm wastes (applied primarily to the silage conservation areas). The crop rotation that has been established is: Year 1 cereals (undersown), Year 2-3 Italian ryegrass/red clover (*Lolium multiflorum* L./*Trifolium pratense* L.), Year 4 cereals and Years 5-8 perennial ryegrass/white clover (*Lolium perenne* L./*Trifolium repens* L.). The establishment of Italian ryegrass/red clover swards has led to the production of high herbage yields, providing 50% of the conserved forage required for feeding during the winter.

The main change in the diet of the Holstein/Friesian dairy cows has been the replacement of a conventional commercial compound concentrate by acceptable (non-chemically extracted) concentrate supplements including organic cereals, full-fat soya beans, winter field beans and peas) and also the feeding of mixed grass/clover silage (conserved with a biological additive) as a replacement for grass silage conserved with an organic acid.

ANIMAL PERFORMANCE AND HEALTH

The mean stocking rate (LSU/ha) declined from 2.0 (pre-conversion) to 1.5 and 1.4 during the 2-year conversion period, increasing to 1.5 and 1.6 when the farm became fully organic. The reduction in stocking rates reduced total milk production. However, when the farm became fully organic, the loss in income was partially offset by the extra income from the receipt of a premium for the organic milk produced and also a small increase in the fat and protein contents of the milk produced. The annual rolling average of the herd (milk yield per cow) during the pre-conversion and conversion periods was 5,040 and 5,047 litres, respectively.

The priority of maintaining herd health and good standards of welfare has been achieved during the conversion period by the withdrawal of the routine use of conventional medicines (including long-acting antibiotics for the dry period) and the introduction and use of alternative remedies for the treatment of some specific ailments. The choice of treatment for specific ailments, with either alternative remedies or conventional drugs, is dependent on the type and severity of the ailment and the advice of the veterinary surgeon. No major health problems were recorded during the conversion period, either with the IGER Ty Gwyn herd or the ten commercial organic dairy herds. There were large differences between herds in the number of cases of both clinical mastitis and lameness, and, compared with conventional herds, the incidence of mastitis was slightly higher and cases of lameness lower. The reproductive performance of all the herds during the conversion period was satisfactory. Despite the grazing of swards with a high clover content few cases of bloat were recorded, either at Ty Gwyn or on the commercial farms.

CONCLUSIONS

Converting from a conventional system, based on high inputs of artificial nitrogen, to an organic system, based on clover as the main source of nitrogen, reduced herbage yields, stocking rates and total milk production during the 2-year conversion period. At the end of the conversion period, when the farm became fully organic, the beneficial effects of both the establishment of the crop rotation and the increasing clover content of the swards increased herbage yields, leading to higher stocking rates and increased total milk production.

The withdrawal of the routine use of conventional drugs did not lead to any major health problems either in the IGER Ty Gwyn herd or the commercial organic herds.

ACKNOWLEDGEMENTS
The authors would like to acknowledge the financial support of MAFF.

Systems Interactions and the Role of Grassland in Sustainability

D. YOUNIE[1], CHRISTINE WATSON[1], D. A. RAMSAY[2] AND C. K. MACKIE[1]

SAC, [1]581 King Street, Aberdeen, AB9 1UD

[2]The Rural Centre, West Mains, Ingliston, Newbridge, EH28 8NZ

INTRODUCTION

The essential feature of sustainable systems is that they meet the needs of the present generation without compromising the ability of future generations to meet their own needs (WCED, 1987). It follows, therefore, that such systems should make minimal demand on non-renewable resources such as fossil-fuel energy, the main input in the production of nitrogen (N) fertilizer. The objective of the modelling study reported here was to quantify the critical interactions in systems which avoid the use of mineral-N fertiliser.

INTERACTIONS IN SUSTAINABLE SYSTEMS

Organic manures and mineralised soil N are the main sources of N for most arable crops in systems where no fertilizer N is applied. In these systems, the supply of N is derived ultimately from N-fixation by legumes - in cool temperate climates almost universally forage legumes. Fixed atmospheric N can be supplied by grain legumes and by forage legumes grown as annual green manures, but widespread adoption of these is restricted by their limited revenue-earning potential. Hence grass/clover leys, and the ruminant livestock enterprises required for their utilisation, comprise the major source of soil-N enhancement and are essential features of most successful low-external-input systems. The design options for such systems are restricted further by the need for a supply of farmyard manure (FYM), the currency by which nutrients are transferred to different crops around the farm. This requirement for FYM demands a housed cattle enterprise (rather than sheep, which produce less FYM), which in turn makes conserved forage, with its high offtake of soil potassium, also a necessity. These interactions and restrictions have implications for whole farm profitability as well as technical viability and environmental impact, and must be considered within a wider context of greater specialisation of farms, fewer mixed ley/arable farms, and a reduced demand for red meat and dairy products.

METHODOLOGY

Models of five crop rotations were developed for a 100 hectare farm, differing in the proportion of grass/clover ley they contain (and therefore the potential for N fixation, livestock numbers, FYM production and crop yield), as follows:

Rotation A (6-course)   Grass/clover (G/C) → G/C → G/C → G/C →Potatoes/Oats →Oats
Rotation B (6-course)   G/C → G/C → G/C → Oats → Potatoes/Swedes → Oats
Rotation C (8-course)   G/C → G/C →Oats →Potatoes →Oats → G/Red C →Swedes → Oats
Rotation D (6-course)   G/C → G/C → G/C → G/C → Oats → Oats
Rotation E (6-course)   G/C → G/C → G/C → Oats → Oats → Oats

Crop yield and N offtake data were obtained from replicated crop rotations trials undertaken at the SAC organic farms at Tulloch, Aberdeen and Woodside, Elgin. N-fixation values were estimated from a relationship between the amount of N fixed by a grass-clover mixture and the increase in herbage yield of the grass/clover mixture over an unfertilised sward, as used by Barry et al. (1993) for lucerne/grass mixtures. Financial calculations assumed organic costs of production (i.e. no soluble fertilizers or pesticides) but no organic premium prices, and were carried out using SAC farm budgeting software.

RESULTS AND DISCUSSION
The critical technical, environmental and financial parameters from the model outputs are shown in Table 1.

Table 1.   Effect of crop rotation on N dynamics, physical output and financial performance of a 100 hectare farm

	Crop	Rotation			
	A	B	C	D	E
% grass/clover in rotation	67	50	38	67	50
Average N supply/ha (kgN)	110	85	73	105	81
Total cattle numbers (LU)	103	79	60	99	69
Total FYM production (t)	1077	827	628	1038	721
Average grain yield (t/ha)	4.0	3.8	3.1	4.4	3.7
N offtake per hectare (kgN)	38	41	39	40	41
Ratio N supply: N offtake	2.89	2.07	1.88	2.61	1.99
N unaccounted (kg/ha) (N balance)	+72	+44	+34	+65	+40
Gross profit (£)	22636	24906	22425	20385	18974
Gross profit (as % of gross output)	19.4	20.0	16.9	22.5	23.1
Subsidies (as % of gross output)	14.6	15.6	14.2	21.5	29.4

A higher proportion of grass/clover in the rotation increased total N supply through more fixed N, more livestock and greater FYM production, resulting in higher crop yields. Rotation A (67% grass/clover) sustained 29% higher grain yields than C (38% grass/clover). The levels of N offtake per hectare from all five rotations were very similar, in contrast to the wide range in N supply. The ratio of N supply to offtake was much greater in A than C, suggesting that A has greater reliability in crop growth potential, but also greater risk of N loss to the environment. However, in SAC crop rotation field trials, average soil nitrate-N content over winter was greatest in C, indicating that the risk of loss was greater in this rotation, at least in terms of N-leaching. In fact, all the N surplus values are relatively low and losses to the environment are likely to be low as a result. Some loss is unavoidable - potential losses in the range 50 - 90 kgN/ha have been reported for low-input systems (Wilkins, 1993) - but it is essential to maintain a positive N balance if agricultural production is to be sustained in the long term and, if N losses of this magnitude were to be included in the calculation, some of these rotations (e.g. C) may be in negative N balance and, therefore, technically unsustainable.

Financial analysis reflected the high output/high costs associated with root crops. Gross output was highest in C (38% G/C), but gross profit was greater in B (50% G/C), with its higher yields and lower production costs. Further research is necessary to quantify these relationships, particularly the influence of N loss to the environment, but the data illustrate the crucial importance of grass/clover leys in maintaining the N supply, and hence the technical and financial sustainability of low-external-input farming systems.

ACKNOWLEDGEMENT
SAC receives financial assistance from the Scottish Office Agriculture, Fisheries and Environment Department.

REFERENCES
BARRY D. A. J., GOORAHOO D. and GOSS M.J. (1993) Estimation of nitrate concentrations in groundwater using a whole farm nitrogen budget. *Journal of Environmental Quality*, **22**, 767-775.
WILKINS, R.J. (1993). Environmental constraints to production systems. In: *The Place for Grass in Land Use Systems*. The British Grassland Society, Reading, 19-30.
World Commission on Environment and Development (WCED) (1987) *Our Common Future*. UN World Commission on Environment and Development. Oxford University Press.

Suitability of Pasture Grasses in Morainic Soil and the Economic Evaluation of their Cultivation

C. A. CENCI, F. DONATI AND S.CLOCCHIATTI

Dipartimento di Biologia ed Economia Agro-industriale
via delle Scienze, 208-1-33100 UDINE, ITALIA

INTRODUCTION

Italy has undergone a complete modernisation of its agricultural methods in recent years. This evolution is still continuing as a result of the European Agricultural Policy. Some hilly and mountain fields, previously cultivated, have been abandoned or turned into grassland. In this case it is necessary to grow artificial grass swards.

The results of this process, common in the last ten years, has often fallen short of farmers' expectations since foreign seeds are not suitable for the pedo-climatic conditions of these areas. On the other hand, Italian varieties and seeds collected from natural local populations have given very good results in various trials by lasting several years and spreading over the nearby plots. For this reason, during the 1980s, national varieties have been created from the most common herbage species, some of them have been especially selected for the pedo-climatic conditions of Central Italy. Their success has allowed them to be tested in a Northern zone (hills near Lake Garda) too.

METHODS

This study aimed to evaluate the suitability of Italian and foreign varieties of *Dactilis glomerata*, *Festuca arundinacea* and *Lolium perenne* characterized by different classes of precocity (early, medium, late class) in a piedmont area of Northern Italy.

The procedure was carried out on a morainic stony soil, adopting an experimental method (split-split-plot) with four replications. After sowing, pasture was utilised 20 times during the following four years (1991-1994). Sixty to eighty sheep were grazed on the trial plots, with a sward height of 20-25 cm. The animals were allowed to graze until no further material was available.

Data were collected on; the percentage ground cover of the sown species and the wild flora; grazing activity; vegetative activity (using a score related to the green colour of the herbage).

RESULTS

Agronomy

During the latter years differences emerged between the species, cultivars, measurements and their interactions. The results showed a rapid reduction in ground cover for almost all the varieties, after the second year, whereas *Dactilys*

317

(var. Cesarina) showed a high level of propagation through natural spreading. Generally, varieties with medium precocity had an average ground cover, significantly higher then the varieties with different precocity.

In conclusion the results obtained in this particular environment were a rapid decrease in the ground cover of all *Lolium* and *Festuca* varieties and the better adaptability of *Dactilys* (medium precocity variety) to the conditions. Thus pedo-climatic conditions were very important for the growing of varieties belonging to the wild species.

Economic appraisal

It is well known that the economic advantage of a grassland is directly connected to the life of the grass sward and to the ground cover of the various species. The behaviour of the tested varieties was strictly related to the grazing activity.

A useful method for evaluating the profitability of browsing activity was developed in order to appreciate the advantage in utilizing different varieties. The procedure was based on an estimate of the forage value, during various years, and on the determination of fixed and variable production costs. The parameters relating to the grass yield estimation was obtained through harvest, weighing and chemical analysis of herbage samples. The productivity estimation of the tested species was also made by measuring the ground cover and the grass height before and after grazing, since weighing was used only during the last year of trial. Grazing activity was simulated in a farm field, sown with the varieties used in this study, in order to make an economic appraisal.

Gross and net income, and other economic parameters, were calculated using the gross output and the production costs found in the management accounts of the tested farm.

Clover: Cereal Bi-cropping - A Progress Report

R. O. CLEMENTS[1], E. J. ASTERAKI[1], D. A. KENDALL[2], S. GEORGE[2]

[1]IGER, North Wyke Research Station, Okehampton, Devon, EX20 2SB
[2]IACR - Long Ashton Research, Deptartment of Agricultural Sciences, University of Bristol, Long Ashton, Bristol, BS18 9AF

INTRODUCTION

IGER (North Wyke) and IACR (Long Ashton) together with partners in the EU are developing a system of growing cereals either for grain or whole crop silage that requires greatly reduced inputs of N fertilizer, agrochemicals and management time. The system is potentially straightforward and simple and relies on a permanent, perennial understorey of white clover (*Trifolium repens*). A sward of pure white clover is established and is then defoliated by grazing or by cutting for silage, in the autumn. Cereal seeds are direct-drilled into the clover and the two crops develop together. The cereal is harvested the following summer using conventional equipment, either for whole crop silage or is left to mature and harvested for grain.

Provided that certain simple guidelines are followed the clover understorey survives, is allowed to recover and then grazed or cut in the autumn again, prior to direct-drilling a second cereal crop to repeat the cycle. Experiments to date have confirmed that two successive cereal crops can be grown in this way and work is continuing to investigate how many further crops can be obtained.

REDUCTION OF INPUTS

The need for N fertilizer is greatly reduced, presumably because the cereal benefits from N fixed by the clover. Pest, especially aphid, problems are generally reduced. The reduction in pests probably occurs because large numbers of predatory beetles and spiders build-up in the perennial, permanent understorey of white clover. These predators probably feed avidly on aphids and other pests as they arrive in the crop. Fungal disease occurrence and severity is also greatly reduced. This is partly because the progress of splash-borne diseases is halted by the presence of the clover (Deadman and Soleimani, 1994). Other fungal diseases rely on organic trash at the base of the crop for their progress, but in bi-cropped areas the rate of disappearance of the litter layer is very rapid - possibly as a result of enhanced earthworm activity. Consequently many diseases which depend partly on the trash for their carry-over fail to develop in bi-cropped areas (M. Deadman, personal communication)

Virtually all broad-leaved weeds are suppressed by the clover understorey, eliminating the need for herbicide to control them. Grass weeds especially *Poa* spp. have, however, been troublesome on some occasions. They can be controlled at least experimentally, in clover/cereal bi-cropped areas after emergence of the cereal by the use of the herbicide isoproturon. Treating the clover crop with one of a number of herbicides before drilling the cereal is another possibility. Grass weed problems appear to be exacerbated by over-grazing, leading to bare patches in the clover sward which are all too easily colonised by *Poa*. Clearly a better approach to the problem is to avoid over grazing. Plots cut for silage and not grazed are usually virtually free of weeds.

CEREAL YIELD

The bi-cropping system that we are developing seems to be better suited to growing winter wheat, of which there are 1.7 million ha in the UK, than other cereals. Grain yields of bi-cropped wheat are about 60% of those of conventionally grown crops, but, since inputs are greatly reduced, gross margins remain at around 90% of that for conventional crops.

Work is in hand to develop more cost effective methods of establishing the clover understorey, to capitalise on the reduction in soil erosion that bi-cropping also results in and to explore the growth and suitability of clover and wheat varieties not yet tested.

ACKNOWLEDGEMENT

This work is funded by MAFF and the EU.

REFERENCES

DEADMAN M. and SOLEIMANI M.J. (1994) Cereal : clover bi-cropping - implications for crop disease incidence. *Proceedings Fourth Research Meeting, British Grassland Society, Reading 1994*, 79-80.

Low Input Grass/Clover Sheep Systems

J.R. JONES[1] AND A.R. SIBBALD[2]

[1]IGER, Bronydd Mawr Research Station,
Trecastle, Brecon, Powys, LD3 8RD
[2]Macaulay Land Use Research Institute,
Craigiebuckler, Aberdeen, AB9 2QJ

INTRODUCTION

Against a background of pressure for extensification of farming systems, there is a need to extend the understanding gained from upland sheep systems experiments in terms of the utilisation of grass/clover swards in the absence of nitrogen fertiliser input. There is the further requirement for information on the consequences of running more extensive systems at sward height profiles which are higher than those regarded as the most efficient for animal production on a per hectare basis. The experiment reported here examined the effect of nitrogen fertiliser, sward height and flock stocking rate on animal production and feed self sufficiency and followed on from studies carried out in the Welsh uplands since 1984 (Jones *et al.*, 1988; 1992 and 1995; Sibbald *et al.*, 1994).

MATERIALS AND METHODS

The experiment was located at Bronydd Mawr Research Station, in south Powys (330 masl, 1500 mm annual rainfall). The swards used were perennial ryegrass (*Lolium perenne*)/timothy, (*Phleum pratense*)/white clover (*Trifolium repens*), (commercial mixture) reseeded in 1991. Ewes were Beulah Speckled Face with Suffolk cross lambs at a ewe:lamb ratio of 1:1.4

The experiment started in the spring of 1993 and investigated the biological and economic consequences of changes in management. Treatments, all with no nitrogen fertilizer (NO) were:- two grazed sward heights (3.5 (N) and 5.5 cm (H) to weaning, representing different grazing pressures) and two stocking rates (12 (SR12) and 9 (SR9) ewes plus lambs per hectare). A further treatment with 50 kg nitrogen per hectare per annum (N5O), 3.5 cm sward height and 12 ewes plus lambs per hectare was included to provide continuity with previous experiments. All treatments were replicated three times. Fertilizer was applied in April of both years with all treatments given 50 kg/ha/annum P and K.

After weaning sward surface height was maintained at 4-6 cm and 6-8 cm respectively for the low and high sward height treatments up to the end of September with a difference of 2 cm between the treatments at all time. Grazed sward surface height was controlled by closing surplus areas of pasture using moveable electric fences. Surplus pasture was conserved as silage. Lambs were weighed regularly, weaned on July 27 and sent to slaughter at 34 kg liveweight. After weaning, lambs were retained on their treatment plots, weighed every 2 weeks and removed at 34 kg liveweight. Remaining lambs were weighed and removed at the end of September.

RESULTS AND DISCUSSION

Results as means of the first two years are shown in Table 1. Lamb liveweight gain on the higher sward height treatments was greater than that on the lower sward height treatments (P=0.02), resulting in higher lamb weight (P=0.01) and percentage lambs finished (P=0.02) at weaning. At the same stocking rate lamb production at weaning and total lamb production (P=0.001) at the end of September was greater at the higher sward height. Silage made, measured as kg DM/ewe, within stocking rate treatment was greater on the lower swards (P=0.017). In the second year all treatments produced silage in excess of a self sufficiency level of 110 kg DM/ewe, while in the first year the low sward height/higher stocking rate treatment did not reach that requirement.

Table 1.   Results from the first two years of the experiment.

	N50 SR12N	NO SR12N	NO SR9N	NO SR12H	NO SR9H
Lamb wt. (kg wean)	30.7	32.4	32.0	35.8	34.9
Lamb (kg/ha)(wean)	528	549	413	616	449
Lamb prodn. (kg/ha)	608	596	441	635	467
% finished (wean)	28.3	43.3	36.7	65.0	58.0
Stolons (m/m^2) 1993	23.6	40.2	43.2	50.8	33.4
1994	77.0	71.0	68.0	57.0	43.0
Silage/ewe (kg)	311	146	361	128	250
Lwg (g/d to wean)	212.6	222.6	225.1	261.8	252.0
Conc (£/ewe)	0.94	0.75	0.02	0	0
Gross margins (1993)					
- £/ewe - no subsidy	34.53	30.05	42.08	34.92	37.00
- subsidy	58.58	54.10	66.13	58.97	61.10
- £/ha - no subsidy	414	361	379	419	333
- subsidy	703	649	595	708	550

Clover stolon length (m/m^2) increased from year one to year two by 101% and 19% respectively on the lower and higher sward height treatments with clover growing point numbers following a similar pattern. Concentrate, fed when sward surface height was below 3.5 cm in spring or autumn, was not fed in the spring of either year. Autumn feeding was only necessary for the low sward height treatments.

The results indicate that spring application of nitrogen at 50 kg per hectare had little or no effect on animal production and was not detrimental to clover growth but that there was a positive effect on the amount of winter fodder conserved. Lamb live weight gain, production and percentage finished at weaning still favoured this higher sward height treatments in the second year but to a lesser degree than in the first year. This may indicate falling pasture quality in those swards.

Potential lambing rates (ns) suggest that the treatments imposed have not compromised ewe fertility. Economic assessment of the treatments is only available for the first year and shows that the low stocking rate treatments at both sward heights gave higher gross margins per ewe. Gross margins per hectare, however, were higher from the high stocking rate treatments. It is hoped to continue this study for a further two to three years to cover annual climatic variations and any deterioration in pasture quality, resulting from higher than recommended spring sward surface height.

REFERENCES

JONES J.R., JAMES M.E., MUNRO J.M.M., MAXWELL T.J. and SIBBALD A.R. (1988) Evaluation of systems of upland sheep production from two Welsh breeds. *BGS Research meeting, Aberystwyth.*

JONES J.R., MUNRO J.M.M., SIBBALD A.R., REES M.E., PREEN R.N., VALE J.E., DONAGHY D.T. and DEANS E.V. (1992). Evaluation of lower input upland sheep systems. *BGS 3rd Research conference, Northern Ireland.* 87-88.

SIBBALD A.R., MAXWELL T.J., MORGAN T.E.H., JONES J.R. and REES M.E. (1994) The implications of controlling grazed sward height for the operation & productivity of upland sheep systems in the UK. 2. Effects of two annual stocking rates in combination with two levels of fertilizer nitrogen. *Grass & Forage Science,* **49,** 89-95.

JONES, J.R., REES, M.E., VALE, J.E. and SIBBALD, A.R. (1995) Low input grass/clover sheep systems. *Third International Livestock Farming Systems Symposium, Aberdeen, Scotland.* (In press).

The Performance of a Progressive Hill Sheep System following Conversion to Organic Management

R. KEATINGE AND B. G. MERRELL

ADAS Redesdale, Rochester, Otterburn, Newcastle upon Tyne, NE19 1SB

INTRODUCTION

In an effort to improve financial returns, significant land improvement has taken place in the hill and uplands of the UK, particularly up to the mid 1980s. However, more recently the emphasis is on agri-environmental packages designed to reduce stocking rates and maintain, or improve, botanical diversity in these areas. In May 1991, approximately 500 ha at ADAS Redesdale (carrying 800 Scottish Blackface ewes and 30 spring calving suckler cows) was assigned to a research project investigating the effects of organic farming on the physical and financial performance of a progressive hill and upland system. In a MAFF-funded study, over 400 ha were put into conversion following standards laid down by the United Kingdom Register of Organic Food Standards (UKROFS), while 92 ha continued to be managed conventionally to act as a control. This paper summarises the main results from the first 3 years of the study, including the two year conversion period and one year of full organic production.

EXPERIMENTAL METHOD

Direct comparison of organic and conventional farming practices was achieved by carefully splitting one complete heft to form two sub-units of comparable carrying capacity. Both sub-flocks, each of approximately 180 ewes, were run under a 'Two Pasture' system. This integrated the use of three distinct types of grazing - native hill, improved hill and in-bye fields (representing 73%, 23% and 4% of the area respectively). The policy was to farm as profitably as possible within UKROFS standards, maintaining output and continuing to home-finish all lambs. Rather than impose an arbitrary cut in stocking rate at the outset, original stocking rates were maintained for both flocks. Seasonal stocking rates peaked at 2.5, 7.5 and 25 ewes plus their lambs per ha, for each grazing type. All in-bye fields were reseeded just before, or during, the conversion period. Because of the low clover content in the swards initially, and difficulties in transporting and applying slurry, some purchased nitrogen (either a keratin-based, or dried poultry manure) was applied to organically managed ground. Over 27% of the area (representing the in-bye and improved hill), this amounted to 49, 28 and 8 kg/ha total N during 1992, 1993 and 1994 respectively. Comparable inputs to the conventionally-managed area were 86, 53 and 51 kg/ha total N. Data were collected on forage production, botanical change, soil fertility, animal health and productivity, and financial performance.

RESULTS

Direct measurement of forage production was confined to the in-bye fields. In terms of LUGD, organic swards performed at comparable levels (98% and 102%, for 1993 and 1994) to those managed conventionally. Little change in botanical composition occurred on the native or improved hill. This could be expected, given the relatively short period of study and the maintenance of overall stocking rates. On in-bye fields, clover content in newly sown swards was high, peaking at 60% clover content by dry matter. Following reseeding, annual weeds were a problem but these did not persist. However, perennial weeds (notably docks) made a significant impact on some areas of the in-bye land and will prove difficult to control under organic management.

Formerly, control measures for leatherjackets (*Tipula* spp) were considered above threshold populations of 2.5 million larvae/ha. On the organic unit, leatherjacket numbers increased steadily reaching damaging levels on improved areas of the hill by spring 1995. Biological control methods have shown promise experimentally but are not commercially available for grassland. Potash levels fell on in-bye fields under both management regimes.

Organic standards permit the use of some, mainly rock-based, sources of K. These generally have slow degradation characteristics in the soil. Following consultation with UKROFS, a limited remedial application of 60 kg/ha of sulphate of potash was made, in addition to an approved potash (Kali vinesse).

Sheep stocking rates were maintained in both flocks and all lambs were successfully home finished. However, the price of purchased nitrogen increased the cost of forage production in the organic flock by approximately £5 per ewe. For breeding stock within LFAs, an allowance to feed up to 20% of annual DM requirements from non-organic sources reduces the problem of winter fodder production. Feeding high clover silage to finishing lambs has been shown to increase DLWG by approximately 20%, reducing the need for expensive organically grown concentrates. Levels of sheep performance have broadly been similar. Significant reductions were made in veterinary inputs, but trace element status and parasite control are likely to be ongoing issues. While it has been possible to sell organic store cattle at a premium, all lambs so far produced on the unit were sold through conventional outlets.

DISCUSSION

Organic farming will be slow to develop in the hills and uplands unless financial incentives increase. Technical issues, such as long-term productivity, weed control, animal disease patterns remain to be resolved. Nevertheless, organic farming could potentially provide a further mechanism to adjust stocking rates and modify farming practice in the hills and uplands.

Winter Feed Production Potential of Grass and Grass/Clover Swards

E. G. O'RIORDAN

Grange Research and Development Division, Dunsany, Co. Meath, Ireland.

INTRODUCTION

White clover has been the accepted legume choice for a range of grazed pasture conditions in temperate climates. Although white clover is perceived to be a desired sward component, from an animal nutritional standpoint, sward productivity is generally less than similar swards receiving inorganic fertiliser nitrogen. Fertiliser nitrogen applications are, however, considered to be detrimental to clover survival in swards. The present study assesses the dry matter production potential of grass/clover swards as a source of winter feed and determines the effect of fertiliser nitrogen on yields and clover content.

MATERIALS AND METHODS

Six *Lolium perenne* cultivars, representing both diploid (D) and tetraploid (T) grasses from each of the early (E) intermediate (I) and late (L) heading-date categories, were sown in binary combinations with five *Trifolium repens* varieties representing small (S), medium (M) and large (L) leafed categories. The ryegrass cultivars were Yatsyn (E, D), Green Isle (E, T), Magella (I, D), Everest (I, T), Tyrone (L, D) and Tivoli (L, T), while the clovers were represented by Gwenda (S), Huia (M), Susi (M), Menna (M), and Aran (L). The 30 grass/clover combinations, in conjunction with the 11 monoculture treatments, were laid out in a randomised complete block design in plots measuring 5 x 2 m, and replicated 6 times. Swards were sown in August 1992 and seeding rates, based on '1000 seed weight' and germination rates were such as to give equal plant stands, on all combinations. Swards were managed in a uniform manner throughout 1993. In late March 1994, three replications (blocks) received 100 kg fertiliser N/ha while the remaining three received no added nitrogen. Dry-matter production was determined on 19 May 1994. The respective blocks again received fertiliser at either 0 or 80 kg N/ha in late May and were harvested for a second time on 7 July 1994. Representative herbage samples were removed from each plot for the quantification of the clover content.

RESULTS AND DISCUSSION

Dry-matter yields and sward clover content for both harvests are summarised in Tables 1 and 2. Herbage dry-matter production following the application of 100 kg N/ha for ryegrass sown is monoculture or with each of the five clovers was not significantly different for the first harvest. Herbage clover content was low, but the contents in the Magella/Gwenda (16.3%) and Everest/Huia (12.0%)

combinations was greater (P<0.05) than in other treatments. In the absence of nitrogen, only the Magella/Gwenda, Magella/Huia and Magella/Menna combinations resulted in higher (P<0.05, P<0.01, P<0.05, respectively) dry-matter yields in Harvest 1. There was a higher clover content in the Gwenda, Menna, and Aran clovers when sown with Magella and for Gwenda and Huia with Everest as well as in the Tyrone/Aran and Tivoli/Menna treatments. In the absence of nitrogen, relative dry-matter production for the respective monoculture grass was 0.59 compared to 100 kg N/ha and in the presence of nitrogen ranged from 0.91 to 1.09 for the grass/clover mixtures.

Table 1. Effect of grass cultivar, clover variety and nitrogen application rate (kg N/ha) on herbage dry matter yields (kg/ha) on May 19 (Harvest 1) and July 7 (Harvest 2).

Ryegrass Cultivar	N Rate	Control		Gwenda		Huia		Susi		Menna		Aran	
		Harvest											
		1	2	1	2	1	2	1	2	1	2	1	2
Yatsyn	0	5480	1077	6037	1891	5986	1671	5914	1660	6597	1738	5855	2173
	100	8797	3322	8278	3297	8397	3271	8012	3493	9584	3255	9220	3769
Green Isle	0	5859	1192	5139	1994	6086	1589	5732	1769	5627	1712	5534	2258
	100	8116	3309	7562	3594	8764	3603	7672	3446	7469	3184	8096	3301
Magella	0	3545	1859	4979	3155	5399	2668	4034	2755	4945	3280	4425	3486
	100	6641	3944	6276	3812	6872	3793	7083	4144	6616	3738	6917	4228
Everest	0	3684	1751	4944	2859	4460	3238	3981	2702	4360	2790	4278	2733
	100	7138	3949	7193	4123	6015	3869	6817	4247	7136	3770	7556	4220
Tyrone	0	4099	2038	4446	2888	4227	2345	4425	3130	4182	2598	4043	3200
	100	6659	4093	7114	4077	7199	4141	6905	3999	6783	3608	6556	4097
Tivoli	0	3231	2838	3461	3337	3461	2810	4179	3421	3918	3584	3775	3135
	100	6266	4381	5971	4298	6486	4219	6352	4315	6428	4175	6181	4382

Harvest 1 s.e. = 660.6;   Harvester 2 s.e. = 321.1 Control = grass monoculture

In Harvest 2, all treatments that received nitrogen had similar dry matter yields. In the absence of nitrogen, there were significant yield increases in some grass/clover combinations, especially with Magella and Everest and to a lesser extent with Tyrone. While clover content in Harvest 2 was higher than in Harvest 1, difference between treatments did not attain significance in the presence of nitrogen. In the absence of nitrogen, treatment differences did emerge. Relative dry matter production in Harvest 2 for the monoculture grasses was 0.46 in the absence of nitrogen but ranged from 0.88 - 1.13 for the grass/clover combination.

Table 2. Effect of grass cultivar and clover variety on the clover content (%) of herbage harvested on May 19 and July 7 (Harvest 1 and 2, respectively).

Ryegrass Cultivar	N Rate	Gwenda		Huia		Susi		Menna		Aran	
		Harvest 1	2	1	2	1	2	1	2	1	2
Yatsyn	0	8.0	23.7	8.0	23.7	3.0	22.3	1.7	9.7	9.3	24.3
	100	7.3	12.3	4.7	7.7	2.0	4.0	0.3	1.7	1.3	12.7
Green Isle	0	8.3	18.7	2.0	12.3	3.3	18.7	8.0	23.7	8.3	38.0
	100	6.3	5.3	2.7	7.3	1.7	4.3	4.7	6.0	2.7	12.7
Magella	0	23.0	38.7	7.0	20.7	13.0	30.0	20.3	40.3	18.7	34.7
	100	16.3	23.0	6.7	7.0	4.7	8.0	18.0	15.0	6.7	18.3
Everest	0	12.3	44.7	20.3	39.3	5.3	35.3	9.3	31.0	2.0	21.7
	100	9.7	12.7	12.0	10.0	5.3	9.7	9.0	9.7	4.0	5.7
Tyrone	0	5.3	30.0	5.3	18.7	14.0	22.7	10.3	26.0	12.0	38.0
	100	5.0	11.0	3.3	5.0	3.7	7.3	6.0	10.7	10.0	10.7
Tivoli	0	13.3	30.0	14.0	24.3	10.7	17.0	19.0	28.0	12.7	22.3
	100	8.0	8.3	6.7	5.0	6.3	2.7	6.0	10.0	5.0	4.3

Harvest 1 s.e. = 4.10; Harvest 2 s.e. = 7.48

SECTION 4

TECHNOLOGY INTERACTION

The Milk Development Council

J. E. MOFFITT
Westside, Newton, Stocksfield, Northumberland, NE43 7TW

INTRODUCTION
The dairy industry of the United Kingdom was reorganised in 1994, with major changes to the arrangements for the marketing of milk from British farms. Since the 1930s, the Milk Marketing Boards had been responsible for purchasing all the milk sold off farms, and finding markets for it. They had also run an extensive network of services for dairy farmers and provided information for the industry.

From 1 November 1994, farmers were free to sell their milk to any individual or company, and dairy companies were free to buy milk direct from individual farmers or groups of farmers. Many of the other functions of the Milk Marketing Boards became established as independent businesses.

With the Government's decision in the late 1980s to concentrate their agricultural research budget towards basic science, the Milk Marketing Boards had agreed to fund research which was more 'near market'. With the abolition of the Boards, farmers were asked to vote on a proposal to set up a levy-funded body to fund various activities which had previously been financed by the Boards. These included production research and development, livestock improvement, human nutrition and education programmes, and the gathering and publication of dairy industry statistics.

A statutory producer levy
Farmers in Great Britain voted in favour of a statutory producer levy, and the Government brought in the necessary legislation under the terms of the Milk Development Council Order 1995, which became effective on 7 February 1995.

It is not easy to come up with a precise figure as to how much was being deducted from the farmers milk cheques to support advertising promotion of milk, education, NMR and the BCEU etc. prior to the dissolving of the Milk Boards. Administration appeared to cover a multitude of things but a penny per litre (ppl) would not be too far away from the true figure. The Milk Development Council's levy of 0.04 ppl is over 25 times less than was previously being payed.

It is interesting to reflect on the actual price paid for milk since the inception of the Milk Boards using the retail price index of each year in question and converting old pounds per gallon to the new pound per litre (Table 1). In 1950, when the price was equivalent to 40 ppl, there were 200,000 milk producers in the United Kingdom and this will soon be down to 30,000. The average herd size during the same period has risen from 16 cows to approaching 90 cows.

Table 1.   Average net price received by producers from MMB for wholesale milk, 1934-1990 (ppl).

	Actual price	Price at 1990 values[1]
1934-43	1.45	27.69
1944-1953	2.81	40.19
1954-1963	3.21	31.49
1964-1973	3.89	26.92
1974-1983	11.17	24.48
1985-86	15.42	19.35
1989-90	18.94	19.53

[1] Converted using the Retail Price Index

APPOINTMENT OF THE MILK DEVELOPMENT COUNCIL
The Agriculture Ministers appointed a council of 11 people, under my chairmanship, with a defined schedule of responsibilities. Broadly, these fall into the following areas:-

1.   To support the technical strength, and maintain the competitive position of Britain's dairy farmers through funding production research and development.
2.   To provide funding for nutrition, education, and crisis management through the National Dairy Council. (Jointly funded by the Dairy Industry Federation).
3.   To improve the genetic base of the British cattle population, by funding the work of the Animal Data Centre.
4.   To collect, monitor and publish statistics about the British and European dairy industry.

MINISTERIAL APPOINTMENTS AND STAFF
The Council itself has been appointed by the Agriculture Ministers, and is subject to ministerial review at the end of three years. The Council has taken a lease on a vacant office within the building occupied by the National Dairy Council, and a Chief Executive, Peter Merson, was appointed on 1 June 1995 with a Financial Manager and Office Manager taking up office in July 1995.

A STRATEGY FOR DAIRY FARMING RESEARCH AND DEVELOPMENT
The funding of production research and development is a key task for the newly-formed Milk Development Council - but the investment in research will only bring a dividend to levy-paying farmers if the right projects are supported, they are properly monitored, and the results communicated quickly and effectively to

the industry. Practically all of our European partners have a producer levy to support their members and attend to their industry needs. The same is true for Australasia and North America; so it cannot be said that UK farmers will be disadvantaged - in fact without such support it would be UK producers who would be disadvantaged.

The world of the British dairy farmer has changed rapidly in the past decade and this is a process which is bound to continue. Dairy farmers' profits will be directly related to their ability to cope with that change. Only by attaining world-class levels of technical and cost efficiency will they continue to compete in the markets of the 21st Century.

Factors likely to influence the dairy industry

- A freer world market in dairy products, with changes and possible abolition of EU milk quotas. There is likely to be downward pressure on the price of milk and dairy products.
- Increased pressure from consumers, and more particularly, from the supermarkets, demanding milk produced and handled to more exacting standards.
- Continued, and possibly increased, activities from a wide range of pressure groups with an interest in the activities of farmers.
- Increasingly stringent environmental controls on farming.
- The emerging availability of new tools to aid animal breeding and management, particularly as a result of advances in molecular biology.

The Milk Development Council's R&D strategy must anticipate the changes that these pressures will bring, to enable Britain's dairy farmers to remain competitive in the future. A careful balance needs to be struck between solving today's problems and preparing the industry for the future.

Making appropriate use of producer funding

The levy paid by farmers to the MDC (0.04 ppl) will generate about £5 million, some two thirds of which will be spent on supporting research and development projects. In deciding where milk producers' money should be spent, the first consideration must be to improve the profitability and competitiveness of Britain's dairy farmers. Proposals which are unable to show this benefit will not receive MDC support. The determination of cost/benefit ratios for research projects is notoriously difficult, but projects will nevertheless be subjected to financial scrutiny in all cases. Projects which are able to show benefits at the level of individual farms are more credible than those which can only show 'global' figures, which can be more easily massaged.

Beside the principal objective of improving farm profitability, other benefits will also be sought. These include improvements in cattle welfare, increases in consumer choice and safety, and environmental benefits. Projects which are neutral in respect of some these benefits may be appropriate for MDC funding but any with likely negative impact will be rejected.

Effective selection and monitoring of projects

All proposals will be systematically assessed against a standard set of criteria. Most important will be the economic benefits indicated above. The expertise of the research team will be carefully assessed. The MDC will use independent experts to evaluate the competence of teams, and the scientific and innovative merit of projects. To qualify for MDC support, projects will have to have clearly stated objectives. Wherever possible, these should be quantifiable. Defined, measurable milestones will be built into the proposal, against which the progress of the project can be objectively assessed. There is little point in discovering that a project is not going anywhere six months before the end of MDC funding!

A Project Manager will be assigned to each project, and projects will be subject to regular scientific and financial scrutiny. Trials and experiments must be set up in a way which enables the results to be statistically meaningful.

The MDC will seek to fund work which is innovative, and does not merely repeat what has already been done elsewhere. An exception to this might be made in the case of a project aiming to test the applicability of work done in a research institute to practical farm conditions. It may also be appropriate to repeat overseas work under UK farming conditions.

Priority areas for research

- Economic feeding of cattle. Feed represents the major cost on most diary farms. New systems of feeding dairy cows to produce the quality of milk demanded by the market are of vital interest to the industry.
- Hygienic and safe food production. MDC will do everything in its power to foster positive images of dairy farming and dairy foods, both through R&D projects, and by financial support to the National Dairy Council (jointly funded with the Dairy Industry Federation).
- Reduction of productivity loss. The three most important areas of productivity loss in dairy cattle are reproductive inefficiency, lameness and mastitis. Projects with realistic chances of reducing these losses will be supported by MDC.
- Cattle housing, equipment and environment. The changing structure of the industry, and changes to cows themselves, means that research is needed into these aspects of dairy cow management.
- Genetic tools. Great strides are being made in molecular biology. The MDC is keen that these should be applied at a practical farm level. Genetic tools are becoming available to reduce disease, as well as increase productivity.

Database of existing research knowledge
An early priority for the MDC is to establish a database of existing and current research. This will be valuable in several ways:
1. To establish gaps in current programmes.
2. To identify centres of research excellence.
3. To provide a basis for the early dissemination of results to farmers, and to associate these with the MDC brand.

The MDC will achieve this database by checking existing sources, e.g. MAFF, ADAS, SOAFD, BBSRC, MLC etc. and will also ask research institutes and universities to detail their current areas of expertise, and are considering commissioning a graduate student to establish a database for MDC.

Build on links with other research bodies
The MDC is by no means alone in supporting research of benefit to dairy farmers. MAFF, SOAFD, BBSRC and other bodies already spend considerably more than the MDC budget on cattle R&D. By linking MDC programmes to other sponsors, not only will levy payers' money go further, but through MDC, farmers will be able to influence the research policies of other bodies. The Council will seek to build on these links to maximise the benefits to dairy farmers. Money is available from the European Union to support appropriate R&D projects. The MDC is in an ideal position to help to obtain EU support by collaboration with other European bodies.

Establish and develop a 'brand image'
MDC must demonstrate that the levy collected from milk producers is used for their direct and indirect benefit. To this end, brief summaries of findings from all MDC funded projects will be sent to producers by means of a regular newsletter. Where research findings merit the publication of more detailed advice, this will be made available, on demand, free of charge to levy payers, and at a realistic charge to others. An example of this type of publication is the recent booklet on *Mixed Forage Diets for Dairy Cows*, which reports on work funded by the Milk Marketing Board and published by MDC.

Farmers must know where their money is being spent, and a Communications Committee has been formed by MDC to oversee this key function. Successful communications management will establish the credibility of MDC with all sides of the industry and further extend our ability to exercise influence.

Above all, the Milk Development Council must establish its own areas of priority, driven primarily by farmer needs. This is particularly important in the context of Government funded research, which is frequently driven by wider political perspectives, and the priorities of the research community, which may be driven by the need to publish in scientific journals.

NATIONAL DAIRY COUNCIL

It was soon apparent that there were quite a number of issues which had been left unresolved after the demise of the Milk Marketing Boards. The National Dairy Council was one of the more urgent areas to address. It had previously been funded jointly by the dairy industry and milk producers, to the tune of around £150 million per annum paid for through their respective organisations, The Dairy Industry Federation and the MMBs. The majority of this was for the generic promotion of milk.

Education and nutrition

The MDC's current responsibility in education and nutrition, again jointly funded by the Dairy Industry Federation and MDC, is primarily directed towards education in schools, doctors and hospital staff. Its aim is to redress the balance, often put out by the media, regarding dietary health problems of dairy products. Some 60,000 leaflets are despatched to schools, hospitals, surgeries etc. containing information about the value of milk and backed up by the best nutritional advice available.

Crisis management

A fighting fund is available to react when health problems arise; for example listeria, salmonella etc. There is always a risk of possible contamination with any perishable food and the industry has to be ready in that emergency.

  These are just two areas of the MDC's work which are essential for it to continue to support, and the MDC has to make farmers much more aware of the need to protect our main product - milk.

THE MILK DEVELOPMENT COUNCIL

John Moffitt, CBE	MDC Chairman	John Gibson	Communications
Alex Brown	Communications	David Harden	R & D
Ben Boot	R&D	Martin Stanbury	Finance
Malcolm Crabtree	R&D (C'tee Chair)	Hugh Wilson	Finance
Irene Unsworth	Communications (Consumer affairs)		
Philippa Foster Back	Finance (C'tee Chair)		
Chris French	Communications (C'tee Chair)		

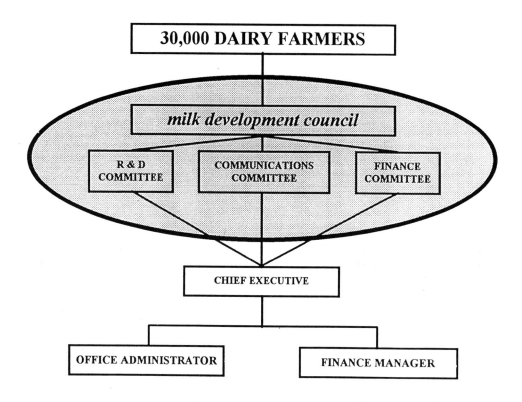

STRUCTURE OF THE MILK DEVELOPMENT COUNCIL

Problem-led R & D

JANICE JIGGINS
De Dellen 4, 6673 MD, Andelst, Netherlands

ABSTRACT

Some of the key theoretical, methodological, and practical challenges facing problem-led R & D are explored with reference to the development of the social agency to act, stakeholder participation in research, PRA, the Local Consensus Data technique, and Farm Inventories. The implications for investment and management are then analysed.

INTRODUCTION

Scientists, research funders, advisers, and producers rightly can claim that 'problem-led' R & D, in the laboratory, at the research station, and in farmers' fields, always has been an important and valued component of total R & D activity. The process involved has been modelled as a chain-linked or design-driven process characterised by; market- or client-based definition of problems and anticipation of opportunity; a dual role for science, as a body of knowledge which can be accessed at any point along the chain of problem solution, and as a tool for enquiry and problem-solving which can be called into play as required; and strong feed-back from, and interaction throughout the process with, clients and end-users of products and technologies (Kline and Rosenberg, 1986).

However, the definition of the market, the client, and the user have come to be narrowly defined, the focus of attention concentrated on smaller and smaller components and interactions, and feedback and interaction with end users and/or clients attenuated. In brief, pasture and livestock units have come to be treated as if they belonged to a relatively closed system devoted to a single (or limited range of) purpose.

The new challenge

In recent years, grassland R & D has been challenged the world over to acknowledge that there are more people than pasture and livestock farmers who have a stake in the future of grasslands. For multiple uses, the challenge that many problems in need of urgent solution cannot be addressed solely at the level of the plant, paddock, or farm has arisen. In addition, system change is being driven by forces exogenous to, and beyond the control of, individual producers. The questions of **what** grasslands are for, **who** should be involved in problem definition and the search for solutions, and **how** R & D can be conducted to take account of systemic interactions at societal and ecological levels, come into prominence.

APPROACHES AND METHODS

The 'what' and 'who' questions

The 'what' and 'who' questions are closely intertwined. Recognition of multiple

337

users and multiple uses leads to the necessity for 'platform-building' i.e. the development of social agency (the 'who' question), in order to define the desired emergent properties of the resource to be managed (the 'what' question), and to manage the resource in ways which promote and sustain their emergence (Röling, 1994).

The Landcare groups in Australia may be taken as examples (Campbell and Woodhill, 1995). Each group of farmers and/or graziers sets its own agenda and priorities. Although government, extensionists, and researchers support the groups, they do not initiate or determine problems or solutions. A group, or groups together, operate at the level of a district, catchment, or community to include nearly all those people within a collectively constructed 'Landcare neighbourhood', which defines social and ecological boundaries. The definition of 'stakeholders' is thus significantly different to that of commodity producer groups.

Although groups typically begin working on single issues, such as salination of grazing land, their problem definition tends to evolve over time toward definitions of sustainability as the desired emergent property of the whole social, economic and physical landscape. This requires a multi-faceted search for 'solutions' at both individual and collective levels. Over 2200 groups were active by 1994, involving about a third of Australia's farming families (Campbell, 1994). While documentation of the results, in social, environmental and economic terms is only recently becoming available, the indications are positive (Campbell and Woodhill, 1995), with group activity continuing even in conditions of negative income and drought.

The concept of Landcare groups as generators of valid knowledge calls into question the argument of Richards (1993:pp67) that a producer's local knowledge and experimentation constitutes an idiosyncratic performance, and not socialised and socialisable knowledge. At the theoretical and field research levels, Darré (1989) has shown the importance of distinguishing between what researchers can learn from material phenomena and practices, researchers' and producers' contrasting decision processes and the forms of knowledge or epistemologies of the different actors. The **fact** that producers make a particular decision, and that makes itself evident in particular material phenomena, does not in itself allow inference concerning the **principles** upon which the decision is made. Researchers typically mis-apply the logic of their way of knowing to draw deterministic and predictive conclusions about producers' decisions concerning why, what, and how they manage resources.

The practical implications of this insight can be examined in producer-to-producer movements, such as the Wisconsin rotational graziers association (Hassanein and Kloppenberg, in progress). Input-intensive dairy producers responded to economic and environmental crises by developing mechanisms for the development of their collective knowledge about management-intensive, grass-based, rotational grazing. They drew from science universal principles rather than specific recommendations or technologies. This was only one kind of information input to guide their rapid evolution of practice, based on actual experimentation, observing, and interpreting for themselves.

Study tours (including visits to rotational graziers in New Zealand), pasture walks and an annual, producer-run, grazing conference were three important mechanisms for socialising the action-learning experiences of individuals. Latterly, a private foundation, the Center of Integrated Agricultural Systems, has provided a home for the Grazing-based Dairy Systems project, which brings together the self-styled 'grass-farmers', extensionists, and scientists into a common platform for further development of knowledge and practice.

Ison *et al.* (1989) report an effort to build a national platform among disparate, and somewhat antagonistic, organisational stakeholders in relation to the herbage seed industry in Australia through action research and participatory learning. A series of workshops were run with key stakeholders, viz: (i) extension and regulatory officers; (ii) seed producers; (iii) seed merchants and wholesalers, using modified soft systems methodology, SWOT analysis, and dialogue around a number of conceptual models developed by the facilitators. The outputs from these workshops were consolidated, together with secondary data, into a monograph which was circulated to all workshop participants, together with a questionnaire based on key questions and indicators of progress identified during the workshops. A concluding workshop, with members drawn from the earlier workshop series, monitored and evaluated progress and organisational change and reviewed and validated the questionnaire results. The results were summed-up by one grower participant to the final workshop as: "The study has caused the industry to move over fifty years in the last two" (Ison *et al.*, 1989; pp686).

The 'How'

Three approaches and methodologies are presented here as among the more innovative of the many creative ways stakeholders are seeking to deal with grass-lands as a resource management concern.

Participatory Rural Appraisal (PRA) encompasses a wide range of approaches with strong conceptual and methodological similarities, which are making a significant contribution in both industrial and developing country settings (IIED, 1994). PRA methods are being applied with great effect to carry out joint diagnosis of problem situations by cattle-keepers and researchers, and for the development of partnerships among cattle-keepers, researchers and extensionists to address the problems defined by the diagnosis (Biggs and Pound, 1992; IIED/Farm Africa, 1991). There is explicit recognition that while specific parts of the problems defined require the power of positivist science to resolve, such problem-parts are embedded in specific environments, which require investigation, experimentation, action, and resolution on larger scales.

The Local Consensus Data (LCD) technique (Clark, 1991) is being applied by the Department of Primary Industry in Queensland, Australia, in conditions where the production environment is largely uncontrolled, rainfall is erratic and variable, and major changes in ecological conditions are the result of climatic events rather than management. Since researchers can never develop adequate knowledge about enough sites to conduct experiments on-farm that are meaningful in management terms, the LCD seeks to capture the long time-series information and experience of individuals through systematic group communication. It also aims to build the capacity for real-time learning and development of understanding of systemic performance on scales which are significant in both ecological and industry terms, and to develop a process of change toward a shared set of goals.

Groups of participants are asked to describe the size and characteristics of 'a typical property in their area. They are then asked to use their experience to develop management recommendations for sustainable optimal production and minimal degradation of natural resources with respect to the hypothesised property. In subsequent meetings they compare and contrast their own management practices in the light of the hypothesised property, and to develop action learning strategies that would enable them to move towards the desired optima and minima. At repeat meetings, participants discuss feedback against agreed physical, economic and social indicators and review strategies. In one such series of meetings in the Black Speargrass country, participants came to realise that around 40 % of their properties faced severe resource degradation and/or indebtedness unless the management and technology employed were changed. It is interesting that recent reviews of the experience of trying to develop Africa's arid and semi-arid rangelands has led leading researchers and practitioners to a similar focus on 'tracking and buffering' methods and strategies (Behnke *et al.*, 1993).

Farm Inventories. Dr. Liz Wedderburn and her colleagues at Whatawhata Research Station, Hamilton, New Zealand, are working with dairy, sheep, and beef farmers to take farm inventories (E. Wedderburn, personal communication), a systematic procedure conducted as follows. Through group discussion, **lifestyle, viability, profitability, and productivity** were identified as co-necessary elements of sustainability. Sustainability in turn was defined by participants using the criteria of efficiency, contented animals, productive pastures, clean water, access to markets, good lifestyle and family health, and control of feral pests. Each criterion was then analysed in turn to develop indicators and characteristics by which condition and performance could be measured. Each of these in turn was linked to management practice. Finally, participants were invited to assess the current status of their own properties against each criterion on a scale of 0 to 20. They agreed that their collective goal was to move in the direction from 0 to 20, with 20 understood as a moving scale, as understanding and learning developed.

One of the key challenges researchers face as a result of this process is to develop (a) new monitoring tools, cheap and accessible to producers on their own properties; (b) new and improved interpretation tools for the data generated.

IMPLICATIONS FOR INVESTMENT AND MANAGEMENT

Funders of research typically invest in a packet of activities with fixed goals and objectives, a limited range of identified actors, and finite time horizons, i.e. the investment pattern is predicated on the linear assumption that given inputs lead to determinable outputs, and that the pathway for achievement can be specified in advance (Jiggins, 1995). Management concerns focus on efficiency, which is fairly easy to identify and measure, and sometimes also effectiveness, as a measure of whether the approach, technology or project does in fact do the job it was designed to do. Impact assessment procedures assume that the intervention (the research project) is the largest source of variance in actual outcomes.

The approaches and methods presented here require a different pattern of investment and different management and assessment procedures. The investment process must begin with support for the identification of stakeholders, and activities to build among them a shared vision of the nature and state of the resource to be managed, the problems associated with current resource use, and what they would like the resource to look like (i.e. its emergent properties) over time. The process typically involves clarification of areas of agreement concerning the information and data sets available for scrutiny but also of areas of disagreement where further investigation, data-gathering or monitoring is required.

The action research and learning process, which then unfolds, might be described in terms of a guided random walk, with periodic revision of the pathway in the light of organised feedback on key societal and natural processes. It is predicated on an understanding of the relationship between material resources and societal processes as a dynamic coupled system. Intended outcomes are describable in terms of Bayesian probability; the initial expectation that any one outcome will be achieved is modified iteratively in the light of what actually occurs.

The probabilistic nature of events in turn implies that standard research management tools, such as pre-project determination of fixed targets and milestones, typically described as specific events or in quantitative terms, are inappropriate. Goals, targets, and milestones are rather to be seen as dynamic moments in an unfolding process, expressed as a broad range of measures, both quantitative and qualitative, which are iteratively renegotiated in the light of changing circumstances. The Sustainable Grazing Communication Project attached to the GLASS sustainable grazing research study, conducted by the CSIRO Division of Tropical Crops and Pastures, Queensland, Australia, provides an instance of these challenges. The team took the innovative step, in the prevailing research culture, of designing input from graziers at key points of the property- and paddock-based experimental research programme. These took the form, for example, of key informant interviews, collaborative site assessments, and joint research review panels. These activities were designed as milestone events in the project proposal, with careful consideration given as to how the output from one would feed back as an input into the on-going programme. But the reality turned out differently. The interviews revealed that, with respect to certain key features in the experimental design (important to answer scientists' questions), the graziers had other ideas, based on their own knowledge and experience of the condition, trends, and the management practices used on their own properties. Further, particular parts of the experimental portfolio did not work well in scientific terms, so there was nothing much, in terms of expected results, for the graziers to look at when the scheduled time for site review arrived. While the graziers were keen to learn from what went wrong, as far as the scientists were concerned, the experiments were better written off as failures. Then the drought intervened, and some experiments never became established at all. Graziers still thought there was much to be learned, since drought is a 'normal' hazard which they have to manage in order to survive, but the absurdity of carrying out predetermined 'dialogues' of a specific kind at a pre-set moment was felt keenly by the research team, who felt obligated to 'perform' according to the project proposal. If these activities were to be jettisoned, and/or others substituted, then what, if anything, would be learned about grazier-scientist communication from the project?

The experience highlighted the importance of a stakeholder-based approach to research and the changes in research management practice required to guide a participatory process; add-on participation rarely satisfies anyone's need or interest. The key management questions change to: are we still moving toward where we want to go? and do we need to re-define where we want to go in the light of our emerging understanding? Research establishments have yet to learn how to respond flexibly to such signals from other stakeholders and changes in natural resource conditions.

There are further implications if research funders are to be included among the set of stakeholders: (a) when funders participate directly in the learning process, the pattern of investment is shaped through collective negotiation; (b) since budgets cannot be set in advance with exactitude, either by item, total amount, or timing, iterative, rolling budgeting procedures are required. This in turn demands investment decision-making as close as practicable to where the experience is being generated. Let it be noted that the process does not necessarily preclude commitment to fund longer term research; the process often throws up questions and problems which only longer term research can address. The point is that such needs are identified from within the process by stakeholders, and no longer by a narrow, elite group of outside 'experts'; (c) it follows that the portfolio of investment widens, both in terms of who receives funding and of what is funded. A local environmental activist group is as likely a recipient as the more traditional pasture specialist or university department.

There are yet further implications. The Foundation for Research, Science and Technology, a major public domain funder of agricultural research in New Zealand, for example, has realised that the participation of funders as stakeholders in action research and learning leads to greater emphasis on evaluation and review activities rather than pre-investment appraisal of research projects. Also the familiar end-of-project review of research results by a scientific peer group gives way to periodic consideration of (i) process outcomes;(ii) research-in-progress; and (iii), feedback from monitoring, by the set of stakeholders, with as much participation by research users as by research providers.

In addition, the question of efficacy assumes greater prominence, as a measure of whether an activity is, in fact, the right thing to be doing to achieve the collective vision. Assessment of efficacy cannot be an exact science but it serves as a useful touchstone for selecting and prioritising among investment choices and activities.

The above analysis sheds additional light on questions of power and the democratisation of science. Many scientists seem to fear the kinds of processes described in this paper as a species of popularisation that will lead to anarchy among competing claims to knowledge. It is more exact, and more helpful, to view them as simply another epistemology, with their own parameters of use and rigour (Jiggins and Röling, 1995). It would be naive to assume that stakeholder participation and the approaches and methods outlined in themselves obviate struggles about power and claims to knowledge of either personal or institutional kinds, or guarantee that decisions will not be made that later turn out to have been mistakes. Yet such struggles are manageable, indeed may become both enriching and empowering, if three important lessons are heeded:

1. If stakeholders are encouraged to negotiate resource management on the basis of their present position, then the process stalls, with no one actor willing to compromise his or her own power base for the sake of an as yet undefined common good. However, experience indicates that it is possible to overcome such an impasse by moving discussion from 'positions' to 'interests', by investing in the development of the collective vision, and by creating the space for stakeholders to work on local solutions (rather than to adapt to centrally imposed conditions) (Wagemans, 1996; Susskind and Cruikshank, 1987).

2. While resource management problems initially tend to present themselves as problems susceptible to technical solutions, the technocratic assumption typically hides underlying differences in perception of what the problem is really about and forces premature closure on a limited range of options. Much negative energy is then wasted in fighting over 'solutions' which prove

unacceptable to one or other stakeholder interest (leaving scientists in despair at the apparent irrationality of others).

3. It is not sufficient to gather together a range of disciplinary and other expertise considered relevant to the case in hand. Neither 'inter-disciplinarity' nor 'multi-disciplinarity' adequately describes what may be better defined as 'trans-disciplinarity', that is the need for stakeholders (including scientists and lay publics) to build together an integrative conceptual framework.

An integrative conceptual framework often is taken to mean a computer-based model. Interactive Multiple-Goal Simulation Models (Fresco et al., 1994) which allow interrogation of policy scenarios from a variety of technical perspectives; Crop Process models, such as those generated by the APSRU team of the DPI/CSIRO Division of Tropical Crops and Pastures in Queensland, Australia, which allows farmers and other users to explore the yield and income consequences over time of a range of resource management options in relation to interactive rainfall-soil fertility scenarios; and probabilistic models which allow updating of model coefficients, such as that being developed at Whatawhata research station in New Zealand, are representative of the range of effort now being devoted to this approach, but a number of caveats should be noted. First, they serve the purpose of an integrative conceptual framework only to the extent that all stakeholders are involved in design and interpretation. Secondly, where researchers are largely or entirely responsible for design and interpretation, there is a tendency for them to make claims for accuracy, precision, and generality which cannot be sustained under scrutiny i.e. the models become an assertion of power rather than instruments for understanding. Thirdly, computer-based modelling may prove to be an expensive distraction to the definition of problem-led R & D and the management of resources. As the experience documented by Scoones and Thompson (1994) demonstrates, there are effective alternatives to high-tech approaches. Even illiterate men and women are perfectly capable of generating powerful conceptual and physical models of resource states and trends which integrate societal and physical processes, and which are manipulable for exploration of scenarios, given an appropriate methodology and facilitation support.

CONCLUSIONS

Problems of natural resource management and the environment and of the social viability of rural areas, cannot be addressed solely on the basis of technocratic approaches focused on individual properties or components of grassland systems. Approaches and methods which combine societal and technical change, and at larger scales than the individual property, are required.

REFERENCES
BEHNKE R.H., SCOONES I., and KERVEN C., (eds) (1993) *Range Ecology at Disequilibrium: New models of natural variability and pastoral adaptation in African savannas*, London: Overseas Development Institute.

BIGGS S. and POUND B. (1992) *Farmers' participatory research.* A review of FARM AFRICA's Project in Africa. Norwich. University of East Anglia/Chatham. Natural Resources Institute.

CAMPBELL A. (1994) *LANDCARE - communities shaping the land and the future.* Sydney: Allen and Unwin.

CAMPBELL A. and WOODHILL J., compiled and edited with J. FRANKENBERG, P. GRICE, J. HARDY and P. TREVETHEN (1995 in press) *Landcare: a new horizons case study.* London: IIED.

CLARK R. (1991) *How To Notes*: using the Local Consensus Data Technique to develop farm management strategies, No. 1. Regional Extension Office. Rockhampton: Department of Primary Industries

DARRÉ J.P. (1989) Introducing livestock farmer's ways of thinking in the study of grazing systems. *Etudes et recherche sur les systèmes agraires et le développement* **16**, 173-179.

FRESCO L.O., STROOSNIJDER L., BOUMA J. and VAN KEULEN H. (eds) (1994) *The future of the land*, Chichester:John Wiley and Sons Ltd.

HASSANEIN N. and KLOPPENBURG J.R. (1995 in progress) Where the grass grows again: Knowledge exchange in the sustainable agriculture movement.

IIED (1994) *RRA Notes.* **20**. Special issue on livestock. Sustainable Agriculture Programme. London:IIED.

IIED/FARM AFRICA (1991) *Farmer participatory research in North Omo, Ethiopia.* Report of a Training Course. London: IIED.

ISON R.L., POTTS W.H.C. and BEALE G. (1989) Improving herbage seed industry productivity and stability through action research. *Proceedings of the XVI International Grassland Congress.* Nice, France, 685-686.

JIGGINS J. (1995) Development impact assessment: Impact assessment of aid projects in non-western countries. *Journal of Impact Assessment,* **13(1)**, 47-69.

JIGGINS J. and RÖLING, N. (1995) Action research in natural resource management. In: Albaladejo C. and Casabianca, F. (eds), *Pour une méthodologie de la rechereche action*, [A methodology for action research]. Paris: INRA/SAD.

KLINE S. and ROSENBERG N. (1986) An overview of innovation. In: Landau R., Rosenberg, N. (eds), *The Positive Sum Strategy*: harnessing technology for economic growth. Washington D.C.: National Academy Press. 275-306

RICHARDS, P. (1993) Cultivation: knowledge or performance? In: Hobart, M. (ed) *Anthropology of development.* London:Routledge. pp 61-78.

RÖLING N.(1994) Creating human platforms to manage natural resources: First results of a research program. In: CIRAD-SAR *Systems-oriented research in agriculture and rural development.* Montpellier:CIRAD. 391-395.

SCOONES I. and THOMPSON J. (eds) (1994) *Beyond farmer first; rural people's knowledge, agricultural research and extension practice.* London:Intermediate Technology Publishers.

SUSSKIND L. and CRUIKSHANK J. (1987) Breaking the impasse. Consensual approaches to resolving public disputes. MIT-Harvard Public Disputes Program. New York: Basic Books Publishers.

WAGEMANS M. (1995 in progress) The Role of Communication in the Development of Policy in the Netherlands. The Case of the Grote Peel. In: Röling, N. and Wagemakers, M. (eds), *Facilitating Natural Resource Management* Department of Innovation and Communication Studies. Wageningen Agriculture Unviersity.

Agriculture into the 21st Century: Technology Interactions for Science-Led R&D

PENNY MAPLESTONE AND T. L. BLUNDELL

Biotechnology and Biological Sciences Research Council,
Polaris House, North Star Avenue, Swindon, SN2 IUH

ABSTRACT

Although existing agricultural practices and technologies have much to contribute in the future, the 'new biology' and information technology must also be exploited. These provide opportunities to satisfy many of the demands of the public as consumers, as environmentalists and as members of the rural community. The new technologies can be used to improve the quality of food, decrease the use of agrochemicals and assist in diversification to other products such as fibres, specialist chemicals, pharmaceuticals and fuels. They can help sustain integrated farming systems, the creation of wealth in the countryside and the provision of a greener alternative to town-based industries.

The recent White Paper on science, engineering and technology emphasises the need for close and continuous interactions between universities, research institutes, and the industries that will apply the new science. Although agricultural scientists have traditionally had close contacts with the farming community, they have tended to emphasise production, rather than efficiency, product quality, market demands and diversification. Both farmers and scientists have failed to make close links with the food processor and the retailer. The BBSRC will focus on the complex interactions that will be needed in the 21st Century between the science base, the new technologies, the products, the needs in the market place and the beneficiaries of the new technologies. The BBSRC must balance market pull and science drive, in order to make sure that knowledge is transferred in both directions and the new science is usefully incorporated into new products and processes.

THE CHALLENGE

In May 1993 the UK Government published a White Paper on Science, Engineering and Technology entitled *Realising our Potential*. Although the paper reasserted the importance of Government funding for fundamental research, its main theme was the role of science, engineering and technology in underpinning wealth creation and the quality of life. The White Paper called for more attention to technology interaction between the science base and industry. It threw down the challenge to ensure that excellent science is exploited to the advantage of the UK plc.

One of the main actions of the White Paper was to set up six mission-oriented research councils. In establishing the new Biotechnology and Biological Sciences Research Council (BBSRC), the Government recognised the revolutionary potential of biology and agriculture for a wide range of industrial users. The new Research Council builds on the innovative and internationally competitive biotechnology and biological science of SERC and the plant, animal, food and

346

agricultural sciences developed in the AFRC over the previous decade.

The increased emphasis on technology interaction and wealth creation in the BBSRC, together with the more multidisciplinary science environment, is a new setting for agricultural research. This paper addresses the question of how this has affected our approach to the funding and exploitation of agricultural research in general and grassland research in particular. What are the implications and the opportunities for science-led research in the future?

THE SCIENCE OPPORTUNITY

The greatest single opportunity that can change agriculture for the 21st Century is that afforded by the revolution in biology. The biorevolution has given us a detailed insight into the molecular mechanisms of life and offers the possibility of optimising biological processes for the benefit of mankind. It is now possible to re-examine traditional agriculture and ask how the new technology can contribute towards the sustainability of the agricultural industry.

Although the revolution in biology began with the definition of the structure of DNA by Watson and Crick in the 1950s, it was not until the 1970s that it was understood how to sequence genes and recombine them in micro-organisms. Even more recently, scientists have learnt how to introduce genes into more complex animals and plants. Thus, although it had its roots in the 1950s, the biorevolution was realised only in the 1970s and 1980s.

The biorevolution offers opportunities at many different levels of biological complexity. These include the engineering of individual DNA or protein molecules, the modification of complex molecular assemblies like viruses, the manipulation of micro-organisms and the transfer of genes between different plants or animals. Each has its analogies in traditional agricultural biotechnology, and the new technologies can be seen as making traditional biological processes more competitive with the products of town-based production, that rely on non-renewable resources.

At the molecular level

At the most basic level, that of the DNA or protein molecule, there are many new opportunities. In crop protection, discrimination between closely related pathogens, pathogen variants or different parasites and predator clones or biotypes, frequently requires the use of laborious plant-based tests or phenotypic assays. Assays and tests, based on specific antibodies or on the identification of DNA polymorphisms, offer rapid and reliable methods for discrimination. Combined with forecasting techniques based in epidemiology and IT-based expert systems these can allow a more targeted and rational use of chemical controls for the farmer. The technology is important not only for the farmer and advisor but also for those in the seed industry interested in the health of their stock material.

The same technologies can be used for the diagnosis of animal disease. BBSRC scientists for example, developed an antibody-based test for detection of the rinderpest virus and have been closely involved in transferring this technology to developing countries. It is being used for monitoring in national disease eradication campaigns in Africa and Asia.

It may also be possible to use these molecular diagnostic tools in environmental policing. For example, the addition of genetically marked strains of bacteria to silage clamps could make it possible to identify the source of a particular pollution incident.

Using viruses

Diagnostics exploit naturally occurring genetic variation; there are also opportunities to modify the genetic material. Viruses are perhaps the simplest to modify and there is much interest in their use. In the past attenuated viruses have been used as vaccines for livestock and these have involved real risks that have often become greater than the risk of infection from natural causes. However, specific regions of the virus can now be identified and synthesised to provide safe and effective vaccines. The development of novel vaccines for animal health protection provides opportunities to reduce reliance on excessive, prophylactic use of antibiotics and other medicines leading to build up of resistance and persistence of antibiotics in the food chain and environment.

In a collaboration with Axis Genetics, scientists at JIC have developed 'chimeric viral particle' (CVP) technology in which plant viruses are modified to incorporate the antigenic part of some other, disease-causing virus. These viruses replicate in plants and are immunogenic when injected as a vaccine. The technology has been used to produce vaccines against foot and mouth virus in cowpea by modification of the cowpea mosaic virus to incorporate the antigenic part of the foot and mouth virus particle. Trials of the vaccine are underway; if successful it is anticipated that plants can be used as a relatively cheap manufacturing vehicle for the vaccine.

Similar approaches have been used by scientists elsewhere to produce vaccines by engineering into potato the gene for a surface binding protein of the hepatitis B virus or for a protein from the shell of Norwalk virus which causes diarrhoea in children. In these instances the vaccine is introduced by eating the plant material.

It was recognised as early as 1980 that it might be possible to engineer stable resistance to viruses by introducing, into a plant, part of the viral material, so that it would interfere with the normal life cycle of the virus or prepare the plant for subsequent invasion. Since then there has been an explosion of interest in this technology, and crops protected by coat-protein mediated virus resistance are already in the field in China. The range of targets for this technology is constrained only by the availability of transformation technology for the target crop and by the need for more research on the durability, efficacy and stability of the resistance within real production systems.

Multi-cellular organisms

At the next organisational level are microorganisms. These have been used widely in traditional agriculture and it is not surprising that new opportunities arise with the powerful new technologies. Fundamental studies of bacterial cellulase and hemicellulase enzymes, their structure/function relationships and the genes controlling their expression are opening up possibilities for manipulating bacteria in the rumen or silage inoculum to improve their efficiency. This is collaborative work between scientists at Babraham Institute and the University of Newcastle.

At higher levels of biological organisation, increasingly exciting opportunities for agriculture are opened up. As knowledge of plant and animal genomes grows, the increasing opportunities to exploit that knowledge to speed the identification, selection and incorporation of desirable traits into improved varieties and breeds of crops and livestock becomes evident.

IGER scientists working on a genetic map of *Lolium* spp have located a region of the genome containing several QTLs involved in the control of traits of major agronomic importance, including the timing of inflorescence emergence. The region also contains loci associated with senescence and water soluble carbohydrate content. There is potential to apply this discovery in marker assisted selection for these traits in breeding programmes.

The transfer of useful genes between organisms and the modification of genes within organisms using molecular technologies is already a commercial reality; the first genetically modified oilseed rape (modified for herbicide resistance) is expected on the UK market very shortly. BBSRC's view is that the major opportunities lie with the modification of plants and that in plants, genes affecting storage product quantity and composition, vegetative development, reproduction, pest and disease resistance and response to environmental stresses will be of most value.

Most straightforward, scientifically, will be to introduce or modify a single gene that affects a single protein product. A programme of research at IGER aimed at understanding the fundamental basis of leaf senescence led to the discovery of the stay-green character caused by a mutation in a gene required for normal senescence. The gene has been introduced to a range of genetic backgrounds in grasses, which have been found to have enhanced nutritional and aesthetic characteristics. Commercialisation will be through the Institute's industrial partners, Germinal Holdings. The stay-green character could be especially valuable in dry-land agricultural systems and ODA is providing support to investigate its potential in sorghum, maize and beans.

There are also real possibilities now of introducing genes which give resistance to various herbicides, pests and diseases. The introduction of herbicide resistance is well advanced, being a potentially lucrative commercial opportunity for the agrochemical and breeding companies. It is also a use for molecular biology which has given rise to some concern amongst the public. These concerns may or may not be realised but it does seem that the public would find the engineering of disease or pest resistance more acceptable.

Plants can be protected from pest attack through the introduction of genes from other species or from organisms other than plants. The US Environmental Protection Agency has recently approved applications from Mycogen and Ciba Seeds to market maize seed containing a gene from *Bacillis thuringiensis* that produces a protein toxic to the European corn borer. Other companies have similar products in the pipeline.

Basic research on plant-pathogen interactions at the molecular level is uncovering the mechanisms which provide plants with their natural resistance to disease. The first specific resistance genes have been isolated from plants in the last year and many more are expected soon. Resistance genes might be used in breeding programmes but care will need to be taken to utilise them in strategies designed to give durable resistance to a broad range of pathogens and to minimise the likelihood of rapid evolution of resistance-breaking pathogen strains.

The introduction of durable resistance into plants has many advantages. The trait can be transferred into many local varieties by traditional breeding or genetic transformation and therefore the new plants will disrupt traditional agricultural patterns to a smaller extent than the products of the 'green revolution'. Once the techniques have been developed, the transformed plants are cheap to produce and will decrease the requirement for expensive agrochemicals to control disease vectors. They will also decrease the use of insecticides, fungicides and other chemicals that impact on our environment and carry over into our food and water.

Animal biotechnology

Similar transfers of genes can be achieved in animals. In general this will be much less acceptable to the public. The most important applications in animals of the new biology will come in making traditional breeding techniques more efficient. Mapping of livestock genomes should allow the identification of genes that contribute to particular traits, such as meat quality or disease susceptibility, in a way at speeds up the breeding process. The pig and chicken genome are those which have received the greatest attention in the UK to date but work is beginning on the bovine genome.

The 'new biology' whether it produces molecules, cells, tissues or whole plants, must be seen as part of a system and must be tested thoroughly within the context of that system to provide a sound ecological and economic basis for the development of more sustainable farming systems and to ensure the expected benefits are realised without unforeseen side effects. The agricultural system of the 21st Century which incorporates DNA and antibody diagnostic tests for pests, disease and nutrient status, biological control agents and crops modified for pest and disease resistance or other traits must also incorporate knowledge-based systems which will allow decisions to be made; access to information and information technology will be crucial to the successful implementation of these new farming systems.

TECHNOLOGY INTERACTIONS
A new model
The White Paper emphasises the need for close and continuous interactions between universities and research institutes and the industries that will apply the new science. It rejects the linear model in which scientific opportunities are seen as the single drivers of the research agenda. Rather it stresses the importance of both market pull and science drive mediated by continuous interactions between scientists, technologists, industrialists and customers.

At one level agricultural scientists have probably been less guilty of pursuing a simple linear model than most others. They have traditionally had very close contacts with the farming community and the agricultural research institutes have involved farmers and farming organisations, many of whom played a role in establishing the first research foundations with private funds. The farming industry is receptive to the introduction of new technologies and keen to participate in their development and implementation. There is evidence for this in the active support for R&D from the levy organisations.

But there are still many problems. The present organisation of research in the UK still reflects the linear model with existing mechanisms focused on transfer of results and information when R&D is close to the point of application. Basic science is often assumed to flow from the universities into institutes, from institutes to research associations or advisory services, and from these to the industry or to the policy maker. Whereas it would seem to be good sense that the institutes, with their longer term strategic science programmes, should pull back from the market place and leave the interactions with the customer to the research associations, this can now be seen to have serious consequences. The BBSRC sees it to be of primary importance that its scientists in universities and institutes interact closely together, and are in close touch with the advisory service, the industry and the customer.

In the increasingly competitive research market, institutes have worked hard to strengthen their links with industry through specific collaborations such as the IGER strategic alliance with the breeding companies Germinal Holdings and Semundo. This covers breeding and marketing of improved varieties of forage grasses, clover and oats. Within the framework of the agreement varieties remain the property of the institute and the companies have exclusive licences to market them world-wide. Both sides benefit; the industrial partners from access to the science base and the institute from relatively stable funding, scientific freedom and access to markets for the products of its science. The first ryegrass and white clover varieties developed within this alliance have recently appeared on the Recommended List.

More generally, institutes place great emphasis on disseminating their science to a specialist audience through articles in the trade press, technical publications, open days for specific sectors of the industry and undertaking consultancies. These interactions may be formalised through associations such as ARIA, the Arable Research Institute Association, which aims to foster a free interchange of information between researchers, farmers, trade organisations and arable advisers. Membership is open to anyone with an interest in the application of science to the practice of farming and currently stands at around 400.

The widest audience is reached through the activities of the Council and individual institutes at events such as the Royal Show, BAAS, through the publication of annual reports and through work with schools and women's organisations.

Research in agricultural systems

Interaction implies that there must also be feedback from the industry to those making decisions about science policy and the future direction of research. Institutes increasingly seek to have industrial representation on their Governing Bodies. BBSRC Council members now include about 50% industrialists and policy makers. The Agricultural Systems Directorate (ASD) has an advisory Management Committee including farmers, breeders, representatives of the agrochemical industry, retailers and consumers as well as scientists.

The Directorate funds research in both universities and institutes grant-aided by BBSRC. It has defined its priorities for future support of the Councils agricultural systems research and put in place priority programmes which exploit opportunities not only from biotechnology but from the biological and related sciences more widely to address the strategic needs of its users. Grassland systems, as would be anticipated from their importance to UK agriculture, feature strongly in those programmes. Grassland agriculture is based on an inefficient process. The conversion efficiency of plant material into meat, milk and fibre by the grazing animal is low and the process generates large amounts of waste which as well as being economically inefficient, can contribute significantly to environmental pollution. ASD's research programme aims to improve the efficiency of feeding the grazing animal. Its priorities are to understand behavioural factors in grazing, to improve the efficiency of feed conversion in the rumen and to study the processes involved in the internal control of nutrient partitioning after absorption. Farmers need these improvements to fulfil their obligations to the environment without losing profitability.

The soil is a critical component of any farming system, grassland or other. A central question is how to maintain an appropriate supply of nutrients for sustainable primary production. Despite the intensive research effort on nutrient cycling in soils, virtually nothing is known about the contribution of soil organic matter to the process. ASD's programme will bring the disciplines of soil science, microbiology, organic and physical chemistry and mathematical modelling to bear on this topic to underpin better management of soil organic matter for improved nutrient availability to plant and reduce wasteful and polluting losses to the environment.

A further, related, priority is minimising waste in agricultural systems where the aims are to target reduction in applied inputs, the integration of waste management at farm and landscape level and the application of life-cycle analysis to decision support.

Modern intensive management systems, geared to high productivity, have led to greater uniformity in the agri-environment. ASD's programme will provide underpinning research on ways to maintain and extend environmental diversity within current agricultural systems with the emphasis on management for ecological diversity, novel management and production systems and on the exploitation of naturally occurring diversity for example in biological pest control.

Sustainable farming must also take into account the health and welfare of livestock. High standards prevent economic loss and also give the farmer a competitive advantage in a market in which consumers are more often demanding to know that the meat and eggs they purchase have been produced from animals who have been protected from pain and disease and whose welfare needs have been met. ASD will give priority to both health and welfare research. There will be a special emphasis given to the welfare of the dairy cow. ASD plans to work closely with other research sponsors to set national goals for reducing the incidence of mastitis, lameness, metabolic diseases and culling in dairy cows, to identify the priorities for research needed to provide the information to achieve this and to put in place the appropriate research programme. Technology interaction will be central to this programme and BBSRC will seek to ensure that the results of the research are translated into advice for the stockman and implemented as early as possible.

Beyond the farm gate

A significant impediment to technology interaction in agricultural research is the farm gate, which has separated the farmers from their real customers, the food processor, the retailer and the consumer. This has also been reflected in the distant relationships between agricultural scientists (and the sponsors of agricultural research) and those involved in food quality, food processing, food safety and diet and health. BBSRC has tried to deal with this concern by introducing a major programme that spans both sides of the farm gate. The Raw

Material Quality programme aims to provide the knowledge to link consumer and manufacturer assays of quality to the fundamental attribute of the raw material and, in particular, to identify how raw materials are specified by the interaction of the genetic constitution of the organism and environmental factors. Both food and feed will be tackled and the issue to be covered will include:

* identification of the sensory and functional qualities of raw materials required by both the consumer and manufacturer;
* development of strategies for the production of modified raw materials with the desired characteristics;
* investigating how the interaction between genetic and environmental factors affect the variability of product quality;
* understanding how food safety, throughout the food chain is influenced by the primary production process.

Evidence for the novelty of the approach is seen in the very small number of research groups in the UK already addressing this kind of problem. There are small pockets of excellent science. At, IGER for example, scientists have been producing genetically modified *Lotus corniculatus* in which antisense technology has been used to alter the content of condensed tannins, anti-nutritional factors associated with bloat. The material will be tested to see whether it produces silage of improved nutritional quality and whether there is a beneficial effect on the efficiency of protein conversion in the rumen.

This trend will probably be accelerated by the supermarkets' demand for reliability of supply and high quality of produce which is now beginning to encourage vertical integration through producer-retailer contracts. The diversification to non-food products will make the vertical integration even more challenging. The farmer will need to interact with a far greater range of industries, including chemicals, construction and energy. The interaction of the research base with these industries, new to agriculture, is being addressed by BBSRC through ACTIN, the Alternative Crops Technology Interaction Network. BBSRC has linked up with a consortium of companies from the plant breeding and seeds industries to provide a platform for research and development leading to commercialisation of alternative crop technologies and products. ACTIN will establish and maintain databases of main users of alternative crop technologies and products and of current research and development; it will promote uptake and exploitation of available technology and stimulate research and development by creating synergy between and within UK industry, Government and academia.

This paper has described some of the present challenges for technology interaction in the agricultural sector; particularly the new challenges and also opportunities which are presented by the potential to exploit the biorevolution. These challenges must be met, but at the same time lessons from the past must be learnt to ensure that the same, or greater, technological success than resulted from the green revolution of the 1960s and 70s is achieved. This achievement must be made with a sense of social responsibility and an awareness of the long term human and environmental consequences of the results of these methods.

CONCLUSIONS

The BBSRC will focus on the complex interactions between the science base, the new technologies, the products, the needs in the market place and the beneficiaries of the new technologies. It must balance market pull and science drive, in order to make sure that knowledge is transferred in both directions and the new science is usefully incorporated in new products and processes.

Through the Directorate strategy, BBSRC is attempting to target its resources for strategic science to the areas in which it sees greatest potential for effective technology interaction to address real and urgent concern of its user communities. BBSRC policy for strategic science is influenced by:

*   the ability of the user base to exploit the potential value of science to the UK in terms of wealth creation and/or quality of life;
*   the ability of the UK science and engineering base to deliver;
*   the scope for high quality science input and appropriateness for the research base to pursue.

The development of this strategy has closely paralleled the National Technology Foresight and, although it is perhaps no great surprise, it is reassuring to note that many of the priorities identified match those which have emerged from 'Foresight'. The emphasis over the coming year will be to implement Directorate strategy coupled with maintaining the flexibility to respond to new 'Foresight' priorities.

Technology Interaction in Herbage Plant Breeding

D. H. Hides

IGER, Aberystwyth, Dyfed, SY23 3EB

Publicly funded biological research often results in the development of products which can make a contribution to the competitiveness of the agricultural sector. However, transferring these products successfully to the market place is not always easy. Herbage breeding research at the Institute of Grassland and Environmental Research (IGER) produces grass and clover cultivars as one of its end products. Until 1987, this work was wholly funded by MAFF. The resulting cultivars were marketed by the National Seed Development Organisation (NSDO) who acted as brokers for all cultivars emanating from publicly funded plant breeding. In the period 1987/88 two events occurred which forced change in this situation. Firstly NSDO was privatised, leaving IGER without marketing arrangements and, secondly, MAFF withdrew a proportion ('near-market') of its funding to the breeding programmes. In the subsequent search for new funding and marketing arrangements it became evident that, for IGER, both would have to be linked and that the most realistic option was to ally the Institute to a company, or group of companies, with an established reputation in herbage seed marketing and with a strong commitment to the UK herbage seed industry. After open competition Germinal Holdings Ltd (British Seed Houses in England and Wales and David Bell in Scotland) agreed to pay the 'near market' costs of the IGER herbage breeding programmes in return for the world marketing rights of the varieties.

This relationship, which began in 1988, has now developed into a true technology interaction which is much more than the simple transfer of cultivars from MAFF funded research to the UK grassland sector. Herbage breeding research in IGER concentrates on improving traits such as nutritive value, nitrogen use efficiency and grass clover compatibility, all of which can assist with reducing costly inputs to forage production. To maximise the benefits of cultivars combining these traits there is a major requirement for increasing user awareness. For their part, Germinal Holdings publicise the possible benefits and bring farmers and seed merchants to IGER to hear directly from the breeders how their varieties should be managed. IGER researchers, with Germinal Holdings, also contribute widely to grassland associations and other gatherings of interested farmers and researchers. A series of evening meetings with farmers have also been organised by British Seed Houses for the coming winter to maximise user awareness of the potential of IGER-bred varieties. In an era when the grassland sector of the agricultural industry is under severe economic pressure, IGER and Germinal Holdings working together can provide both the new cultivars and the methodology for improving the efficiency of production of livestock products from grass. This link between publicly funded research and a UK commercial company enables the products of breeding research to realise their full potential and make a significant contribution to wealth creation.

GLOSSARY OF ABBREVIATIONS USED IN THE TEXT

ADAS	Agricultural Development and Advisory Service
ADF	Acid detergent fibre
AFRC	Agriculture and Food Research Council
AGM	Annual General Meeting
ANE	Apparent nitrogen efficiency
ANR	Apparent recovery of nitrogen
APSRU	Agricultural Production Systems Research Unit
ARC	Agricultural Research Council
ARIA	Arable Research Institute Association
ASD	Agricultural Systems Directorate of BBSRC
ATP	Adenine triose phosphate
asl	above sea level
BAAS	British Association for the Advancement of Science
BBSRC	Biotechnology and Biology Research Council
BCEU	Bull and Cow Evaluation Unit
BCPC	British Crop Protection Council
BES	British Ecological Society
BGS	British Grassland Society
BOD	Biochemical oxygen demand
BSAP	British Society of Animal Production
BST	Bovine somatotropin
CAP	Common Agricultural Policy of the EU
CD	Cow day
CF	Crude fibre
COMA	Committee on Medical Aspects of Food Policy
COST	European Cooperation in the Field of Science and Technology
CP	Crude protein
CSIRO	Commonwealth Scientific and Industrial Research Organisation
CV	Coefficient of variation
cv	cultivar
CVP	Chimeric viral particle
CWD	Cell wall degradability
DCD	Dicyandiamide
DLWG	Daily liveweight gain
DM	Dry matter
DMD	Dry matter digestibility
DNA	Dioxy ribonucleic acid
DOE	Department of the Environment
DOMD	Digestible organic matter in dry matter
DPI	Department of Primary Industry
DUS	Distinctiveness, uniformity and stability assessment
D-value	See DOMD

EAGGF	see FEOGA
EC/EC12	European Community
ECU	European currency unit
EE	Ear emergence
EEC	European Economic Community
EGF	European Grassland Federation
EHF	Experimental Husbandry Farm
ESA	Environmentally sensitive area
EU	European Union
FACE	Free air carbon dioxide enrichment
FAO	The Food and Agriculture Organisation of the United Nations
FEOGA	Fonds Européean d'Orientation et de Garantie Agricole
FM	Fresh matter
FME	Fermentable metabolisable energy
FYM	Farmyard manure
GATT	General Agreement on Tariffs and Trade
GC-MS	Gas chromatography/ mass spectometry
GIS	Grassland Improvement Station
GLASS	Grazing Legumes/Landscapes and Sustainability of Pastures in the Sub-tropics
GMP	Ground mineral phosphate
GRI	Grassland Research Institute
HFRO	Hill Farming Research Organisation
HMSO	Her Majesty's Stationery Office
HVS	Higher Voluntary Standards
IACR	Institute for Arable Crop Research
ICI	Imperial Chemical Company
IGER	Institute for Grassland and Environmental Research
IGC	International Grassland Congress
IGS	Intergenic spacer
ITEB	Institut Technique d'Élevage Bovin
IVDMD	*In-vivo* dry matter degradation
JIC	Joint Industry Council
JNCC	Joint Nature Conservancy Council
LAB	Lactic acid bacteria
LAI	Leaf area index
LCD	Local Consensus Data
LFA	Less favoured area
LSU/LU	Livestock unit
LUGD	Livestock unit grazing day
LWG	Liveweight gain
MADF	Modified acid detergent fibre
MAFF	Ministry of Agriculture, Fisheries and Food
MAS	Marker assisted selection
MDC	Milk Development Council

ME	Metabolisable energy
MLC	Meat and Livestock Commission
MMB	Milk Marketing Board
NDF	Neutral detergent fibre
NFU	National Farmers' Union
NFS	National Food Survey
NIAB	National Institute of Agricultural Botany
NIRS	Near infra-red spectroscopy
NMR	National Milk Records
NRA	National Rivers Authority
ns	not significant
NSA	National Sheep Association
NSDO	National Seed Development Organisation
NVC	National Vegetation Classification
OAP	Old age pensioner
ODA	Overseas Development Administration
OECD	Organisation for European Cooperation and Development
OEEC	Organization of European Economic Cooperation/ Economic Planning Agency
OMD	Organic matter digestibility
OSTS	Official seed testing station
P	Probability
PLFA	Phospholipid fatty acid analysis
ppl	Pence per litre
PRA	Participative rural appraisal
QTL	Quantitative trait loci
r	correlation coefficient
R & D	Research and development
RAPD	Random amplified polymorphic DNA
RASE	Royal Agricultural Society of England
RFLP	Restriction fragment length polymorphism
RH	Relative humidity
RSPB	Royal Society for the Protection of Birds
SAC	Scottish Agricultural College
se	standard error
sed	standard error of the difference
sem	standard error of the mean
SERC	Science and Engineering Research Council
SOAFD	Scottish Office: Agriculture and Food Department
SR	Stocking rate
SSH	Sward surface height
SWOT	Strengths, weaknesses, opportunities and threats
TNC	Total non-structural carbohydrate
UK	United Kingdom
UKROFS	United Kingdom Register of Organic Food Standards

UME	Utilisable metabolisable energy
USA	United States of America
USE	Utilised Starch Equivalent
UVB	Ultra violet band
VCU	Value for cultivation and use trials
VFA	Volatile fatty acid
WCW	Whole crop wheat
WOAD	Welsh Office Agricultural Division
WPBS	Welsh Plant Breeding Station
WSC	Water-soluble carbohydrate

LIST OF AUTHORS

PUBLICATIONS IN THE BGS OCCASIONAL SYMPOSIUM SERIES

1.*   **The Agronomic Evaluation of Grassland** (Eds) Baker, H.K. & Tayler, R.S. (1963).

2.*   **Beef Production and Marketing** (Ed) Cannell, R.Q. (1966).

3.*   **Fodder Conservation** (Ed) Wilkins, R.J. (1967).

4.*   **Hill-Land Productivity** (Ed) Hunt, I.V. (1968).

5.*   **Grass and Forage Breeding** (Eds) Phillips, L.I. & Hughes, R. (1969).

6.*   **White Clover Research** (Ed) Lowe, J. (1970).

7.   **Forage on the Arable Farm** (Ed) Kimber, D.S. (1972).

8.*   **Pasture Utilisation by the Grazing Animal** (Eds) Hodgson, J. & Jackson, K. (1974).

9.   **Green Crop Fractionation** (Ed) Wilkins, R.J. (1977).

10.   **Changes in Sward Composition and Productivity** (Eds) Charles, A.H. & Haggar, R.J. (1979).

11.   **Forage Conservation in the '80s** (Ed) Thomas, C. (1980).

12.   **Effective Use of Forage and Animal Resources in the Hills and Uplands** (Ed) Frame, J. (1981).

13.*   **Plant Physiology and Herbage Production** (Ed) Wright, C.E. (1981).

14.   **Efficient Grassland Farming** (Ed) Corrall, A.J. (1983).

15.   **Money from Grass** (Ed) Corrall, A.J. (1984).

16.   **Forage Legumes** (Ed) Thomson, D.J. (1984).

17.   **Machinery from Silage** (Eds) Nelson, J.K. & Dinnis, E.R. (1985).

18.   **Weeds, Pests and Diseases of Grassland and Herbage Legumes** (Ed) Brockman, J.S. (1985).

19.   **Grazing** (Ed) Frame, J. (1986).

20.   **Grassland Manuring** (Eds) Raymond, W.F. & Cooper, J.C. (1986).

21.   **Efficient Sheep Production from Grass** (Ed) Pollott, G.E. (1987).

22.*   **Efficient Beef Production from Grass** (Ed) Frame, J. (1988).

23.   **Silage for Milk Production** (Ed) Mayne, C.S. (1989).

24.   **Milk and Meat from Forage Crops** (Ed) Pollott, G.E. (1990).

25.   **Management Issues for the Grassland Farmer in the 1990's** (Ed) Mayne, C.S. (1991).

26.   **Grass on the Move - a positive way forward for the grassland farmer** (Ed) Hopkins, A. (1992).

27.   **Forward with Grass into Europe** (Eds) Hopkins, A. & Younie D. (1993).

28.   **Grassland Management and Nature Conservation** (Eds) Haggar, R.J. & Peel, S. (1993)

29.   **Grassland Into the 21st Century: Challenges & Opportunities** (Ed) Pollott, G.E. (1995)

*   **Out of print**